Autodesk®Inventor®2015 Essentials Plus

Daniel T. Banach & Travis Jones

SDC
Publications

SDC Publications
P.O. Box 1334
Mission, KS 66222
913-262-2664
www.SDCpublications.com
Publisher: Stephen Schroff

ISBN-13: 978-1-58503-903-6
ISBN-10: 1-58503-903-9

Printed and bound in the United States of America.

Table of Contents

Table of Contents

INTRODUCTION

Welcome to the Autodesk Inventor 2015 Essentials Plus manual. This manual provides a thorough coverage of the features and functionalities offered in Autodesk Inventor.

Each chapter in this manual is organized with the following elements:

Objectives. Describes the content and learning objectives.

Topic Coverage. Presents a concise, thorough review of the topic.

Exercises. Presents the workflow for a specific command or process through illustrated, step-by-step instructions.

Checking Your Skills. Tests your understanding of the material using True/False and multiple-choice questions.

Note to the Learner

Autodesk Inventor is designed for easy learning. Autodesk Inventor's help system provides you with ongoing support as well as access to online documentation.

As described above, each chapter in this manual has the same instructional design, making it easy to follow and understand. Each exercise is task-oriented and based on real-world mechanical engineering examples.

Who Should Use This Manual?

The manual is designed to be used in instructor-led courses, although you may also find it helpful as a self-paced learning tool.

Recommended Course Duration

Four days (32 hours) to seven days (56 hours) are recommended, or used through a semester.

User Prerequisites

It is recommended that you have a working knowledge of Microsoft® Windows 7 or Windows 8 as well as a working knowledge of mechanical design principles.

Manual Objectives

The primary objective of this manual is to provide instruction on how to create part and assembly models, document those designs with drawing views, and automate the design process.

Upon completion of all chapters in this manual, you will be proficient in the following tasks:

- Basic and advanced part modeling techniques
- Drawing view creation techniques
- Assembly modeling techniques

While working through these materials, we encourage you to make use of the Autodesk Inventor help system, where you may find solutions to additional design problems that are not addressed specifically in this manual.

Book Description

This book provides the foundation for a hands-on course that covers basic and advanced Autodesk Inventor features used to create, edit, document, and print parts and assemblies. You learn about the part and assembly modeling through the real-world exercises in this manual.

Essentials Exercise Files

The exercise files for each chapter can be downloaded from: www.SDCpublications.com.

Projects

Most designers and engineers work on several projects at a time, with each project consisting of a number of files. To accommodate this, Autodesk Inventor uses projects to help organize related files and maintain links between files.

Each project has a project file that stores the paths to all files related to the project. When you attempt to open a file, Autodesk Inventor uses the paths in the current project file to locate other necessary files.

For convenience, a project file is provided for the exercises.

Using the Project File

Before starting the exercise, you must complete the following steps:

1. Start Autodesk Inventor.
2. On the Get Started tab Launch panel, click Projects.
3. In the Projects window, select Browse. Navigate to the folder, or click the Application Menu Manage Projects, where you placed the Essentials Exercises, and double-click the file "*Inv 2015 Ess Plus.ipj*".
4. The "Inv 2015 Ess Plus" project will become the current project.
5. Click Done in the Projects dialog box.
6. You can now start doing the exercises.

Acknowledgements

The authors would like to thank the SDC Publications staff for their expertise, knowledge, and attention to detail, as they have added a great deal to this book.

Chapter 1 – Getting Started

INTRODUCTION

In this chapter you learn about the following: Inventor's user interface, application options that control how Inventor looks and acts, how to start commands, create and control projects, and how to change your viewpoint to view parts from different perspectives. The knowledge that you learn in this chapter will lay a strong foundation for you to master Inventor.

OBJECTIVES

After completing this chapter, you will be able to do the following:

- [ ] List the main areas of Inventor's user interface
- [ ] Open files
- [ ] Create new files
- [ ] List the file types used in Autodesk Inventor
- [ ] Explain how to use the three save commands
- [ ] Use the Application Options to control how Inventor looks
- [ ] Start commands
- [ ] Describe how to use Inventor's help system
- [ ] Describe the purposes of a project file
- [ ] Create a project file for a single user
- [ ] Use navigation commands to change how you view a part

GETTING STARTED WITH AUTODESK INVENTOR

Autodesk Inventor's My Home screen looks similar to the following image. From here you access help, learn how to use Inventor, create a new file, open an existing file, see a list of recent files, and set the current project. You can return to the home screen by selecting the My Home tab My Home at the bottom of the screen or from the Get Started tab > Launch panel > click My Home.

Figure 1-1

USER INTERFACE

The default sketch environment of a part (.ipt) in the Autodesk Inventor application window is shown in the following image.

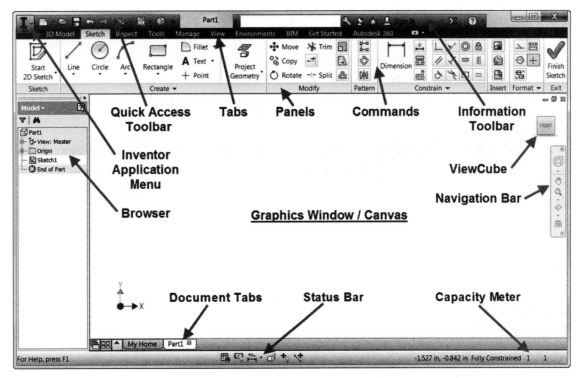

Figure 1-2

The screen is divided into the following areas:

Inventor Application Menu
Contains common commands for working with files. More information about the Application Menu is available in the next section.

Quick Access Toolbar
Access common commands as well as commands that can be added or removed.

Tabs
Changes available commands by clicking on a tab.

Panels
The panels will change to show available commands for the active tab, click on a tab to display a set of new panels and commands.

Commands
Access basic Windows and Autodesk Inventor commands. The set of commands will change to reflect the environment in which you are working.

Information Toolbar
Displays common help commands as well as Subscription services.

ViewCube
Displays the current viewpoint and allows you to change the orientation of the view.

Navigation Bar

Displays common viewing commands. Viewing commands can be added by clicking the bottom drop arrow.

Capacity Meter

Displays how many occurrences (parts) are in the active document, the number of open documents in the current session, and how much memory is being used. Note: The capacity meter that shows memory usage is available only on 32-bit computers.

Status Bar

Displays text messages about the current process.

Document Tabs

Each open file will be displayed on its own tab, and the My Home tab takes you to the Home screen if it has not been closed.

Browser

Shows the history of how the contents in the file were created. The browser can also be used to edit features and components.

Graphics Window/Canvas

Displays the graphics of the current file.

INVENTOR APPLICATION MENU

Besides selecting commands for working with files, you can control how the recent or open documents are listed in the menu. The following image shows the functionality available from the Inventor Application Menu.

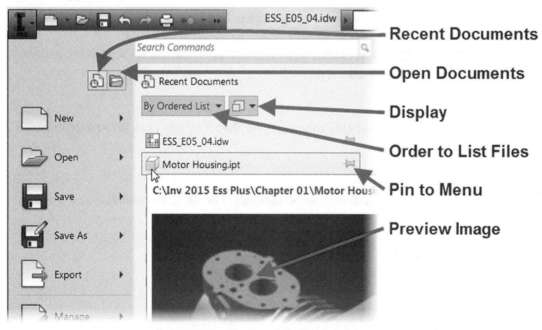

Figure 1-3

Recent Documents
Displays documents that were previously opened.

Open Documents
Displays documents that are opened.

Display
Controls what is displayed in the list: icons or images and what size.

Order to List Files
Controls the order that the files are listed: by Ordered List, by Access Date, by Size, or by Type.

Pin to Menu
Click the push pin to keep the file in the list no matter when it was last opened.

Preview Image
Hover the cursor over a file to see a larger image of the file when it was last saved.

 TIP: Double-click on the Inventor Application button, and a dialog box will appear asking you to save each unsaved document and then Inventor will close.

RIBBON
The ribbon displays commands that are relevant to the selected tab. The current tab is highlighted in green and is also green if it supports the current environment. The commands are arranged by panels. The most common commands are larger in size while less used commands are smaller and positioned to the right of the larger command. Commands may also be available in the drop list of a command or in the name of the panel. For example there is a drop list available under the Circle icon located in the Create panel, as shown in the following image that shows the Sketch tab active in a part file.

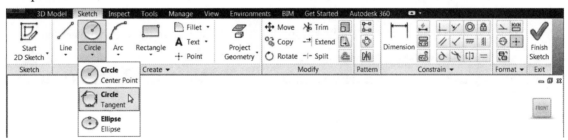

Figure 1-4

The ribbon can be modified by right-clicking on the Panel; the following image on the left shows the main options or you click the down arrow to the right of the panel to turn panels on / off as shown in the following image on the right.

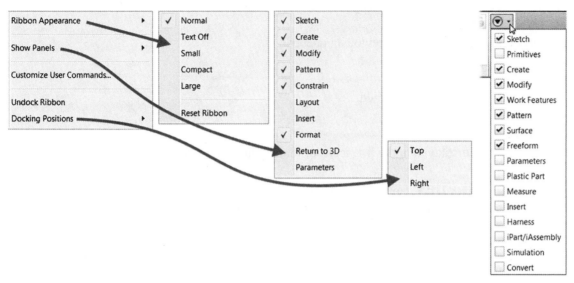

Figure 1-5

- **Ribbon Appearance** – Changes how the Ribbon is displayed, turns text off, and changes the size of the commands
- **Show Panels** – Adds and removes Panels
- **Customize User Commands** – Adds commands to a User Panel
- **Undock Ribbon** – Allows the ribbon to be freely moved
- **Docking Positions** – Changes the location of the Ribbon

QUICK ACCESS TOOLBAR

The Quick Access toolbar is located at the top left corner of the screen and is used to access commonly used commands. Commands can be added or removed from the Quick Access toolbar.

To add a command to the Quick Access toolbar follow these steps

1. Move the cursor over a command that you want to add to the Quick Access toolbar and right-click.
2. Click Add to Quick Access Toolbar from the menu as shown in the following image.

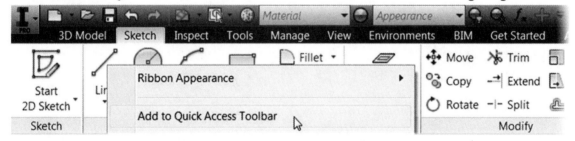

Figure 1-6

To remove a command from the Quick Access toolbar follow these steps

1. Move the cursor over the command to remove and right-click.
2. Click Remove from Quick Access Toolbar as shown in the following image.

Figure 1-7

OPEN FILES

To open files follow one of these techniques:

- Click the Open command in the Quick Access toolbar as shown on the left of the following image.
- Click the Open command in the Get Started tab > Launch panel as shown in the following image in the middle.
- Click the Inventor Application menu in the top-left corner of the screen and click Open as shown in the following image on the right.
- Press CTRL + O.

Figure 1-8

The Open dialog box will appear as shown in the following image. The directory that opens by default is set in the current project file. You can open files from other directories that are not defined in the current project file, but this is not recommended. Part, drawing, and assembly relationships may not be resolved when you reopen an assembly that contains components outside the locations defined in the current project file. Projects are covered later in this chapter.

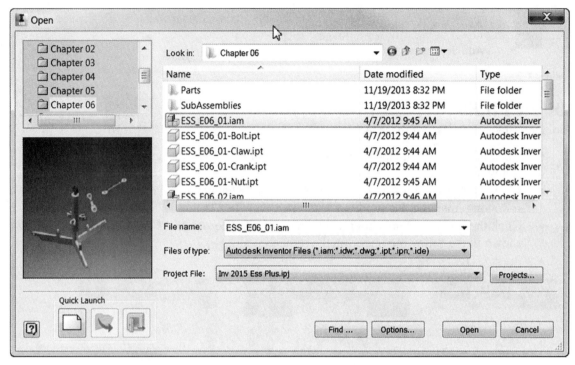

Figure 1-9

Opening Multiple Documents

You can open multiple Autodesk Inventor files at the same time by holding down the CTRL key and selecting the files to open as shown in the following image. Each file will be opened in its own window in a single Autodesk Inventor session. The files can also be arranged to fit the screen or to appear cascaded. If the files are arranged or cascaded, click a file to activate it. Only one file can be active at a time.

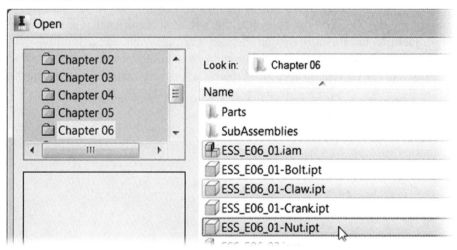

Figure 1-10

Document Tabs

When multiple documents are open in Inventor, each document appears in a tab in the lower left corner of the graphics window. The current document is represented with an "x" to the right of the file name and the tab has a white background. You can see a preview of an open document by hovering the cursor over the tab. In the same area, you can cascade, arrange, or list the open documents as shown in the following image.

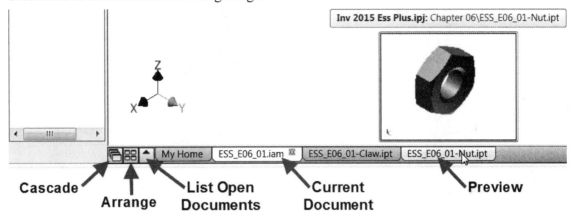

Figure 1-11

NEW FILES

Like the Open command there are many ways to create a new file. To create a new Inventor file, follow one of these techniques:

- Click the New command in the Quick Access toolbar as shown in the following image on the left.
- To start a new file based on one of the default templates click the down arrow next to the New icon in the Quick Access toolbar as shown in the following image, second from the left.
- Click the New command in the Get Started tab > Launch Panel as shown in the following image, third from the left.
- Click the Inventor Application menu in the top-left corner of the screen and click New as shown in the image on the right.
- Click New on the Home page.
- Press CTRL + N.

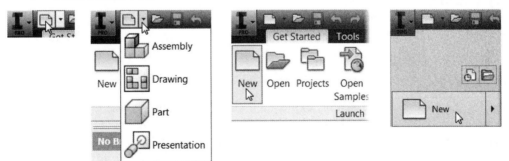

Figure 1-12

The Create New File dialog box will appear as shown in the following image. Begin by selecting the type of file to create or one of the folders from the left column, and then click on a template from the Part, Assembly, Drawing or Presentation section. A preview and a description will appear on the right side of the dialog box. To start a new file double-click on a template or after a template is selected, click Create on the bottom-right of the dialog box. If Autodesk Inventor Professional is installed, a Mold Design folder will exist in the list of template folders.

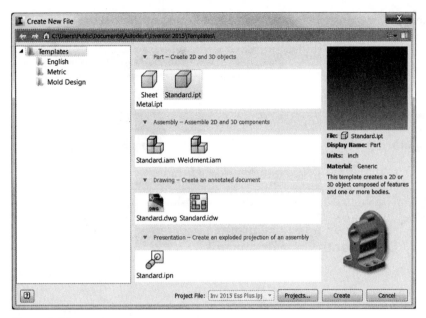

Figure 1-13

FILE INFORMATION

While creating parts, assemblies, presentation files, and drawing views, data is stored in separate files with different file extensions. This section describes the different file types and the options for creating them.

File Types

The following section describes the main file types that you can create in Autodesk Inventor, their file extensions, and descriptions of their uses.

Part (.ipt)

Part files contain only one part, which can be either 2D or 3D.

Assembly (.iam)

Assembly files can consist of a single part, multiple parts, or subassemblies. The parts themselves are saved to their own part file and are referenced (linked) in the assembly file. See Chapter 6 for more information about assemblies.

Presentation (.ipn)

Presentation files show parts of an assembly exploded in different states. A presentation file is associated with an assembly, and any changes made to the assembly will be updated in the presentation file. A presentation file can be animated, showing how parts are assembled or disassembled. The presentation file extension is ipn, but you save animations as an AVI or WMV file. See Chapter 6 for more information about presentation files.

Sheet Metal (.ipt)

Sheet metal files are part files that have the sheet metal environment loaded. In the sheet metal environment, you can create sheet metal parts and flat patterns. You can create a sheet metal part while in a regular part. This requires that you load the sheet metal environment manually.

Drawing (.dwg and .idw)

Drawing files can contain 2D projected drawing views of parts, assemblies, and/or presentation files. You can add dimensions and annotations to drawing views. The parts and assemblies in drawing files are linked, like the parts and assemblies in assembly and presentation files. See Chapter 5 for more information about drawing views.

Project (.ipj)

Project files are structured XML files that contain search paths to locations of all the files in the project. The search paths are used to find the files in a project.

iFeature (.ide)

iFeature files can contain one or more 3D features or 2D sketches that can be inserted into a part file. You can place size limits and ranges on iFeatures to enhance their functionality.

SAVE FILE OPTIONS

There are three options on the Inventor Application button for saving your files: Save, Save Copy As, and Save All as shown in the following image.

Figure 1-14

Save

The Save command, saves the current document with the same name to the location where you created it. If this is the first time that a new file is saved, you are prompted for a file name and file location.

 TIP: To use the Save command, click the Save icon on the Quick Access toolbar, use the *shortcut keys CTRL + S, or click Save on the Inventor Application menu.*

Save All

Use the Save All command to save all open documents and their dependents. The files are saved with the same name to the location where you created them. The first time that a new file is saved, you will be prompted for a file name and file location.

Save As

Use the Save As command to save the active document with a new name and location, if required. A new file is created and is made active.

Save Copy As

Use the Save Copy As command to save the active document with a new name and location, if required. A new file is created but is not made active. You can also save the current file as different file formats that other CAD systems can open.

Save Copy As Template

Use the Save Copy As Template command to save the current file to the template folder. New files can be based on the template file. Templates can be saved in the existing folders, or you can create a subdirectory in the Autodesk\Inventor (version number)\ templates directory, and add a file to it. A new template tab, with the same name as the subdirectory, is created automatically when a file is added to the new folder.

Pack and Go

Use the Pack and Go command to copy all the files that are used to create the current file to a specified location.

Save Reminder

You can have Inventor remind you to save a file. Inventor will NOT automatically save the file. After a predetermined amount of time has expired without saving the file, a notification bubble appears in the upper right corner of the screen as shown on the left of the following image. The time can be adjusted via the Application Options Save tab as shown on the right of the following image. The time can be adjusted from 1 minute to 9999 minutes, or uncheck this option to turn off the notification.

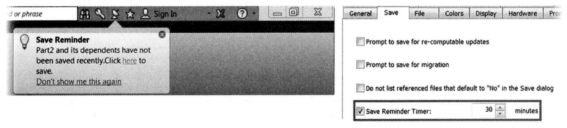

Figure 1-15

APPLICATION OPTIONS

Autodesk Inventor can be customized to your preferences. On the Inventor Application Menu, click Options, or from the Tools tab > Application Options, to open the Application Options dialog box as shown in the following image. You set options on each of the tabs to control specific actions in the Autodesk Inventor software. The application options affect all Inventor documents that are open or will be created. Each section is covered in more detail in the pertinent sections throughout this book. For more information about application options, see the Help system.

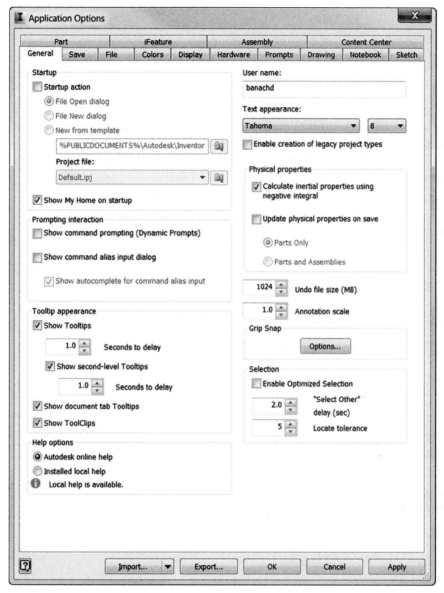

Figure 1-16

General

Set general options for how Autodesk Inventor operates.

Save

Set how files are saved.

File

Set where files are located.

Colors

Change the color scheme and color of the background on your screen. Determine if reflections and textures will be displayed.

Display

Adjust how parts look. Your video card and your requirements affect the appearance of parts on your screen. Experiment with different settings to achieve maximum video performance.

Hardware

Adjust the interaction between your video card and the Autodesk Inventor software. The software is dependent upon your video card. Take time to make sure that you are running a supported video card and the recommended video drivers. If you experience video-related issues, experiment with the options on the Hardware tab. Consult the help system for more information about video cards and drivers.

Prompts

Modify the response given to messages that are displayed.

Drawing

Specify the way that drawings are created and displayed.

Notebook

Specify how the Engineer's Notebook is displayed.

Sketch

Modify how sketch data is created and displayed.

Part

Change how parts are created.

iFeature

Adjust where iFeatures data is stored.

Assembly

Specify how assemblies are controlled and behave.

Content Center

Specify the preferences for using the Content Center.

EXERCISE 1-1: USER INTERFACE

In this exercise, you change the user interface by moving the Ribbon, Quick Access toolbar, and add and remove commands to the Quick Access toolbar.

1. Click the New command from the Quick Access toolbar, in the Create New File dialog box click the English folder on the left column, and in the Part section double-click Standard (in).ipt as shown in the following image.

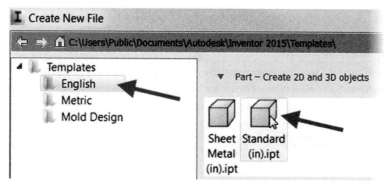

Figure 1-17

2. Move the Ribbon to different locations. Move the cursor anywhere over the Ribbon and right-click, from the menu click Docking Positions > Left as shown in the following image on the left.

3. Repeat the process to move the Ribbon to the Right side.

4. Undock the Ribbon, right-click on the Ribbon, and from the menu click Undock Ribbon as shown in the following image on the right. Move the Ribbon to different locations.

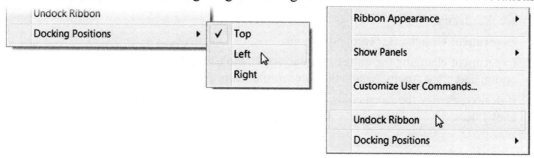

Figure 1-18

5. Move the Ribbon back to its original top position, right-click on the Ribbon, and from the menu click Docking Positions > Top as shown in the previous image on the left.

6. Change the appearance of the Ribbon, right-click on the Ribbon, and from the menu click Ribbon Appearance. Try the different options to change the Ribbon's appearance.

7. Reset the Ribbon back to its original state by clicking Reset Ribbon from the menu as shown in the following image. Click Yes when prompted to reset the ribbon.

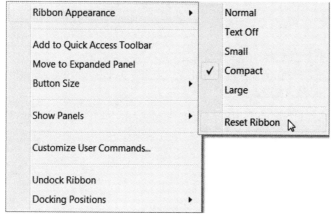

Figure 1-19

8. Add a command to the Quick Access toolbar. Click the Tools tab Options panel and right-click on the Application Options command, and click Add to Quick Access toolbar as shown in the following image on the left.

9. If desired remove the Application Options command from the Quick Access toolbar. Move the cursor over the Application Options command in the Quick Access toolbar, right-click, and click Remove from Quick Access Toolbar as shown in the following image on the right.

Figure 1-20

10. Change the background color of the graphics screen. Click the Application Options command that you just added to the Quick Access toolbar or click Inventor Application Menu and click Options at the bottom of the menu.

11. Click the Colors tab, and from the Color scheme area select a scheme and click Apply to see the change.

12. Experiment with the Background options.

13. Experiment changing the colors of the icons. In the Color Theme area, click the Amber option and click Apply. Notice the color of the icons change.

14. If desired change the icons color back to Cobalt as shown in the following image and click OK.

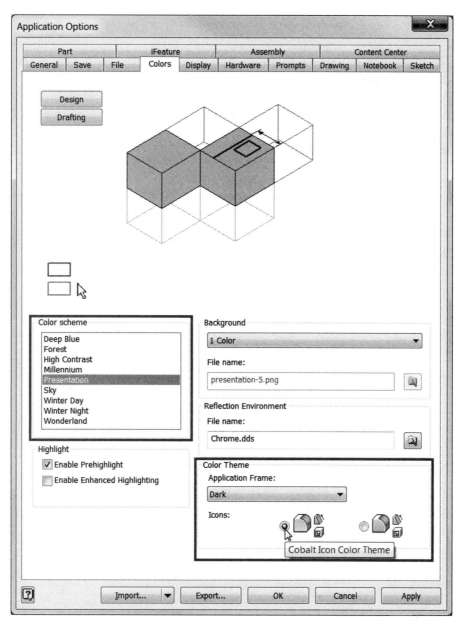

Figure 1-21

15. As you work with Inventor, adjust the user interface to meet your requirements.

16. Close the file. Do not save changes. End of exercise.

COMMAND ENTRY

There are several methods to issue commands in Autodesk Inventor. In the following sections, you will learn how to start a command. There are no right or wrong methods for starting a command, and with experience, you will develop your own preference.

To stop a command, either press the ESC key, right-click, and click Done from the menu or select another icon.

Tooltips

In the last section, you learned how to control the appearance of the Ribbon. The main function of the Ribbon is to hold the commands in a logical fashion, which is done by dividing the commands into panels. To start a command from a panel, move the cursor over the desired icon, and a command tip appears with the name of the command. You can control the tooltip from the Application Options under the General tab as shown on the left in the following image. The first level tooltip displays an abbreviated command description as shown in the middle image. If the cursor hovers over the icon longer, a more detailed command description will appear as shown on the right.

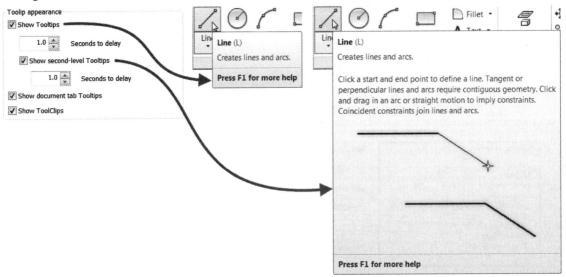

Figure 1-22

Some of the icons in the Panel have a small down arrow in the right side. Select the arrow to see additional commands. To activate a command, move the cursor over a command icon and click. The command that is selected will appear first in the list replacing the previous command.

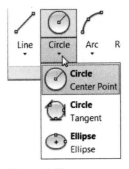

Figure 1-23

Marking Menus and Context (Overflow) Menus

Autodesk Inventor also uses marking menus and context menus also referred to as overflow menus. These menus appear when you press the right mouse button. The marking menu consists of commands that appear around the center of the cursor and consist of commands that are commonly performed for the current environment. The context (overflow) menus appear below the marking menu and contain options that are relevant to the current task. A marking menu only appears when you right-click in the graphics window. The following image on the left shows the marking menu that appears while in the Line command. As you gain experience with Inventor you can start a command from the top portion of the marking menu by right-clicking and moving the cursor (before the menu appears within 250 milliseconds) in the direction of the command and release the mouse button as shown on the right in the following image. This technique is referred to as gesturing.

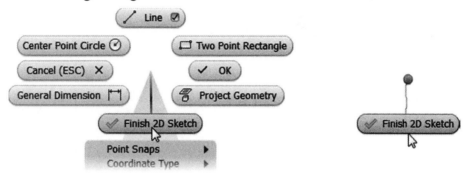

Figure 1-24

Autodesk Inventor Shortcut Keys

Autodesk Inventor has keystrokes called shortcut keys that are preprogrammed. While in a command, the tooltip displays the shortcut key in parenthesis if a shortcut key is available. To start a command via a shortcut key, press the desired preprogrammed key(s). The keys can be reprogrammed by clicking the Tools tab and click Customize.

Repeat Last Command

To restart a command without reselecting the command in a panel bar, either press ENTER or the spacebar, or right-click and click the top entry in the menu, Repeat "the last command." The following image shows the Line command being restarted.

Figure 1-25

Undo and Redo

You may want to undo an action that you just performed, or undo an undo. The Undo command backs up Autodesk Inventor one function at a time. If you undo too far, you can use the Redo command to move forward one step at a time. The Zoom, Orbit, and Pan commands do not affect the Undo and Redo commands. To start the commands, select the command from the Quick Access toolbar as shown in the following image. The Undo command is to the left, and the Redo command is to the right. The shortcut keys are CTRL Z for Undo and CTRL Y for Redo.

Figure 1-26

HELP SYSTEM

The Help system in Inventor goes beyond basic command definition by offering assistance while you design. The commands in the Information Toolbar on the top-right corner of the screen will assist you while you design. To get help on a topic, enter a keyword in the area entitled "Type a keyword or phrase." To see the other help mechanisms that make up the Help System, click the drop arrow to the right of the question mark as shown in the following image.

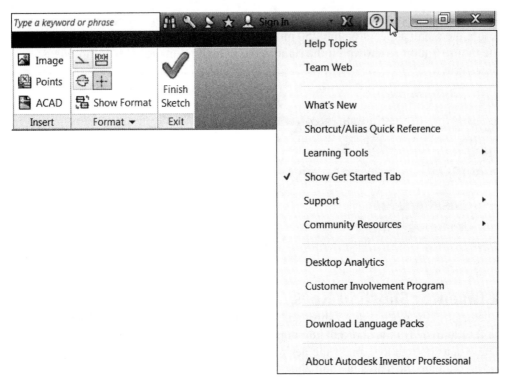

Figure 1-27

Other options to access the Help system include the following methods:

- Press the F1 key, and the Help system assists you with the active operation.
- Click an option on the Help menu.
- Click a Help option on the Information Toolbar.
- In any dialog box, click the 🔡 icon.
- Click an option on the Get Started tab > Videos and Tutorials panel.
- Click on How To or Help Topics on a right-click context menu.

PROJECTS IN AUTODESK INVENTOR

Almost every design that you create in Autodesk Inventor involves more than a single file. Each part, assembly, presentation, and drawing created is stored in a separate file. Each of these files has a unique file extension. There are many times when a design will reference other files. An assembly file, for example, will reference a number of individual part files and/or additional subassemblies. When you open the parent or top-level assembly, it must contain information that allows Autodesk Inventor to locate each of the referenced files. Autodesk Inventor uses a project file to organize and manage these file-location relationships. There is no limit to the number of projects you can create, but only one project can be active at any given time.

You can structure the file locations for a design project in many ways. A single person design shop has different needs from a large manufacturing company or a design team with multiple designers working on the same project. In addition to project files, Autodesk Inventor includes a program called Autodesk Vault that controls basic check-out and check-in file-reservation mechanisms; these control file access for multiuser design teams. Autodesk Inventor always has a project named Default. Specifically, if all the files defining a design are located in a single folder or in a folder tree where each referenced part is located with its parent or in a subfolder underneath the parent, the Default project may be all that is required.

TIP: It is recommended that files in different folders never have the same name to avoid the possibility of Autodesk Inventor resolving a reference to a file of the same name but in a different folder.

Project Setup

To reduce the possibility of file resolution problems later in the design process, always plan your project folder structure before you start a design. A typical project might consist of parts and assemblies unique to the project; standard components that are unique to your company; and off-the-shelf components such as fasteners, fittings, or electrical components.

Project File Search Options

Before you create a project, you need to understand how Autodesk Inventor stores cross-file reference information and how it resolves that information to find the referenced file. Autodesk Inventor stores the file name, a subfolder path (if present) to the file, and a library name (optionally) as the three fundamental pieces of information about the referenced file.

When you use the Default project file, the subfolder path is located relative to the folder containing the referencing file. It may be empty or may go deeper in the subfolder hierarchy, but it can never be located at a level above the parent folder.

When you create a project file, you do not need to add subfolder(s) as search paths. The subfolder(s) are automatically searched and do not need to be added to the project file.

Creating Projects

To create a new project or edit an existing project, use the Autodesk Inventor Project File Editor. The Project File Editor displays a list of shortcuts to previously active projects. A project file has an .ipj file extension and typically is stored in the home folder for the design-specific documents, while a shortcut to the project file is stored in the Projects Folder. The Projects Folder is specified on the File tab of the Application Options dialog box as shown in the following image. All projects with a shortcut in the Projects Folder are listed in the top pane of the Project File Editor.

Figure 1-28

You create or edit a project file by clicking the Projects button in the New or Open dialog box or by clicking Projects from the Get Started tab > Launch panel, as shown in the following image on the left, or from the Inventor Application Menu click Manage and click Projects as shown on the right of the following image.

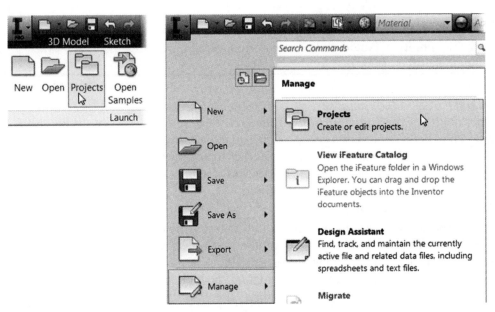

Figure 1-29

The Projects dialog box will appear as shown in the following image. The Projects dialog box is divided into two panes. The top pane lists shortcuts to the project files that have been active previously. Double-click on a project's name to make it the active project. All Inventor files must be closed before making a project active. Only one project file can be active in Autodesk Inventor at a time. The bottom pane reflects information about the project selected in the top pane. If a project file already exists, click on the Browse button on the bottom of the dialog box, then navigate to, and select the project file.

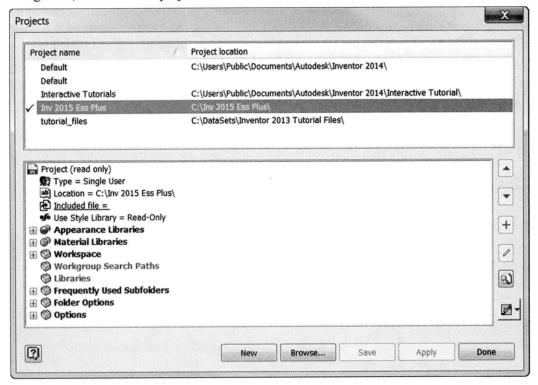

Figure 1-30

TIP: When defining a path to a folder on a network, it is recommended to define a Universal Naming Convention (UNC) path starting with the server name (\\Server\...) and not to use shared (mapped) network drives.

To create a new project, follow these steps:

1. In the Projects dialog box, click the New button at the bottom to initiate the Inventor project wizard.
2. In the Inventor project wizard, follow the prompts to the following questions.

What Type of Project Are You Creating?

If Autodesk Vault is installed, you will be prompted to create a New Vault project or a New Single-User project. If Autodesk Vault is not installed, only a New Single-User project type will appear in the list.

New Single-User Project

This is the default project type, which is used when only one user will reference Autodesk Inventor files. It creates one workspace where Autodesk Inventor files are stored and any needed library location(s), and it sets the Project Type to Single User. No workgroup is defined but can be defined later. The next section covers the steps for creating a new single-user project. For more information on projects, consult the online Help system.

New Vault Project

This project type is used with Autodesk Vault and is not available until you install Autodesk Vault. It creates a project with one workspace and any needed library location(s), and it sets the multiuser mode to Vault. More information about Autodesk Vault appears later in this section.

Creating a New Single-User Project

Click on New Single User Project as shown in the following image. If Autodesk Vault is not installed, New Single User Project will be the only available option.

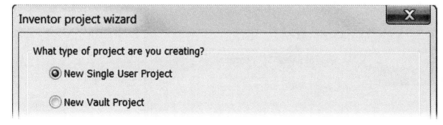

Figure 1-31

Name

Click the Next button, and specify the project file name and location on the second page of the Inventor project wizard. Enter a descriptive project file name in the Name field as shown in the following image. The project file will use this name with an .ipj file extension.

Project (Workspace) Folder

This specifies the path to the home or top-level folder for the project. You can accept the suggested path, enter a path, or click the Browse button (...) to manually locate the path. The default home folder is a subfolder under My Documents, or wherever you last browsed, that is named to match the project file name.

Project File to Be Created

The full path name of the project file is displayed below the Location field.

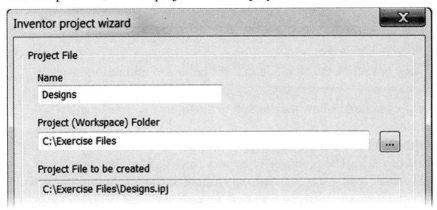

Figure 1-32

 TIP: In the workspace folder it is preferable for the project file (.ipj) to be the only Inventor file stored in this folder. Then create a subfolder under the workspace folder.

Click the Next button at the bottom of the Inventor project wizard, and specify the project library search paths.

You can add library search paths from existing project files to this new project file. The library search paths from every project with a shortcut in your Projects Folder are listed on the left in the Inventor project wizard dialog box as shown in the following image. You can add and remove libraries from the New Project area by clicking on their names in either the All Projects area or the New Project area and then clicking the arrows in the middle of the dialog box. The libraries listed by default in the All Projects list will match those in the project file that you selected prior to starting the New Project process.

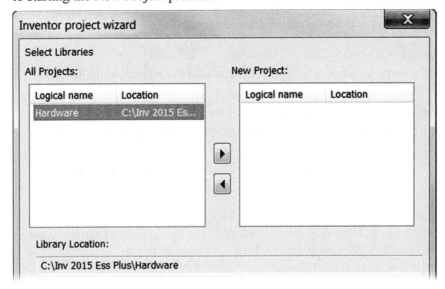

Figure 1-33

Click the Finish button to create the project. If a new directory will be created, click OK in the Inventor Project Editor dialog box. The new project will appear in the Open dialog box. Double-click on a project's name in the Projects dialog box to make it the active project. A checkmark will appear to the left of the active project as shown in the following image.

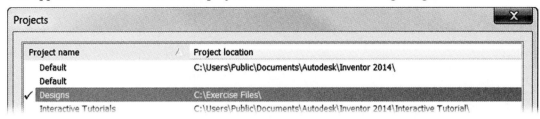

Figure 1-34

AUTODESK VAULT

Autodesk Vault is available when Inventor is installed. The Autodesk Vault enhances the data management process by managing more than just Autodesk Inventor files and by tracking file versions as well as team member access. Controlling access to data, tracking modifications, and communicating the design history are important aspects of managing collaborative data. When working with a vault project, your data files are stored in a central repository that records the entire development history of the design. The vault manages Inventor and non-Inventor files alike. In order to modify a file, it first must be checked out of the vault. When the file is checked back into the vault, the modifications are stored as the most recent version for the project, and the previous version is sequentially indexed as part of the living history of the design.

EXERCISE 1-2: PROJECTS

In this exercise, you create a project file for a single-user project, open existing files, delete the project file, and make an existing project file current.

1. Prior to creating a new project file, close all Inventor files and ensure that the exercise files have been copy to your computer, the default folder is *C:\Inv 2015 Ess Plus*. To download the exercise, see the Essentials Exercise Files section in the Introduction section in the front of the book.

2. From the Get Started tab > Launch panel click Projects.

3. You now create a new project file. Click the New button at the bottom of the Projects dialog box.

4. For the type of project to create, click New Single User Project, and then click Next.

5. In the next dialog box of the Inventor project wizard, enter ABC Machine in the Name field.

6. In the Project (Workspace) Folder field type C:\My First Project as shown in the following image.

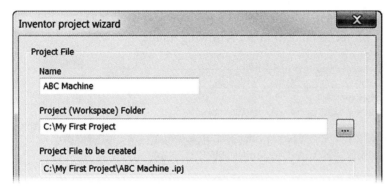

Figure 1-35

 TIP: It is a good practice to place files such as parts, assemblies, and drawings in sub-folders below the top-level folder, where the project file is located.

7. Click Next to see a list of Libraries that are used in other projects library search paths. The New Project list on the right side should be blank. For this project no libraries will be added.

8. Click Finish and then click OK to create the new project path. The new project file is highlighted in the upper pane of the Project File Editor and should have a check mark to the left of its name indicating that it is the active project.

9. The options for the active project are listed in the lower pane. In the lower pane expand Workspace and notice that the Workspace search path is listed as a period "." as shown in the following image. The "." denotes that the workspace location is relative to the location where the project file is saved.

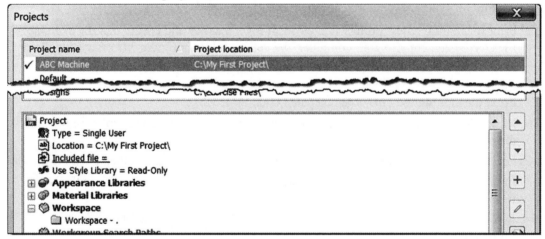

Figure 1-36

 TIP: To make it easier to use subfolders that are below the workspace, you can add them to the Frequently Used Subfolders setting by right-clicking on the Frequently Used Subfolders option, and click Add Paths from Directory as shown in the following image. The project file that you will use for the remaining exercises has the frequently used subfolders added.

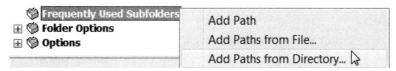

Figure 1-37

10. In the bottom of the Projects dialog box, click Done.

11. Click the Open icon on the Quick Access toolbar. Notice that the Look in: location is in the My First Project folder and the active project is ABC Machine as shown in the following image.

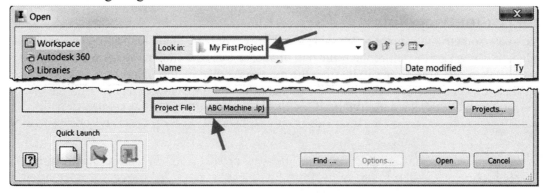

Figure 1-38

12. Close the Open dialog box by clicking the Cancel button.

13. You must change the active project file to successfully complete the remaining exercises. Close all files currently open in Autodesk Inventor.

14. Click Inventor Application Menu then click Manage > Projects.

15. To add an existing project file to the current list, click the Browse ... button at the bottom of the dialog box. Navigate to and select *C:\Inv 2015 Ess Plus\Inv 2015 Ess Plus.ipj*. This project should now be the current project. This project will be used for the remaining exercises. Expand the Frequently Used Subfolders section to verify that each chapter has its own subfolder.

16. Right-click on the project ABC Machine in the upper pane and select delete as shown in the following image.

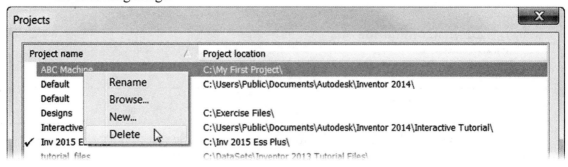

Figure 1-39

17. Close the Projects dialog box by clicking Done.

18. End of exercise.

VIEWPOINT OPTIONS

When you work on a 2D sketch, the default view is looking straight down at the XY plane, which is often referred to as a plan view. When you work in 3D, it is helpful to view objects from a different viewpoint and to zoom in and out or pan the objects on the screen. The next section guides you through the most common methods for viewing objects from different perspectives and viewpoints. As you use these commands, the physical objects remain unmoved. Your perspective or viewpoint of the objects is what creates the perceived movement of the part. If you are performing an operation while a viewing command is issued, the operation resumes after the transition to the new view is completed.

Home (Isometric) View

Change to an isometric viewpoint by pressing the F6 key, click the home icon above the ViewCube as shown on the left of the following image, or by right-clicking in the graphics window and then selecting Home View from the menu as shown on the right of the following image. The view on the screen transitions to a predetermined home view. You can redefine the home view with a ViewCube option. The ViewCube is explained later in this section.

Figure 1-40

Navigation Bar

The Navigation bar, as shown in the following image, contains commands that will allow you to zoom, pan, and rotate the geometry on the screen. The default location for the Navigation bar is on the right side of the graphics window, but it can be repositioned. Commands are also available below the displayed commands. When commands are selected, they will become the top level command. Descriptions of the viewing commands follow.

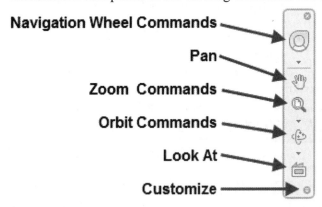

Figure 1-41

TIP: The navigation commands are also available on the View tab > Navigate panel.

Navigation Wheel

Click the Navigation Wheel icon to turn on the steering wheel, which contains eight viewing options.

Pan

Moves the view to a new location. Issue the Pan command, or press and hold the F2 key. Press and hold the left mouse button, and the screen moves in the same direction that the cursor moves. If you have a mouse with a wheel, hold down the wheel, and the screen moves in the same direction that the cursor is moved.

Zoom Commands

- **Zoom:** Zooms in or out from the parts. Issue the Zoom command, or press and hold the F3 key. Then, in the graphics window, press and hold the left mouse key. Move the mouse toward you to make the parts appear larger, and away from you to make the parts appear smaller. Another method is to roll the wheel on the mouse toward you, and the parts appear larger; roll the wheel away from you, and the parts appear smaller.
- **Zoom All:** Maximizes the screen with all parts that are in the current file. The screen transitions to the new view.
- **Zoom Window:** Zooms in on an area that is designated by two points. Issue the Zoom Window command and select the first point. With the mouse button depressed, move the cursor to the second point. A rectangle representing the window appears. When the correct window is displayed on the screen, release the mouse button, and the view transitions to it.
- **Zoom Selected:** Fills the screen with the maximum size of a selected face, faces, or a part. Either select the face or faces and then issue the Zoom Selected command, or press the END key, or launch the Zoom Selected command. Once the command is started, select the face or faces to which you wish to zoom.

Orbit Commands

- **Free Orbit:** Rotates your viewpoint dynamically. Issue the Free Orbit command; an Orbit symbol - circular image with lines at the quadrants and a center point appears. To rotate your viewpoint, click a point inside the circle, and keep the mouse button pressed as you move the cursor. Your viewpoint rotates in the direction of the cursor movement. When you release the mouse button, the viewpoint stops rotating. To accept the view orientation, press the ESC key or right-click and select Done from the menu. Click the outside of the circle to rotate the viewpoint about the center of the circle. To rotate the viewpoint about the vertical axis, click one of the horizontal lines on the circle and, with the mouse button pressed, move the cursor sideways. To rotate the viewpoint about the horizontal axis, click one of the vertical lines on the circle and, with the mouse button pressed, move the cursor upward or downward. The Constrained Orbit command is available below the Orbit command.
  - A shortcut to start the Free Orbit command is to press and hold down the F4 key and a circular image appears with lines at the quadrants and center. With the F4 key depressed, rotate the viewpoint. When you finish rotating the viewpoint, release the F4 key. If you are performing an operation while the F4 key is pressed, that operation will resume after you release the F4 key.
  - Another option to quickly rotate your viewpoint is to hold down the Shift key and press down the middle mouse button or wheel on the mouse. Once the rotate glyph appears on the screen, you can release the Shift key. While holding down

the wheel, move the mouse, and your viewpoint will rotate. With this option, no other options are available. Release the wheel to complete the operation.

- **Constrained Orbit:** Use the Constrained Orbit command to rotate the model about the horizontal screen axes like a turntable. Click one of the horizontal lines on the circle and, with the mouse button pressed, move the cursor sideways. The model is rotated about the model space center point set in the Navigation Wheel CENTER command.

Look At

Changes your viewpoint so that you are looking perpendicular to a plane or rotates the screen viewpoint to be horizontal to an edge. Issue the Look At command or press the PAGE UP key; then select a plane or edge. The Look At command can also be issued by selecting a plane or edge, right-clicking while the cursor is in the graphics window, and selecting Look At from the menu.

Customize the Navigation Bar

To modify the Navigation bar, click the down arrow on the bottom of the Navigation Toolbar as shown in the following image. Click a command to add or remove it from the Navigation bar. You can also reposition the toolbar by clicking the options under Docking positions.

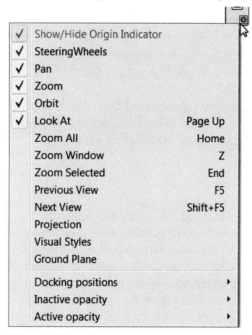

Figure 1-42

ViewCube

The ViewCube allows you to quickly change the viewpoint of the screen. With the ViewCube turned on, move the cursor over the ViewCube. Move the cursor over the home in the ViewCube to return to the default home (isometric) view as shown in the following image.

Figure 1-43

Change the viewpoint by using one of the following techniques.

Isometric
Change to a different isometric view by clicking a corner on the ViewCube as shown in the following image, second from the left.

Face
Change the viewpoint so it looks directly at a plane by clicking a plane on the ViewCube as shown in the following image, third from the left.

Rotate in 90 Degree Increments
When looking at the plane of a ViewCube, you can rotate the view 90 degrees by clicking one of the arcs with arrows or one of the four inside facing triangles as shown in the following image, fourth from the left.

Edge
You can also orientate the viewpoint to an edge. Click an edge on the ViewCube as shown in the following image on the right.

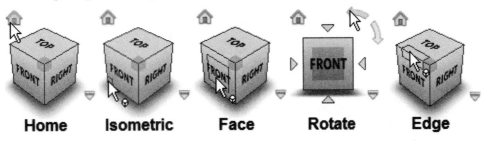

Home   Isometric   Face   Rotate   Edge

Figure 1-44

Dynamic Rotate via ViewCube
To dynamically rotate your viewpoint, click on the ViewCube and keep the mouse button pressed as you move the cursor. Your viewpoint rotates in the direction of the cursor movement. When you release the mouse button, the viewpoint stops rotating. When the viewpoint does not match a defined viewpoint, the ViewCube edges appear in dashed lines from one of the corners as shown in the following image. To smooth the rotation, right-click on the ViewCube and click Options and uncheck Snap to closest view.

Figure 1-45

Dynamically Rotate Viewpoint Shortcuts
While working, press and hold down the F4 key. The circular image appears with lines at the quadrants and center. With the F4 key still depressed, rotate the viewpoint. When you finish rotating the viewpoint, release the F4 key. If you are performing an operation while the F4 key is pressed, that operation will resume after you release the F4 key.

Another option to quickly rotate your viewpoint is to hold down the Shift key and press the middle mouse button (or mouse wheel). Once the rotate glyph appears on the screen, you can release the Shift key and while holding down the wheel, move the mouse, and your viewpoint will rotate. With this option, no other options are available. The model(s) are rotated about the center of the model(s). Release the wheel to complete the operation.

EXERCISE 1-3: VIEWING A MODEL

In this exercise, you use Navigation commands that make it easier to work on your designs.

1. Open *C:\Inv 2015 Ess Plus\Chapter 01\ESS_E01_03.ipt*. Click the Chapter 01 subfolder from the Frequently Used Subfolders area on the left side of the dialog box, and then double-click on the file name as shown in the following image.

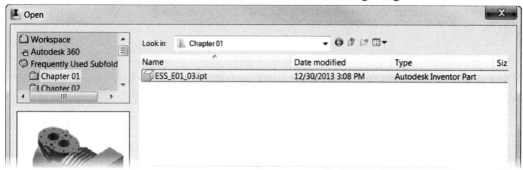

Figure 1-46

2. Move the cursor over the lower left foot of the motor housing and spin the wheel toward you. Inventor will zoom into the location of the cursor. This will fill the screen as shown in the following image.

Figure 1-47

3. Press F5 a few times to change the viewpoint to the previous views.
4. Press the F6 key to change the viewpoint to the home view.
5. Next rotate the viewpoint, from the Navigation bar, click the Free Orbit command. The Orbit symbol appears in the graphics screen as shown in the following image.

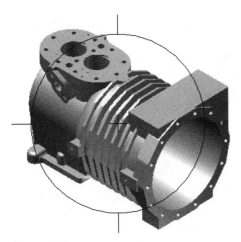

Figure 1-48

6. Move the cursor inside the circle of the Orbit symbol; notice how the cursor (glyph) changes as the cursor moves inside the orbit's circle.

7. Click and drag the cursor to rotate the model.

8. To return to the Home View, press F6, the Free Orbit command will still be active.

9. Place the cursor on one of the horizontal handles of the Orbit symbol, noting the cursor display.

10. Drag the cursor right or left to rotate the viewpoint about the Y axis. As you rotate the viewpoint, you will see the bottom of the assembly.

Figure 1-49

11. Cancel the command by pressing the ESC key.

12. Next you use the same Free Orbit command but use the shortcut key, press and hold down the F4 key, move the cursor inside the orbit's circle and click and hold down the left mouse button, and move the mouse to rotate the viewpoint. Soon as you release the F4 key the command will stop.

13. Press and hold down the Shift key and click and hold down the wheel on the mouse. Move the mouse to rotate the viewpoint.

14. Return to the home view by clicking the Home symbol above the ViewCube.

15. To change the viewpoint to predetermined isometric views, or directly at a plane, use the ViewCube. Click the Top-Front left corner of the ViewCube as shown on the left of the following image. Continue clicking the other corners of the ViewCube as shown in middle two images.

16. Change to the front view by clicking the Front plane on the ViewCube as shown on the right of the following image.

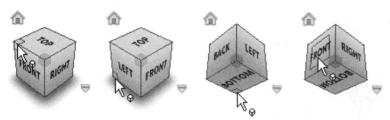

Figure 1-50

17. Rotate the view 90 degrees by clicking the arc with arrow in the ViewCube as shown on the left of the following image.

18. To look at the Top view that is also rotated by 90 degrees, click the left arrow as shown on the right of the following image.

Figure 1-51

19. Practice changing views by clicking the corners, faces, and edges of the ViewCube.

20. Click the Look At command from the Navigation bar as shown in the following image on the left. Select the planar face on the part as shown in the following middle image. The viewpoint will change so you are looking perpendicular to the selected plane as shown in the following image on the right.

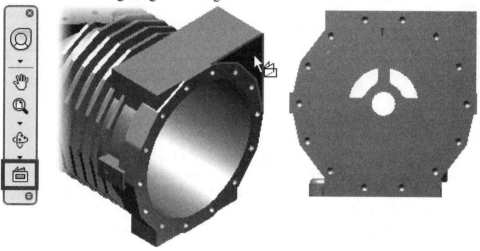

Figure 1-52

21. Continue to practice using the navigation commands.

22. Close the file. Do not save changes to the model. End of exercise.

CHECKING YOUR SKILLS

Use these questions to test your knowledge of the material covered in this chapter.

1. Explain the reasons why a project file is used.

2. True__ False__ Only one project can be active at any time.

3. True__ False__ Subfolders need to be added to the project file in order for the files to be found.

4. True__ False__ Autodesk Inventor stores the part, assembly information, and related drawing views in the same file.

5. True__ False__ Press and hold down the F4 key to dynamically rotate the viewpoint.

6. True__ False__ The Save Copy As command saves the active document with a new name, and then makes it current.

7. List four ways to access the Help system.

8. Explain how to change the location of the Ribbon.

9. True__ False__ Commands can be added to the Quick Access toolbar.

10. True__ False__ The ViewCube is used to rotate the active part or assembly file about the X axis.

11. True__ False__ Marking menus are used to add annotations to a part file.

12. True__ False__ The settings in the Application Options are global and affect all open and new Inventor files.

13. List three methods to repeat the last command.

14. Explain how to start a command from the marking menu without displaying the marking menu first.

15. True__ False__ By default Inventor will automatically save the current file every 10 minutes.

Chapter 2 – Sketching, Constraining, and Dimensioning

INTRODUCTION

Most 3D parts in Autodesk Inventor start from a 2D sketch. This chapter first provides a look at the application options for creating a part file and sketching. It then covers the three steps in creating a 2D parametric sketch: sketching a rough 2D outline of a part, applying geometric constraints, and then adding parametric dimensions. Lastly, you learn how to use 2D AutoCAD data in a sketch.

OBJECTIVES

After completing this chapter, you will be able to do the following:

☐ Change the part and sketch Application Options to meet your needs

☐ Sketch an outline of a part

☐ Create geometric constraints to a sketch to control design intent

☐ Use construction geometry to help constrain a sketch

☐ Dimension a sketch

☐ Change a dimension's value in a sketch

☐ Insert AutoCAD DWG data into a part's sketch

PART AND SKETCH APPLICATION OPTIONS

Before you start a new part, examine the part and sketch options in Autodesk Inventor that will affect how the part file will be created and how the sketching environment will look and act. While learning Autodesk Inventor, refer back to these option settings to determine which ones work best for you—there is no right or wrong settings.

Part Options

You can customize Autodesk Inventor Part options to your preferences. Click the Inventor Application Menu > Options button, and click on the Part tab, as shown in the following image. Descriptions of a couple of the most common Part options follow. For more information about the Application Options consult the help system. These settings are global—they will affect all active and new Autodesk Inventor documents.

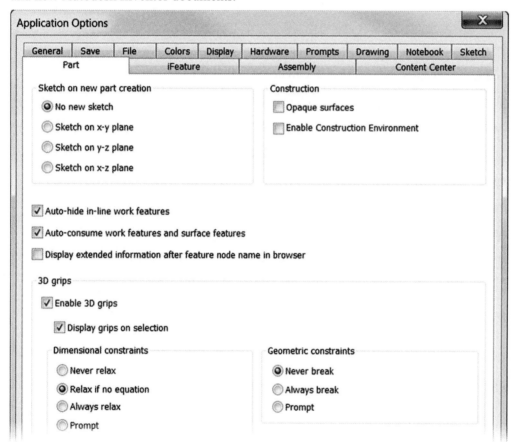

Figure 2-1

A common option that you may want to change is the first option; Sketch on New Part Creation. This option controls if and how a sketch is created when a part file is created.

No new sketch

When checked, Inventor does not set a sketch plane when you create a new part (this is the default setting).

Sketch on x-y plane

When checked, Inventor sets the x-y plane as the current sketch plane when you create a new part.

Sketch on y-z plane

When checked, Inventor sets the y-z plane as the current sketch plane when you create a new part.

Sketch on x-z plane

When checked, Inventor sets the x-z plane as the current sketch plane when you create a new part.

Sketch Options

Autodesk Inventor sketching options can be customized to your preferences. Click Inventor Application Menu > Options, and then click on the Sketch tab, as displayed in the following image. Descriptions of the most common Sketch options follow. For more information about the Application Options consult the help system. These settings are global, and all of them affect currently active Autodesk documents and Autodesk Inventor documents you open in the future.

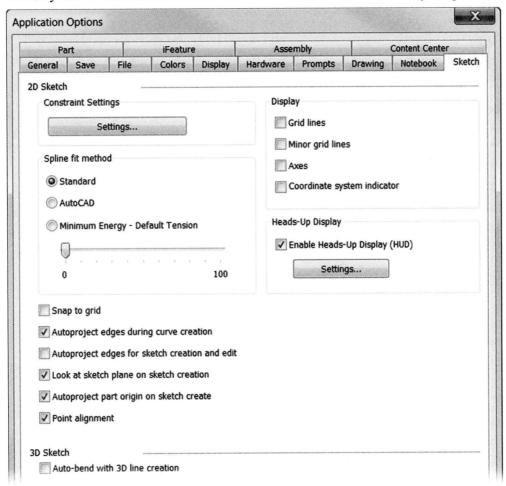

Figure 2-2

Following are descriptions of the common settings that you may want to change.

Constraint Settings

Click the Settings button to control how sketch constraints and dimensions behave.

Display

Grid lines
Toggles both minor and major grid lines on the screen on and off. To set the grid distance, click the Tools tab > Options panel > Document Settings command, and on the Sketch tab of the Document Settings dialog box, change the Snap Spacing and Grid Display.

Minor grid lines
Toggles the minor grid lines displayed on the screen on and off.

Axes
Toggles the lines that represent the X and Y-axis of the current sketch on and off.

Coordinate system indicator
Toggles the icon on and off that represents the X-, Y-, and Z-axes at the 0, 0, 0 coordinates of the current sketch.

Snap to Grid
When checked, endpoints of sketched objects snap to the intersections of the grid as the cursor moves over them.

Autoproject edges during curve creation
When checked, and while sketching, place the cursor over an object and it will be projected onto the current sketch. You can also toggle Autoproject on and off while sketching by right-clicking and selecting Autoproject from the menu.

Autoproject edges for sketch creation and edit
When checked, automatically projects all of the edges that define that plane onto the sketch plane as reference geometry when you create a new sketch.

Look at sketch plane on sketch creation and edit
When checked, automatically changes the view orientation to look directly at the new or active sketch.

Autoproject part origin on sketch create
When checked, the parts origin point will automatically be projected when a new sketch is created. It is recommended to keep this setting on.

Point alignment
When checked, automatically infers alignment (horizontal and vertical) between endpoints of newly created geometry. No sketch constraint is applied. If this option is not checked, points can still be inferred; this technique is covered later in this chapter in the Inferred Points section.

UNITS
Autodesk Inventor uses a default unit of measurement for every part and assembly file. The default unit is set from the template file from which you created the part or assembly file. When specifying numbers in dialog boxes with no unit, the default unit will be used. You can change the default unit in the active part or assembly document by clicking the Tools tab > Options panel > Document Settings button and click the Units tab as shown in the following image. The unit system values change for all of the existing values in that file.

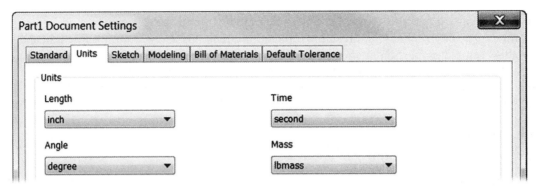

Figure 2-3

 TIP: In a drawing file, the appearance of dimensions is controlled by dimension styles. Drawing settings are covered in Chapter 5.

You can override the default unit for any value by entering the desired unit. If you were working in a metric file whose unit is set to mm, for example, and you placed a 20 mm horizontal dimension as shown in the following image on the left, and you edited the dimension to 1 in (adding the unit) as shown in the middle image, the dimension would appear on the screen in the default units which would be 25.4 as shown in the right image.

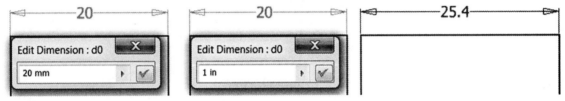

Figure 2-4

When you edit a dimension, the overridden unit appears in the Edit Dimension dialog box. For the previous example when the 25.4 mm dimension is edited, 1 in is displayed in the Edit Dimension dialog box as shown in the following image.

Figure 2-5

TEMPLATES

Each new file is created from a template. You can modify existing templates or add your own templates. As you work, make note of the changes that you make to each file. You then create a new template file or modify an existing file that contains all of the changes and save that file to your template directory, which by default in Windows 7 is *C:\Users\Public\Public Documents\ Autodesk\Inventor 2015\Templates*. You can also create a new subdirectory under the templates folder, and place any Autodesk Inventor file in this new directory. After adding an Inventor file the new tab will appear, and it will be available as a template.

You can use one of two methods to share template files among many users. You can modify the location of templates by clicking the Inventor Application Menu > Options button > File tab, and modifying the Templates location as shown in the following image. The Templates location will need to be modified for each user who needs access to templates that are not stored in the local location.

Figure 2-6

You can also change the unit of measurement (inches or millimeters) for the default part and assembly template files and set the default drawing standard (ANSI, DIN, ISO, etc.) for the default drawing template by clicking Application Option Menu > File tab > Configure Default Template button as shown in the previous image or click Configure Default Templates from the My Home screen as shown in the following image on the left. Then make the changes in the Configure Default Template dialog box as shown in the following image on the right.

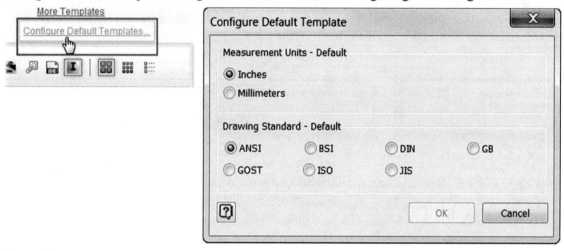

Figure 2-7

You can also set the Templates location in each project file. This method is useful if you need different template files for each project. While editing a project file, change the Templates location in the Folder Options area. The following image shows the default location in Windows 7. The Template location in the project file takes precedence over the Templates option in the Application Options, File tab.

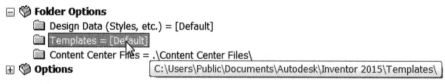

Figure 2-8

TIP: Template files have file extensions that are identical to other files of the same type, but they are located in the template directory. Template files should not be used as production files.

CREATING A PART FILE

The first step in creating a part is to start or create a new part file in an assembly. You can use the following methods to create a new part file:

- In the Quick Access toolbar click the down arrow on the New icon, and click Part as shown in the following image on the left. This creates a new part file based on the default unit as was discussed in the previous Templates section.
- Click Part on the Home page as shown in the middle image.
- From the Inventor Application menu click New > Part as shown in the image on the right.

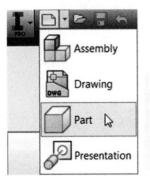  

Figure 2-9

> **TIP:** The default unit for the part and assembly templates and the standard for the drawing template is set in the Application Options dialog box > File tab > Configure Default Template.

You can also create a part file from a template that is not the default location by clicking the New file command from one of these areas:

- Quick Access toolbar as shown in the following image on the left
- Inventor Application menu, as shown in the image second on the left
- Get Started tab > Launch Panel as shown in the image, third from the left.
- On the Home page, as shown in the image, on the right.
- Or press CTRL + N.

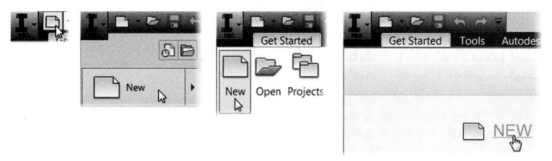

Figure 2-10

The Create New File dialog box appears. Then click the desired templates folder on the left side of the Create New File dialog box and then from the Part section on the right side of the dialog box click on the desired part template file, as shown in the following image.

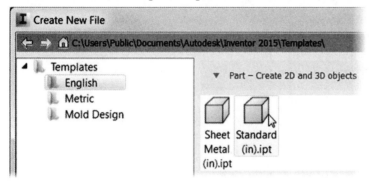

Figure 2-11

After starting a new part file using one of the previous methods, Autodesk Inventor's screen will change to reflect the part environment.

Sketches and Origin (Default) Planes

Before you start sketching, you select a plane on which to draw. A sketch is a plane on which 2D objects are sketched. You can use any planar part face or work plane to create a sketch. By default, when you create a new part file no sketch is created, and you will select an origin plane to sketch on. You can change the default plane on which you will create the sketch by selecting the Inventor Application Menu > Options and clicking on the Part tab. Select the sketch plane to which new parts should default.

Each time you create a new Autodesk Inventor part or assembly file, there are three planes (XY, YZ, and XZ), three axes (X, Y, and Z), and the center (origin) point at the intersection of the three planes. You can use these default planes to create an active sketch. To see the planes, axes, or center point, expand the Origin entry in the browser by clicking on the left side of the text. You can then move the cursor over the names, and they will appear in the graphics window. The following image on the left and the middle image illustrates the default planes, axes, and center point. To leave the visibility of the planes or axes on, right-click in the browser while the cursor is over the name and click Visibility from the menu. When a plane is visible you can display the plane's label by moving the cursor over a plane in the browser or in the graphics window as shown in the following image on the right.

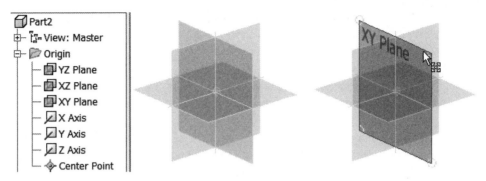

Figure 2-12

Origin 3D Indicator

When working in 3D, it is common to get your orientation turned around. By default in the lower left corner of the graphics screen, there is an XYZ axis indicator that shows the default (world) coordinate system as shown in the following image on the left. The direction of these planes and axes cannot be changed. The arrows are color-coded:

- Red arrow = X axis
- Green arrow = Y axis
- Blue arrow = Z axis

In the Application Options dialog box > Display tab, you can turn the axis indicator and the axis labels on and off as shown in the following image on the right.

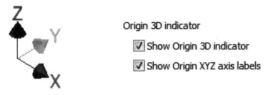

Figure 2-13

By default, Inventor will automatically project the origin point (0,0) when a new sketch is created in a part file. The origin point can be used to constrain a sketch to the 0, 0 point of the sketch. If desired, you can turn this option off by clicking the Tools tab > Application Options or the Application Menu > Options > Sketch tab, and then uncheck Autoproject part origin on sketch create as displayed in the following image.

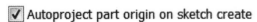

Figure 2-14

New Sketch

By default, when you create a new part file no sketch is active. You can define a plane from the origin folder to be the default by selecting a default plane from the Inventor Application Menu > Options > Part tab. Issue the 2D Sketch command to create a new sketch on a planar part face or a work plane or to activate a non-active sketch in the part. When you are in a part file that does not have a sketch defined and when you start the 2D Sketch command, the origin planes will be displayed in the graphics window, and you can select one of these planes to create the sketch on. To create a new sketch or make an existing sketch active, use one of these methods:

- Click the 3D Model tab > Sketch panel > Start 2D Sketch as shown in the following image on the left or from the Sketch tab > Sketch panel > Start 2D Sketch. Then click a planar face, a work plane, or an existing sketch in the browser.
- Press the S key (a keyboard shortcut) and click a planar face of a part, a work plane, or an existing sketch in the browser.
- While not in the middle of an operation, right-click in the graphics window, and select New Sketch from the marking menu as shown in the middle image. Then click a planar face, a work plane, or an existing sketch in the browser.
- While not in the middle of an operation, click a planar face of a part, a work plane, or an existing sketch in the browser. Then right-click in the graphics window, and click 2D Sketch from the mini-toolbar as shown in the following image on the right.

TIP: You can either start the command first, and then select a plane or you can select a plane and then start the command.

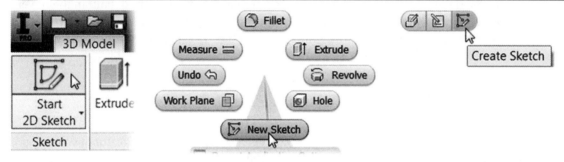

Figure 2-15

After creating a sketch, a Sketch entry will appear in the browser as shown in the following image, and a Sketch tab will appear in the ribbon. By default after you have defined a sketch, the X and Y-axes will align automatically to this plane, and you can begin to sketch.

Figure 2-16

STEP 1 — SKETCH THE 2D OUTLINE OF THE PART

As stated at the beginning of this chapter, 3D parts usually start with a 2D sketch of the outline shape of the part. You can create a sketch with lines, arcs, circles, splines, or any combination of these elements. The next section will cover sketching strategies, commands, and techniques.

Sketching Overview

When deciding what outline to start with, analyze how the finished shape will look. Look for the 2-dimensional shape that best describes the part. When looking for this outline, try to look for a flat 2-dimensional shape that can be extruded or revolved to create a shape that other features can be added to, to create the finished part. It is usually easier to sketch 2-dimensional geometry than

3-dimensional geometry. As you gain modeling experience, you can reflect on how you created the model and think about other ways that you could have built it. There is usually more than one way to generate a given part.

When sketching, draw the geometry so that it is close to the desired shape and size— you do not need to be concerned about exact dimensional values. Even though Inventor allows islands in the sketch (closed objects that lie within another closed object) it is NOT recommended to sketch islands (when you extrude a sketch, island(s) may become voids in the solid). A better method is to place features, which make editing a part easier. For example, instead of sketching a circle inside a rectangle to represent a hole, extrude a rectangle the then place a hole feature.

The following guidelines will help you successfully generate sketches:

- Select a 2-dimensional outline that best represents the part. The 2D outline will be used to create the base feature. A base feature is the first feature and to which other features will add or remove material from.
- Draw the geometry close to the finished size. If you want a 20-inch square, for example, do not draw a 200-inch square. Use dynamic input to define the size of the geometry. Dynamic input is covered in a later section in this chapter.
- Create the sketch proportional in size to the finished shape. When drawing the first object, verify its size in the lower-right corner of the status bar. Use this information as a guide.
- Draw the sketch so that it does not have geometry over geometry, that is, a line on top of another line.
- Do not allow the sketch to have a gap; the geometry should start and end at a single point, just as the start and end points of a rectangle share the same point.
- Keep the sketches simple. Leave out fillets and chamfers when possible. You can easily place them as features after the sketch turns into a solid. The simpler the sketch, the fewer the number of constraints and dimensions that will be required to constrain the model.

Sketching Commands

Before you start sketching the outline of the part, examine the 2D sketching commands that are available. After creating a sketch, the 2D sketch tab is current in the ribbon. The most frequently used commands will be explained throughout this chapter. Consult the help system for information about the remaining commands.

Figure 2-17

Using the Sketch Commands

After starting a new part, a sketch will automatically be active so that you can now use the sketch commands to draw the shape of the part. To start sketching, issue the sketch command that you need, click a point in the graphics window, and follow the prompt on the lower-left corner of the status bar. The sections that follow will introduce techniques that you can use to create a sketch.

Dynamic Input in the sketch environment makes a Heads-Up Display (HUD), which shows information near the cursor for many sketching commands that helps you keep your eyes on the screen. While using the Line, Circle, Arc, Rectangle, or Point commands, you can enter values in the input fields. You can toggle between the value input fields by pressing the TAB key. The following image shows examples of entering Cartesian coordinates and Polar coordinates.

TIP: If no data is entered in the input fields and you click in the graphics window to locate geometry, dimensions will NOT automatically be placed. You can manually place dimensions and constraints after the geometry is sketched.

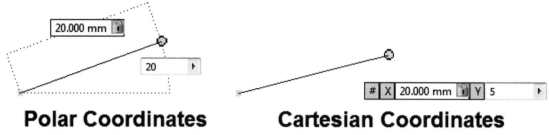

Polar Coordinates   Cartesian Coordinates

Figure 2-18

Dimension Input

When defining lengths and angles for a second point. The dimensional values change as you move the cursor. Press TAB to move to the next input field or click in another cell. After entering a value and pressing the Tab key, the value will be locked and a lock icon will appear to the right of the value as shown in the following image. After a dimension's value is locked, the parametric dimension will be created after clicking a point or pressing the Enter key. You can change the value in an input field by either clicking in the field or pressing the Tab key until the field is highlighted and then typing in a new value.

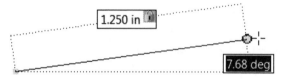

Figure 2-19

Line Command

The Line command is one of the most powerful commands that you will use to sketch. Not only can you draw lines with it, but you can also draw an arc from the endpoint of a line segment. To start sketching lines, click the Line command from the Sketch tab > Create panel as shown in the following image on the left, or right-click in a blank area in the graphics window and click Create Line from the marking menu as shown in the middle image, or press the L key on the keyboard. After starting the Line command you will be prompted to click a first point, select a point in the graphics window, and then click a second point. The image on the right shows the line being created with the dynamic input as well as the horizontal constraint.

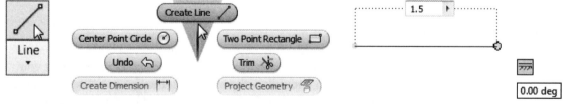

Figure 2-20

You can continue drawing line segments, or you can sketch an arc from the endpoint. Move the cursor over the endpoint of a line segment or arc, and a small gray circle will appear at that endpoint as shown in the following image on the left. Click on the small circle, and with the left mouse button pressed down, move the cursor in the direction that you want the arc to go. Up to eight different arcs can be drawn, depending upon how you move the cursor. The arc will be tangent to the horizontal or vertical edges that are displayed from the selected endpoint. The following image on the right shows an arc that is normal to the sketched line being drawn.

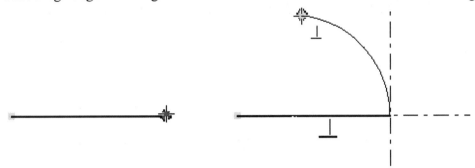

Figure 2-21

 TIP: When sketching, look at the bottom-right corner of the status bar (bottom of the screen) to see the coordinates, length, and angle of the objects that you are drawing. The following image shows the status bar when a line is being drawn.

1.500 in, 0.000 in   x=1.500 in y=0.000 in

Figure 2-22

Object Tracking – Inferred Points

If the Point Alignment On option is checked, from the Sketch tab of the Application Options, dashed lines will appear on the screen as you sketch. These dotted lines represent the endpoints; midpoints; and theoretical intersections of lines, arcs, and center points of arcs and circles that represent their horizontal, vertical, or perpendicular positions. As the cursor gets close to these inferred points, it will snap to that location. If that is the point that you want, click that point; otherwise, continue to move the cursor until it reaches the desired location. When you select inferred points, no constraints (geometric rules such as horizontal, vertical, collinear, and so on) are applied from them. Using inferred points helps create more accurate sketches. The following image shows the inferred points from two midpoints that represent their horizontal and vertical position.

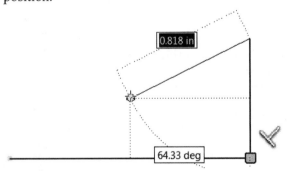

Figure 2-23

Automatic Constraints

As you sketch, a small constraint symbol appears that represents geometric constraint(s) that will be applied to the object. If you do not want a constraint to be applied hold down the CTRL key when you click to create the geometry. The following image shows a line being drawn from the arc, tangent to the arc, and parallel to the angled line, and the dynamic input is also displayed. The symbol appears near the object from which the constraint is coming. Constraints will be covered in the next section.

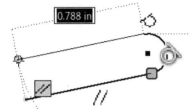

Figure 2-24

Scrubbing

As you sketch, you may prefer to apply a constraint different from the one that automatically appears on the screen. You may want a line to be perpendicular to a given line, for example, instead of being parallel to a different line. The technique to change the constraint is called scrubbing. To place a different constraint while sketching, move the cursor so it touches (scrubs) the other object to which the constraint should be related. Move the cursor back to its original location, and the constraint symbol changes to reflect the new constraint. The same constraint symbol will also appear near the scrubbed object, representing that it is the object to which the constraint is matched. Continue sketching as normal. The following image shows the top horizontal line being drawn with a parallel constraint that was scrubbed from the bottom horizontal line. Without scrubbing the bottom horizontal line, the applied constraint would have been perpendicular to the right vertical line.

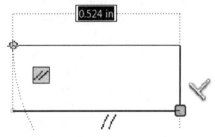

Figure 2-25

Common Sketch Commands

The following table lists common 2D sketch commands. Some commands are available by clicking the down arrow in the lower-right corner of the top command in the panel. Consult the help system for more information about these commands.

Command	Function
Center-point Circle	Creates a circle by clicking a center point for the circle and then a point on the circumference of the circle.
Tangent Circle	Creates a circle that will be tangent to three lines or edges by clicking the lines or edges.
Three-Point Arc	Creates an arc by clicking a start and endpoint and then a point that will lie on the arc.
Tangent Arc	Creates an arc that is tangent to an existing line or arc by clicking the endpoint of a line or arc and then clicking a point for the other endpoint of the arc.
Center-Point Arc	Creates an arc by clicking a center point for the arc and then clicking a start and endpoint.
Two-Point	Creates a rectangle by defining a point and then clicking another point to define the

Rectangle	opposite side of the rectangle. The edges of the rectangle will be horizontal and vertical. If values were entered, dimensions will be placed on the rectangle.
Three-Point Rectangle	Creates a rectangle by clicking two points that will define an edge and then clicking a point to define the third corner. You can also type values to define the three points of the rectangle, and dimensions will be created that define the size of the rectangle.
Two-Point Center Rectangle	Creates a rectangle by defining a center point and another point to define the rectangle's size or type values for the center point and its X and Y values of the rectangle. The edges of the rectangle will be horizontal and vertical, and if values were entered, dimensions will be created.
Three-Point Center Rectangle	Creates a rectangle by defining a center point, a point to define the rectangle's starting point and its angle and another point size or type values for the center point, and size of the rectangle. The edges of the rectangle will be horizontal and vertical, and if values were entered, dimensions will be created.
Center To Center Slot	Creates a slot by defining the center-to-center distance, angle, and then the diameter.
Overall Slot	Creates a slot by defining the overall distance, angle, and then the diameter.
Center Point Slot	Creates a slot by defining the center-to-center distance, angle, and then the diameter.
Three Point Arc Slot	Creates an arc slot by defining a start point, end point and an angle, a radius of the center of the slot and then the diameter of the slot.
Center Point Arc Slot	Creates an angled slot by defining a radius of the center of the slot and a starting angle, an ending angle and then the diameter of the slot.
Fillet	Creates a fillet between two nonparallel lines, two arcs, or a line and an arc at a specified radius. If you select two parallel lines, a fillet is created between them without specifying a radius. When the first fillet is created, a dimension will be created. If many fillets are placed in the same operation, you choose to either apply or not apply an equal constraint.
Chamfer	Creates a chamfer between lines. There are three options to create a chamfer: both sides equal distances, two defined distances, or a distance and an angle.
Polygon	Creates an inscribed or a circumscribed polygon with the number of faces that you specify. The polygon's shape is maintained as dimensions are added.
Mirror	Mirrors the selected objects about a centerline. A symmetry constraint will be applied to the mirrored objects.
Rectangular Pattern	Creates a rectangular array of a sketch with a number of rows and columns that you specify.
Circular Pattern	Creates a circular array of a sketch with a number of copies and spacing that you specify.
Offset	Creates a duplicate of the selected objects that are a given distance away. By default, an equal-distance constraint is applied to the offset objects.
Trim	Trims the selected object to the next object it finds. Click near the end of the object that you want trimmed. While using the Trim command, hold down the SHIFT key to extend objects. If desired, hold down the CTRL key to select boundary objects. While in the Trim command you can also hold down the left mouse button and move the cursor to dynamically trim geometry. While in the Dynamic mode you can hold down the Shift key to dynamically extend geometry.
Extend	Extends the selected object to the next object it finds. Click near the end of the object that you want extended. While using the Extend command, hold down the SHIFT key to trim objects. If desired, hold down the CTRL key to select boundary objects. While in the Extend command you can also click and hold down the left mouse button and move the cursor to dynamically extend geometry. While in the Dynamic mode you can hold down

	the Shift key to dynamically trim geometry.

Selecting Objects

After sketching objects, you may need to move, rotate, or delete some or all of the objects. To edit an object, it must be part of a selection set. There are multiple methods that you can use to place objects into a selection set.

- **CTRL or SHIFT Keys.** You can select objects individually by clicking on them. To manually select multiple individual objects, hold down the CTRL key or SHIFT key while clicking the objects. You can remove selected objects from a selection set by holding down the CTRL or SHIFT key and reselecting them. As you select objects, their color will change to show that they have been selected.
- **Window.** You can select multiple objects by defining a selection window. Not all commands allow you to use the selection window technique and only allow single selections. To define the window, click a starting point. With the left mouse button depressed, move the cursor to define the box. If you draw the selection window from left to right (solid lines), as shown in the following image on the left, only the objects that are fully enclosed in the window will be selected.
- **Crossing window.** If you draw the selection window from right to left (dashed lines), as shown in the following image on the right, a crossing window is used and all of the objects that are fully enclosed in the selection window and the objects that are touched by the window will be selected.
- You can use a combination of the methods to create a selection set.

When you select an object, its color will change according to the color style that you are using. To remove all of the objects from the selection set, click in a blank section of the graphics window.

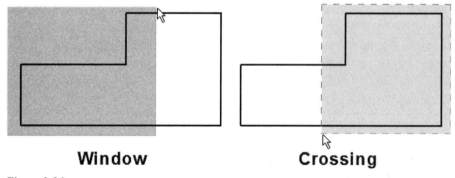

Window   **Crossing**

Figure 2-26

Deleting Objects

To delete objects first cancel the command that you are in by pressing the ESC key. Then select objects to delete, and either press the DELETE key or right-click and click Delete from the menu as shown in the following image.

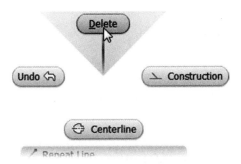

Figure 2-27

Distance Commands

Distance (measure) commands can assist in analyzing sketch, part, and assembly models. The distance command is not a replacement for dimensions; they are additional tools to give you more information. You can measure distances, angles, and loops, and you can perform area calculations. You can start the measure command first and then select the geometry, or select the geometry and then start a measure command.

The Distance commands are located on the Tools tab > Measure panel as shown in the following image on the left. It can also be added to the Quick Access toolbar by clicking the down arrow to the right of the Quick Access toolbar and click Distance from the menu as shown in the middle image. Once the Distance option is added you can access the distance commands as shown in the image on the right.

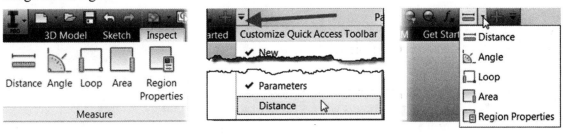

Figure 2-28

Below is a description of measuring loop, area and region properties commands that you could use with 2D geometry. The Distance command will also be covered in Chapter 6 Assemblies.

Measure Loop

Measures the length of closed or open loops defined by face boundaries or other geometry. When moving your cursor over a part face, all edges of the face will become highlighted. Clicking on this face will calculate the closed loop or perimeter of the shape.

Measure Area

Measures the area of enclosed regions or faces. Moving your cursor inside the closed outer shape will cause the outer shape and all holes (referred to as "islands") to also become highlighted. Clicking inside this shape will calculate the area of the shape.

When you click the arrow beside the Measure dialog box, a menu will appear as shown in the following image.

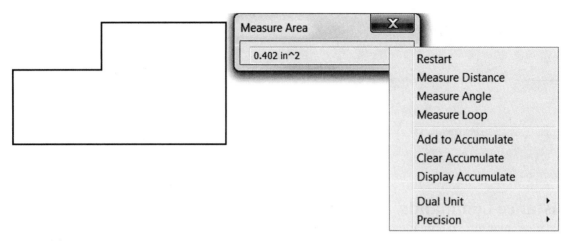

Figure 2-29

Region Properties

While in a sketch you can determine the properties such as the area, perimeter, and Moment of Inertia of a closed 2D sketch. All measurements are taken from the sketch coordinate system (0,0). The properties can be displayed in dual units, the default unit of the document, or a unit of your choice. The following image shows the region properties of two circles.

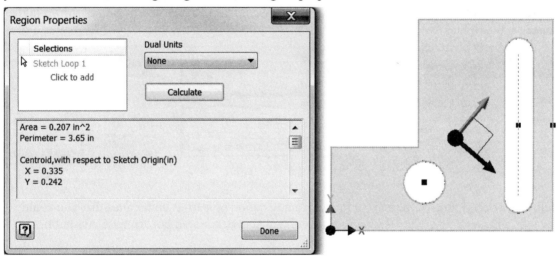

Figure 2-30

EXERCISE 2-1: CREATING A SKETCH WITH LINES

In this exercise, you create a new part file, and 2D Sketch geometry using basic construction techniques. In this exercise no dimensions will be created.

1. Click the New command on the Quick Access toolbar, click the English folder, and then double-click Standard (in).ipt or if inch is the default unit; from the left side of the Quick Access toolbar you can click the down arrow on the New icon and click Part.

2. Click the Start 2D Sketch command on the 3D Model tab > Sketch panel and then select the XY origin plane in the graphics window as shown in the following image.

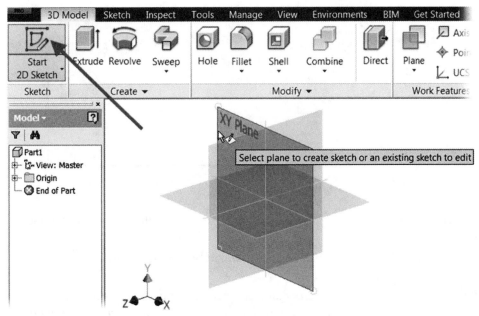

Figure 2-31

3. Start the Line command from the Sketch tab > Create panel.

4. Click on the origin point in the graphics window, move the cursor to the right approximately 4 inches, and, when the horizontal constraint symbol displays, click to specify a second point as shown in the following image. You may need to zoom back and pan the screen to see the entire line.

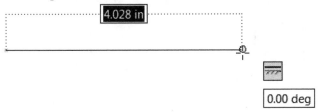

Figure 2-32

 TIP: Symbols indicate the geometric constraints. In the image above, the symbol indicates that the line is horizontal. When you create the first entity in a sketch, make it close to final size.

5. Move the cursor up until the perpendicular constraint symbol displays beside the first line and then click to create a perpendicular line that is approximately 2 inches as shown in the following image on the left.

6. Move the cursor to the left and create a horizontal line approximately 1 inch, that is, parallel to the first horizontal line. The perpendicular constraint symbol is displayed as shown in the following image on the right.

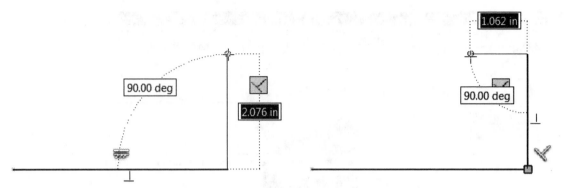

Figure 2-33

7. Move the cursor down, and create a line that is perpendicular to the top horizontal line and is approximately 1 inch.

8. Move the cursor left to create a line that is approximately 2 inches long and is perpendicular to the inside vertical line.

9. Move the cursor up and notice the perpendicular constraint symbol is displayed, to apply a parallel constraint instead, move (scrub) the cursor over the inside vertical line to create a relationship to it. Then click when an inferred line (horizontal dotted line) appears from the top point as shown in the following image on the left.

10. Move the cursor to the left until the perpendicular constraint symbol is displayed, and an inferred vertical line appears from the bottom left point the as shown in the following image on the right and then click to locate the point.

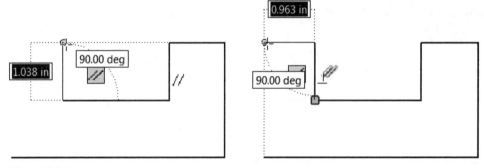

Figure 2-34

11. To close the profile right-click and click Close from the menu.

12. Your screen should resemble the following image.

13. Right-click in the graphics screen, and click Finish 2D Sketch.

14. Close the file. Do not save changes. End of exercise.

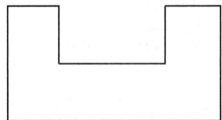

Figure 2-35

EXERCISE 2-2: CREATING A SKETCH WITH TANGENCIES

In this exercise, you create a new part file, and then you create a profile consisting of lines and tangent arcs.

1. Click the New command, and then double-click Standard (inch).ipt; or if inch is the default unit, from the left side of the Quick Access toolbar you can click the down arrow of the New icon, and select Part.

2. Click the Start 2D Sketch command on the 3D Model tab > Sketch panel and then select the XY origin plane.

3. Start the Line command by right-clicking in a blank area in the graphics window and click Create Line from the marking menu.

4. Click on the projected origin point in the middle of the graphics window, and create a horizontal line to the right of the origin point and type **3** (inches will be assumed as the unit because the part file is based on the unit of inch) in the input field. Press the tab key and move the cursor until the horizontal constraint symbol appears and then click. If the second point of the line lies off the screen, roll the mouse wheel away from you to zoom out, hold down the mouse wheel, and drag to pan the view.

5. Create a perpendicular line, move the cursor up until the perpendicular constraint appears, type **1.5** in the input field as shown in the following image on the left, and then press enter.

6. In this step, you infer points, meaning that no sketch constraint is applied. Move the cursor to the intersection of the midpoints of the right-vertical line and bottom horizontal line. Dotted lines (inferred points) appear as shown in image on the right, and then click to create the line. No dimension was created since a value was not entered.

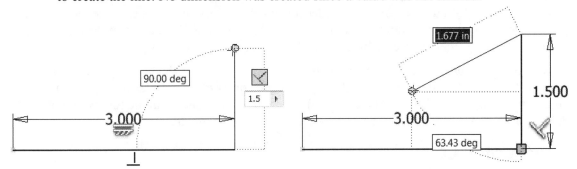

Figure 2-36

7. Next you create a line that is parallel to the bottom line. If needed scrub the bottom line by moving the cursor over the bottom line (do NOT click), and then move the cursor up and to the left until the vertical inferred line and the constraints are displayed as shown in the following image on the left, and then click to create the line.

8. Next you sketch an arc while in the line command. While still in the Line command move the cursor over the left endpoint of the top horizontal line until the gray circle appears, click on the gray dot at the left end of the line, and hold and drag the cursor to the left and then down preview a tangent arc. Do not release the mouse button.

9. Move the cursor over the left endpoint of the first line segment until a coincident constraint (green circle) and the two tangent constraints at start and end points of the arc are displayed as shown in the following image on the right.

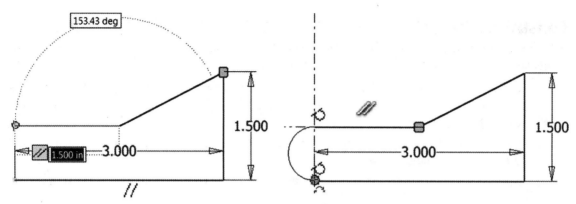

Figure 2-37

10. Release the mouse button to create the arc.

11. Right-click in the graphics window, and then click OK from the marking menu. Later in this chapter you will learn how to create dimensions.

12. Click Finish Sketch from the Sketch tab > Exit panel.

13. Close the file. Do not save changes. End of exercise.

STEP 2 — CONSTRAINING THE SKETCH

After you draw the sketch, you may want to add geometric constraints to it to add design intent. Geometric constraints apply behavior to a specific object or create a relationship between two objects. An example of using a constraint is applying a vertical constraint to a line so that it will always be vertical. You could apply a parallel constraint between two lines to make them parallel to one another; then, as the angle of one of the lines changes, so will the angle of the other line. You can apply a tangent constraint to a line and an arc or to two arcs.

When you add a constraint, the number of constraints or dimensions that are required to fully constrain the sketch will decrease. On the bottom-right corner of Autodesk Inventor, the number of constraints or dimensions will be displayed similar to what is shown in the following image. A fully constrained sketch is a sketch whose objects cannot move or stretch.

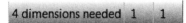

Figure 2-38

Constrain to the Origin Point

When sketching, it is recommended to constrain a point on the sketch to the origin point with a coincident constraint or dimension a point on the sketch to the origin point so it cannot move. You could apply a fix constraint instead of using the origin point, but it is not recommended. When a sketch is constrained to the origin point, Inventor will change the color of constrained objects. If the sketch is not constrained to the origin point, objects are free to move in the sketch and the color of the objects will not change.

 TIP: Autodesk Inventor does not force you to fully constrain a sketch. However, it is recommended that you fully constrain a sketch, as this will allow you to better predict how the change will affect the sketch and part.

Constraint Types

Autodesk Inventor has 12 geometric constraints that you can apply to a sketch. The following image shows the constraint types that can be applied from the Sketch tab > Constrain panel.

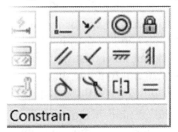

Figure 2-39

The following chart describes the geometric constraints.

Icon	Constraint	Function
	Coincident	A point is constrained to lie on another point or curve (line, arc, etc.).
	Collinear	Two selected lines will line up along a single line; if the first line moves, so will the second. The two lines do not have to be touching.
	Concentric	Arcs and/or circles will share the same center point.
	Fix	Applying a fix constraint to a point will prevent the selected point from moving. Multiple points in a sketch can be fixed. If you select a line segment, the angle of the line will be fixed and only its length can change.
	Parallel	Lines will be repositioned so that they are parallel to one another.
	Perpendicular	Lines will be positioned at 90° angles to one another.
	Horizontal	Line is positioned parallel to the X-axis, or a horizontal constraint can be applied between any two points in the sketch. The selected points will be aligned such that a line drawn between them will be parallel to the X-axis.
	Vertical	Line is positioned parallel to the Y-axis, or a vertical constraint can be applied between any two points in the sketch. The selected points will be aligned such that a line drawn between them will be parallel to the Y-axis.
	Tangent	An arc, circle, or line will become tangent to another arc or circle.
	Smooth (G2)	A spline and another spline, line, or arc that connect at an endpoint with a coincident constraint will represent a smooth G2 (continuous curvature) condition.
	Symmetry	Selected points defining the selected geometry are made symmetric about a selected line.
	Equal	If two arcs or circles are selected, they will have the same radius or diameter. If two lines are selected, they will become the same length. If one of the objects changes, so will the other object to which the Equal constraint has been applied. If the Equal constraint command is applied after one of the arcs, circles, or lines has been dimensioned, the second arc, circle, or line will take on the size of the first one. If you select multiple similar objects (lines, arcs, etc.) before selecting this command, the constraint is applied to all of them.

Adding Constraints

As stated previously in this chapter, you can apply constraints while you sketch objects. You can also apply additional constraints after the sketch is drawn. However, Autodesk Inventor will not allow you to over-constrain the sketch or add duplicate constraints. If you add a constraint that would conflict with another, you will be warned with the message, "Adding this constraint will over-constrain the sketch." For example, if you try to add a vertical constraint to a line that already has a horizontal constraint, you will be alerted. To add a constraint, follow these steps:

1. Click a constraint from the Constrain panel, or right-click in the graphics window and click Create Constraint from the menu. Then click the specific constraint from the menu as shown in the previous image before the chart.

2. Click the object or objects then apply the constraint.

Showing Constraints

To display the geometric constraints that are applied to a sketch, do one of the following:

- Select the geometry in the graphics window by selecting individual objects or by using the window or crossing selection method that was described in the Selecting Objects section that was covered earlier in this chapter.
- Click the Show Constraints command from the Status Bar as shown in the following image on the left or from the Constrain panel as shown in the middle image.
- Right-click in a blank area in the graphics window and click Show All Constraints from the menu.
- Press the F8 key.

The constraints on the selected geometry will be displayed. The yellow squares represent coincident constraints; move the cursor over a yellow square to display the two coincident constraints for the point. The image on the right shows all the constraints in a sketch.

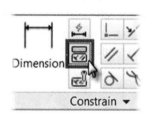
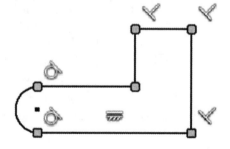

Figure 2-40

Modifying Constraint Size

You can modify the size of the constraint icons displayed on the screen by clicking Tools tab > Application Options > General tab, and then modify the size of the Annotation Scale. The following image shows the Annotation Scale increased from 1.0 to 1.5. This setting also changes the size of the dimensions in a sketch.

1.5   Annotation scale

Figure 2-41

Deleting Constraints

To delete the constraint(s), select a constraint or multiple constraints using one of the selection methods. Right-click and click Delete from the menu as shown in the following image on the left. As an alternate method to deleting constraint, you can press the Delete key once the constraint is selected.

- To delete all constraints except the coincident constraints, use the window or crossing selection technique, right-click and click Delete Constraints from the menu as shown in the image on the right.

Figure 2-42

Hiding Constraints

You can hide the display symbol for individual or all geometric constraints. To perform this task, do one of the following:

To hide a constraint:

- Move the cursor over a constraint, right-click and click Hide from the marking menu as shown in the following image on the left.

To hide all constraints, do one of the following:

- Move the cursor over a constraint, right-click and click Hide All Constraints from the marking menu as shown in the image, second from the left.
- Click Hide All Constraints on the Status Bar as shown in the image, third from the left. This is the same icon you selected to Show All Constraints.
- Right-click in a blank area in the graphics window and click Hide All Constraints on the menu as shown in the following image on the right.
- Press the F9 key

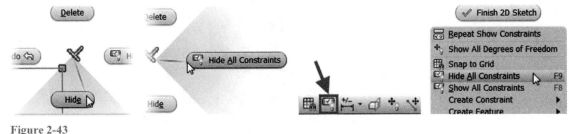

Figure 2-43

Construction Geometry

Construction geometry can help you create sketches that would otherwise be difficult to constrain. You can constrain and dimension construction geometry like normal geometry, but the construction geometry will not be recognized as a profile edge in the part when you turn the sketch into a feature. When you sketch, the sketches by default have a normal geometry style, meaning that the sketch geometry is visible in the feature. Construction geometry can reduce the number of constraints and dimensions required to fully constrain a sketch, and it can help to define the sketch. For example, a construction circle that is tangent to the inside of a hexagon (drawn with individual lines and not the Polygon command) can drive the size of the hexagon. Without construction geometry, the hexagon would require six constraints and dimensions. With construction geometry, it would require only three constraints and dimensions; the circle would have tangent or coincident constraints applied to it and the hexagon. You create construction geometry by changing the line style before or after you sketch geometry in one of the following two ways:

- After creating the sketch, select the geometry that you want to change and click the Construction icon on the Format panel as shown in the following image.
- Before sketching, click the Construction icon on the Format panel, as shown in the following image. All geometry created will be construction until the Construction command is deselected. If you do this, remember to click the Construction icon to turn it off.

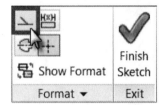

Figure 2-44

After turning the sketch into a feature, the construction geometry will be consumed with the sketch and is maintained in the sketch. When you edit a feature's sketch that you created with construction geometry, the construction geometry will reappear during editing and disappear when the part is updated. You can add or delete construction geometry to or from a sketch just like any geometry that has a normal style. In the graphics window, construction geometry will be displayed as a dashed line, lighter in color, and thinner in width than normal geometry. The following image on the left shows a sketch with a construction line for the angled line. The angled line has a coincident constraint applied to every endpoint that it touches. The image on the right shows the sketch after it has been extruded. Notice that the construction line was not extruded.

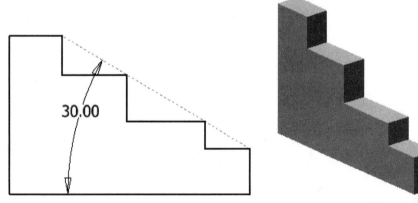

Figure 2-45

Number of Required Constraints or Dimensions

While constraining and dimensioning a sketch, there are multiple ways to determine the number of constraints or dimensions that are required to fully constrain the sketch. When you add a constraint or dimension the number of constraints or dimensions needed to constrain the sketch decreases. A fully constrained sketch is a sketch whose geometry cannot move or stretch.

On the bottom-right corner of the status bar, the number of constraints or dimensions to fully constrain the sketch is displayed similar to what is shown in the following image on the left. When no constraints or dimensions can be added to the sketch, the message Fully Constrained will appear in the bottom-right corner of the status bar as shown in the middle image and in the browser, a pushpin icon will appear to the left of the Sketch entry as shown in the image on the right.

5 dimensions needed   Fully Constrained   ⊢ 🔖 Sketch1

Figure 2-46

Degrees of Freedom

To see the areas in the sketch that are NOT constrained, you can display the degrees of freedom. While a sketch is active, click Show Degree of Freedom on the status bar, as shown in the following image on the left, or right-click in a blank area in the graphics window and click Show All Degrees of Freedom from the menu. Lines and arcs with arrows will appear as shown in the middle image. As constraints and dimensions are added to the sketch, degrees of freedom will disappear. To remove the degree of freedom symbols from the screen, click Hide All Degrees of Freedom on the bottom of the status bar, as shown in the following image on the right, or right-click in a blank area in the graphics window and click Hide All Degrees of Freedom from the menu.

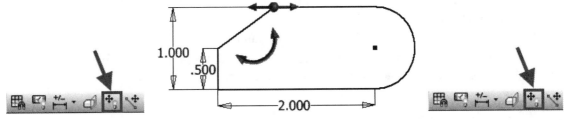

Figure 2-47

Dragging a Sketch

Another method to determine whether or not an object is constrained is to try to drag it to a new location. While not in a command, click a point or an edge, or select multiple objects on the sketch. With the left mouse button depressed, drag it to a new location. If the geometry stretches, it is under constrained. For example, if you draw a rectangle that has two horizontal and two vertical constraints applied to it and you drag a point on one of the corners, the size of the rectangle will change, but the lines will maintain their horizontal and vertical behaviors. If dimensions are set on the object, they will prevent the object from stretching.

EXERCISE 2-3: ADDING AND DISPLAYING CONSTRAINTS

In this exercise, you add geometric constraints to sketch geometry to control the shape of the sketch.

1. Click the New command, click the English folder, and double-click Standard (in).ipt.

2. Click the Start 2D Sketch command on the 3D Model tab > Sketch panel and then select the XY origin plane.

3. Sketch the geometry as shown in the following image, with an approximate size of **2 inches** in the X (horizontal) direction and **1 inch** in the Y (vertical) direction. Do not apply dimensions dynamically. Place the lower-left corner of the sketch on the origin point. Right-click in the graphics window, and then click OK. By starting the line at the origin point, that point is constrained to the origin with a coincident constraint.

4. Click Show All Constraints on the Status Bar, or press the F8 key. Your screen should resemble the following image.

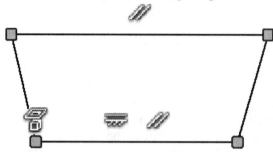

Figure 2-48

5. If another constraint appears, place the cursor over it, right-click, and then click Delete from the marking menu.

6. On the Constrain panel, click the Parallel constraint icon.

7. Select the two angled lines. Depending upon the order in which you sketched the lines, the angles may be opposite of the following image on the left. The constraints that are applied are previewed

8. Press the ESC key twice to stop adding constraints.

9. The new constraints you just added are not displayed. Press the F8 key to refresh the visible constraints. Your screen should resemble the following image.

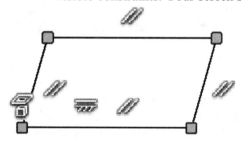

Figure 2-49

10. Select the top horizontal line in the sketch and drag the line. Notice how the sketch changes its size, but not its general shape. Try to drag the bottom horizontal line. The line cannot be dragged as it is constrained.

11. Select the endpoint on the bottom-right horizontal line, and drag the endpoint. The lines remain parallel due to the parallel constraints.

12. Place the cursor over the icon for the parallel constraint on the right-angled line, right-click, and click Delete from the marking menu as shown in the following image on the left. The parallel constraint that was applied to both angled lines is deleted.

13. On the Sketch Tab > Constrain panel, click the Perpendicular constraint icon.

14. Select the bottom horizontal line and the angled line on the right side. Even though it may appear that the rectangle is fully constrained, the left vertical line is still unconstrained

and can move. Notice on the bottom-right of the Status Bar that 3 dimensions are needed to fully constrain the sketch.

15. While still in the Perpendicular Constraint command, select the bottom horizontal line and the left vertical line and then right-click and click OK on the marking menu. Notice on the bottom-right the Status Bar is down to 2 dimensions to fully constrain the sketch. Dimensions would be added to fully constrain the sketch.

16. Press the F8 key to refresh the visible constraints. Your screen should resemble the following image on the right.

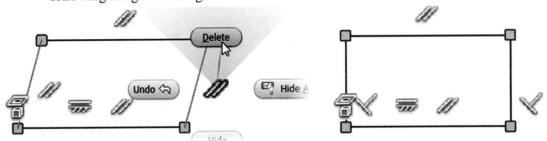

Figure 2-50

17. Click Hide All Constraints on the Status Bar, or press the F9 key.

18. Drag the point at the upper-right corner of the sketch to verify that the rectangle can change size in both the horizontal and vertical directions, but its shape is maintained.

19. Press down the CTRL key and select the four lines or use the window selection technique to select the four lines. Right-click and click Delete from the marking menu.

20. Use the Line command to sketch the geometry as shown in the following image with an approximate size of **2 inches** in the X direction and **1.375 inches** in the Y direction. Place the lower-left point of the sketch on the projected center point. Do not apply dimensions dynamically. Right-click in the graphics window, and then click OK.

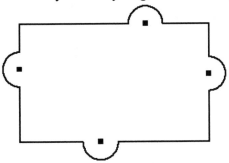

Figure 2-51

21. Inspect the constraints by dragging different points and edges.

22. Next you make the arcs equal in size. On the Constrain panel, click the Equal constraint command or press the = key on the keyboard.

    a. Select the arc on the left and the bottom arc.

    b. Select the arc on the left and the arc on the right side.

    c. Select the arc on the left and the arc on the top.

23. Next you align the line segments if necessary. On the Constrain panel, click the Collinear constraint command.

    If the endpoints and center point of the arcs are aligned horizontally ⌣ or vertically when sketched you will receive a message "Adding this constraint will over-constrain the sketch", if you see this message click Cancel in the dialog box for steps 23 a. b. c. and d.

    a.   Select the two bottom horizontal lines.

    b.   Select the two top horizontal lines.

    c.   Select the two left vertical lines.

    d.   Select the two right vertical lines.

24. To stop applying the collinear constraint, either right-click and click Cancel (ESC) from the marking menu or press the ESC key.

25. Next you will align the arcs. On the Constrain panel, click the Vertical constraint command.

26. Select the center point of the bottom arc, and then click the center point of the top arc.

27. On the Constrain panel, click the Horizontal constraint command.

28. Click the center point of the left arc, and then click the center point of the right arc.

29. To stop applying the constraints, right-click and click Cancel (ESC) from the marking menu, or press the ESC key. If desired you can move the arcs by clicking and dragging on them.

30. Display all of the constraints by pressing the F8 key. Your screen should resemble the following image.

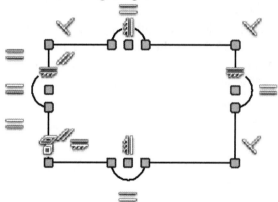

Figure 2-52

31. Hide all of the constraints by pressing the F9 key.

32. Click on an endpoint in the sketch and drag the endpoint. Try dragging different points, and notice how the sketch changes.

33. Next you delete the geometry as shown in the following image on the left. Press the ESC key twice to cancel any command, click a point above and to the left of the top arc, drag a window so it encompasses the arc on the right, release the mouse button, and press the Delete key on the keyboard.

34. Close the open line segments. Drag the open endpoints onto each other until your sketch resembles the following image on the right. A green circle will appear when the two endpoints are near each other; this applies a coincident constraint.

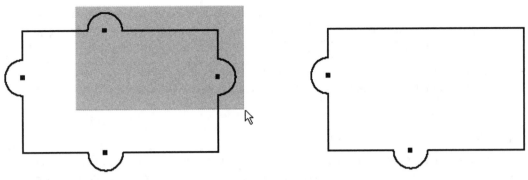

Figure 2-53

35. Next you center the arcs in the middle of the sketch. On the Constrain panel, click the Vertical constraint command.

36. Click the center point on the bottom arc and the midpoint of the top horizontal line as shown in the following image on the left.

37. On the Constrain panel, click the Horizontal constraint command.

38. Click the center point on the left arc and the midpoint of the right vertical line as shown in the following image on the right.

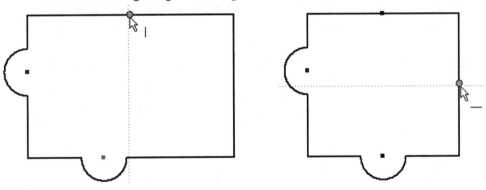

Figure 2-54

39. Click on different points and drag them, notice how the sketch changes shape, but the arcs are always centered as shown in the following image.

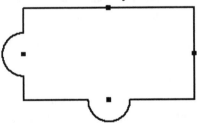

Figure 2-55

40. Close the file. Do not save changes. End of exercise. Note that dimensions would be added to fully constrain the sketch. Dimensions are covered in the next section.

STEP 3 — ADDING DIMENSIONS MANUALLY

The last step to constraining a sketch is to add dimensions that were not added dynamically. The dimensions you place will control the size of the sketch and can also appear in the part drawing views when they are generated. When placing dimensions, try to avoid having extension lines go through the sketch, as this will require more clean up when drawing views are generated. Click near the side from which you anticipate the dimensions will originate in the drawing views.

All dimensions that you create are parametric as well as the dynamic dimensions that are placed automatically when sketching geometry. Parametric means that they will change the size of the geometry.

Scale Sketch

If the sketch is not constrained to the origin point and no dimension was dynamically added to the sketch when it was created, then the entire sketch will be uniformly scaled when the first dimension is added.

General Dimensioning

The General Dimension command can create linear, angle, radial, or diameter dimensions one at a time. The following image on the left shows an example of a dimensioned sketch. To start the General Dimension command, follow one of these techniques:

- Click the General Dimension command from the Sketch tab > Constrain panel as shown in the following image in the middle.
- Right-click in the graphics window and click General Dimension from the marking menu as shown in the image on the right.
- Press the shortcut key D.

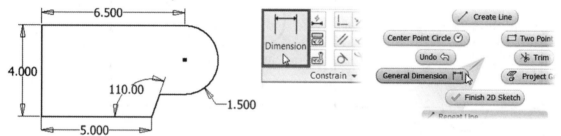

Figure 2-56

When you place a linear dimension, the extension line of the dimension will snap automatically to the nearest endpoint of a selected line; when an arc or circle is selected, it will snap to its center point. To dimension to a tangent point of an arc or circle, see "Dimensioning to a Tangent of an Arc or Circle," later in this chapter.

After you select the General Dimension command, follow these steps to place a dimension:

1. Select the geometry to be dimensioned.
2. After selecting the geometry, a preview image will appear attached to your cursor showing the type of dimension. If the dimension type is not what you want, right-click, and then select the correct style from the menu. After changing the dimension type, the dimension preview will change to reflect the new style.
3. Click to place the dimension.
4. Enter a value for the dimension.

The next sections cover how to dimension specific objects and how to create specific types of dimensioning with the Dimension command.

Dimensioning Lines

There are multiple techniques for dimensioning a line. Issue the Dimension command and do one of the following:

- Click near two endpoints, move the cursor until the dimension is in the correct location, and click.
- To dimension the length of a line, click anywhere on the line; the two endpoints will be selected automatically. Move the cursor until the dimension is in the correct location and click.
- To dimension between two parallel lines, click one line and then the next, and then click a point to locate the dimension.
- To create a dimension whose extension lines are perpendicular to the line being dimensioned, click the line and then right-click. Click Aligned from the menu, and then click a point to place the dimension.

Dimensioning Angles

To create an angular dimension, issue the General Dimension command, click on two lines whose angle you want to define, move the cursor until the dimension is in the correct location, and place the dimension by clicking on a point.

Dimensioning Arcs and Circles

To dimension an arc or circle, issue the General Dimension command, click on the circle's circumference, move the cursor until the dimension is in the correct location, and click. By default, when you dimension a circle, the default is a diameter dimension; when you dimension an arc, the result is a radius dimension. To change a radial dimension to diameter or a diameter to radial, right-click before you place the dimension and select the other style from the Dimension Type menu.

You can dimension the angle of the arc. Start the Dimension command, click on the arc's circumference, click the center point of the arc, and then place the dimension or click the center point and then click the circumference of the arc.

For arcs you can also add an arc length dimension by starting the dimension command: click on the arc, right-click and click Arc Length from the Dimension Type menu, and then click a point to locate the dimension.

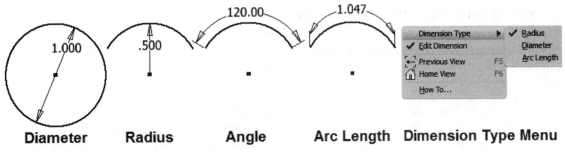

Diameter **Radius** **Angle** **Arc Length** **Dimension Type Menu**

Figure 2-57

Dimensioning to a Tangent of an Arc or Circle

To dimension to a tangent of an arc or circle, follow these steps:

1. Start the General Dimension command.

2. Select a line that is parallel to the tangent arc or circle that will be dimensioned, labeled (1) in the following image on the left.

3. Move the cursor over the arc or circle until the tangent constraint symbol labeled (2) in the following image on the left.

4. Then move the cursor until the dimension is in the correct location and click to create the dimension, labeled (3) in the following image on the right.

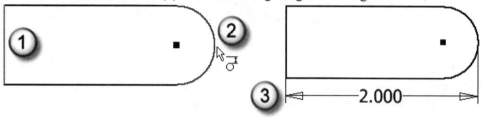

Figure 2-58

To dimension to two tangents, follow these steps:

1. Start the General Dimension command.

2. Select an arc or circle that includes one of the tangents to which it will be dimensioned. The following image illustrates an example of dimensioning a slot, the first selection is labeled (1).

3. Move the cursor over a second arc or circle until the tangent constraint symbol appears, as shown in the following image on the left, labeled (2).

4. Click to select the tangent point and then move the cursor until the dimension is in the correct location. Then click to create the dimension, labeled (3) in the following image on the right.

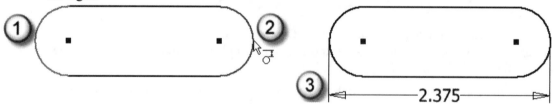

Figure 2-59

Entering and Editing a Dimension Value

After placing the dimension, you can change its value. Depending on your setting for editing dimensions when you created them, the Edit Dimension dialog box may or may not appear automatically after you place the dimension. To set the Edit Dimension option, do one of the following:

*   Click the Tools tab > Options panel > Application Options. On the Sketch tab of the Application Options dialog box, from the Constrain Settings area, click the Settings button and then click the box next to Edit dimension when created as shown in the following image on the left.

*   Or set this option by right-clicking in the graphics window while placing a dimension and click Edit Dimension from the menu as shown in the following image on the right. This method will change the application option Edit Dimension when created as previously described.

If the Edit dimension when created option is checked, the Edit Dimension dialog box will appear automatically after you place the dimension. Otherwise, the dimension will be placed with the default value.

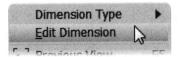

Figure 2-60

To edit a dimension that has already been created, double-click on the dimension, and the Edit Dimension dialog box will appear, as shown in the following image. Enter the new value and unit for the dimension; then either press ENTER or click the checkmark in the Edit Dimension dialog box. If no unit is entered, the units that the file was created with will be used. When inputting values, enter the exact value — do not round up or down. The accuracy of the dimension that is displayed in a sketch is set in the Document Setting. For example, if you want to enter 4 1/16 decimally enter 4.0625 not 4.06.

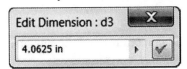

Figure 2-61

Fractions

Inventor also allows you to enter a fraction anywhere a value is required. When the Length unit in the Tools tab > Options panel > Document Settings > Units tab is set to any non-metric unit, as shown in the following image on the left, and a fraction is entered, a fraction will display in the graphics window and will be maintained in the Edit Dimension dialog box. If the Length unit is set to a metric unit and a fraction is entered, the decimal equivalent will be displayed in the graphics window but the fraction will be maintained in the Edit Dimension dialog box. After inputting a fraction you can click on the right-faced arrow and set the type of dimension to display: Decimal, Fractional, or Architectural as shown in the middle of the following image. When entering fractions do not use a dash to separate the fraction, just add a space. For example, enter 4 1/16, not 4-1/16, Inventor would interpret the — as part of an equation and would return the value 3.9375. The following image on the right shows the fraction displayed in the graphics window.

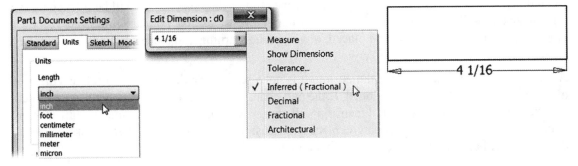

Figure 2-62

 TIP: When placing dimensions, it is recommended that you place the smallest dimensions first. This will help prevent the geometry from flipping in the opposite direction.

Repositioning a Dimension

Once you place a dimension, you can reposition it, but the origin points cannot be moved. Follow these steps to reposition a dimension:

1. Exit the current operation either by pressing ESC twice or right-clicking and then clicking Cancel (ESC) from the marking menu.
2. Move the cursor over the dimension until the move symbol 🁢 appears as shown in the following image.
3. With the left mouse button depressed, move the dimension to a new location and release the button.

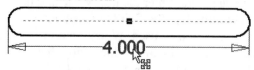

Figure 2-63

Fully Constrained Sketch

As was described in the "Constraining the Sketch" section, as you add constraints and dimensions to a sketch, the number of required dimensions is decreased. When no more constraints or dimensions are needed to constrain the sketch, the number in the "dimensions needed" section on the bottom-right of the status bar will display Fully Constrained as shown in the following image on the left. The icon to the left of the Sketch entry in the browser will also display a pushpin when the sketch is fully constrained as shown in the following image on the right.

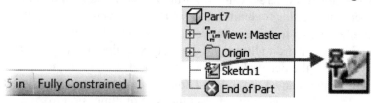

Figure 2-64

Over Constrained Sketch

As explained in the "Adding Constraints" section, Autodesk Inventor will not allow you to over-constrain a sketch or add duplicate constraints. The same is true when adding dimensions. If you add a dimension that will conflict with another constraint or dimension, you will be warned that this dimension will over-constrain the sketch or that it already exists. You can either cancel the operation and no dimension will be placed, or accept the warning and a driven dimension will be created.

A driven dimension is a reference dimension. It is not a parametric dimension—it reflects the size of the points to which it is dimensioned. If the part changes, the driven dimension will be updated to reflect the new value. A driven dimension will appear with parentheses around the dimensions value—for example, (2.500). When you place a dimension that will over-constrain a sketch, a dialog box will appear similar to the following image.

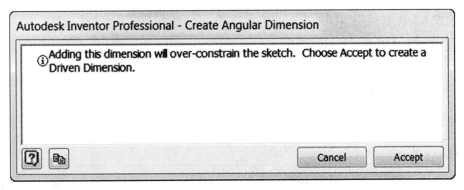

Figure 2-65

Relax Mode

When you try to place a constraint or add a dimension and you receive the over constraint message, and if you want the constraint or dimension to take precedence, you can turn on relax mode. When relax mode is on and you reapply the constraint or add the dimension, it will be applied or created and the conflicting constraint will automatically be deleted, except for Coincident, Smooth, Tangent, Symmetry, Pattern, and Project constraints, and any conflicting dimension will become a driven dimension. While in relax mode, and you are not able to add the new constraint or dimension, you may need to manually delete one of the Coincident, Smooth, Tangent, Symmetry, Pattern, and Project constraints.

Turn on relax mode by clicking the Relax Mode icon on the Status Bar as shown in the following image on the left. When you apply a constraint or dimension that would have over constrained a sketch, a dialog box will appear stating that a constraint or dimension will be deleted to solve the conflict as shown in the following image on the right.

Another method to remove conflicting constraints or dimensions is to drag a point or edge while in Relax Mode and conflicting constraints or dimensions will be deleted.

When done editing the constrained sketch, turn off relax mode. If relax mode is left on, a constrained sketch can inadvertently be altered by dragging constrained objects.

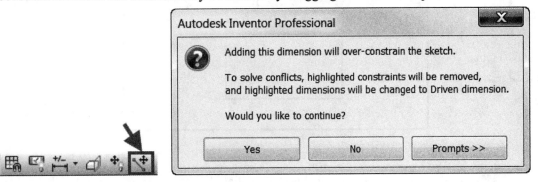

Figure 2-66

For illustration, the following image on the left shows a fully constrained rectangle with the geometric constraints visible. Relax Mode was turned on and a 120 degree angle dimension was located and after clicking Yes in the warning dialog box the dimension was created and the perpendicular constraint in the lower-right corner was deleted as shown in the middle image. To return the geometry back to a rectangle, a perpendicular constraint was applied to the bottom horizontal line and left vertical line and the 120 degree dimension was automatically changed to a driven dimension as shown in the image on the right.

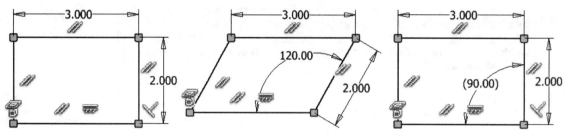

Figure 2-67

 TIP: When done editing the constrained sketch turn off Relax Mode. This returns Inventor to its original editing state. If this is not done, sketches can accidentally be changed by dragging points and objects in the sketch.

Driven Dimension

Another option for creating driven dimensions is to use the Driven Dimension option. A driven dimension does NOT reduce the number of dimensions needed to constrain the sketch it only reflects the length of the object. You would use this option to show reference dimensions.

If you select the Driven Dimension icon from the Sketch tab > Format panel, as shown in following image on the left, any dimension you create will be a driven dimension. Driven dimensions are represented in the sketch with parenthesis around the value, whereas parametric dimensions do not have parenthesis around the value. If the Driven Dimension option is not active, regular parametric dimensions will be created, which is the default.

The same Driven Dimension option can be used to change an existing dimension to either a driven dimension or back to a normal dimension by selecting the dimension and clicking the Driven Dimension option. The following image on the right shows an example of a 5.250 driven dimension referencing the overall length of the sketch. The three parametric dimensions control the length of the sketch. If one of the parametric dimension values change, the driven dimension's value will update to reflect the new overall length.

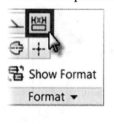

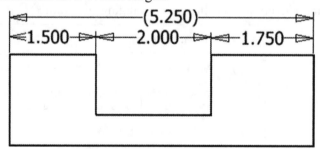

Figure 2-68

 TIP: Avoid over using driven dimensions as they do not parametrically control the size of the sketch, they are only used for reference.

EXERCISE 2-4: CONSTRAINING AND DIMENSIONING A SKETCH

In this exercise, you add dimensional constraints to a sketch. Note: this exercise assumes that the "Edit dimension when created" and "Autoproject part origin on sketch create" options are checked in the Application Options dialog box under the Sketch tab. Experiment with Autodesk Inventor's color schemes to see how the sketch objects change color when they are constrained.

4. Click the New command and click the English folder, and then double-click Standard (in).ipt.

5. Click the Start 2D Sketch command on the 3D Model tab > Sketch panel and then select the XY origin plane.

6. Start sketching by starting the line command in the Sketch tab > Create panel and click the origin point, move the cursor to the right, type **5** in the distance input field, press the Tab key, and then click a point when the horizontal constraint is previewed above the input field for degrees as shown in the following image on the left.

7. Next you place an angle line and a dynamic dimension to define the angle. Press the tab key and type **150** for the angle input field, press the Tab key, and then click a point to the upper right as shown in the following image on the right. The distance should be about 2 inches but the dimension is not needed to define this sketch.

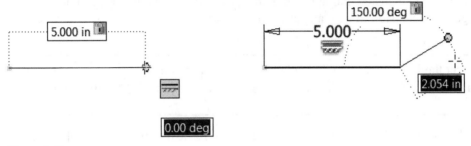

Figure 2-69

8. Sketch the geometry as shown in the following image. When sketching, ensure that a perpendicular constraint is not applied between the two angled lines. If needed, hold down the CTRL key while sketching the top angle line to prevent sketch constraints from being applied. The arc should be tangent to both adjacent lines.

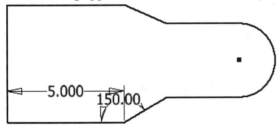

Figure 2-70

9. Add a horizontal constraint between the midpoint of the left vertical line and the center of the arc by clicking the Horizontal Constraint command from the Sketch tab > Constrain panel and select the midpoint of the line and the center point of the arc as shown in the following image on the left.

10. Start the Vertical Constraint command from the Sketch tab > Constrain panel and add a vertical constraint between the endpoints of the angled lines nearest to the right side of the sketch as shown in the following image on the right.

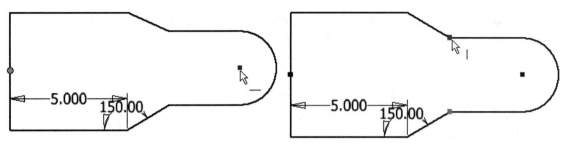

Figure 2-71

11. Make the two angled lines equal in length by adding an equal constraint, press the = key and then select the two angled lines.

12. Click the General Dimension command in the Sketch tab > Constrain panel and add a radial dimension by selecting the arc. Move the cursor until the dimension is positioned near the lower right corner of the sketch and then click a point and then enter **1.5** for its value (if the Edit Dimension dialog box did not appear, double-click on the dimension and change the dimension to 1.5), and click the checkmark in the Edit Dimension dialog box.

 TIP: To set the Edit Dimension dialog box to appear when placing dimensions, while placing a dimension, right-click in the graphics window and click Edit Dimension from the menu.

13. While still in the General Dimension command, add a vertical dimension by selecting the vertical line, position the dimension to the left, click a point to locate it, enter **5**, and click the checkmark. When complete, your sketch should resemble the following image on the left. Notice on the bottom right of the Status Bar, 1 dimension is required to fully constrain the sketch as shown in the following image on the right.

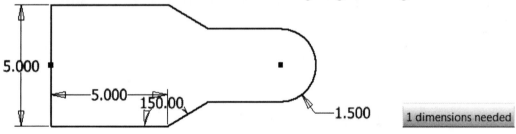

Figure 2-72

14. Add a horizontal dimension by selecting the left vertical line and then select the center point of the arc or on the top of the arc, locate the dimension to the top of the sketch and enter **10** for the value as shown in the following image.

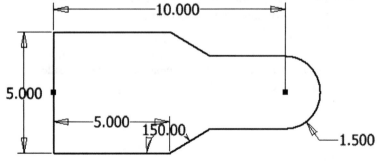

Figure 2-73

15. Press the ESC key twice to end the command. In the Status Bar the, in the number of dimensions required section, it should display "Fully Constrained," and the icon to the left of the sketch in the browser should have a pushpin on it.

16. Try to click and drag on different points on the sketch. The points will not change because they are constrained or dimensioned.

17. Turn relax mode on by clicking the Relax Mode icon in the Status Bar, as shown in the following image.

Figure 2-74

18. Click and drag on different points on the sketch. The dimensions will change to reflect their new value.

19. Return the sketch to the values shown in step 14 by using the Undo command in the Quick Access toolbar.

20. While still in Relax Mode, add an overall horizontal dimension using the General Dimension command by clicking the vertical line (not an endpoint), move the cursor near the right tangent point of the arc until the glyph of dimension with a circle appears, as shown in the following image on the left. Locate the dimension above the 10.000 dimension and accept the default length of **11.500**. The 10.000 was automatically changed to a driven dimension and the sketch should still be fully constrained. Your sketch should resemble the following image on the right.

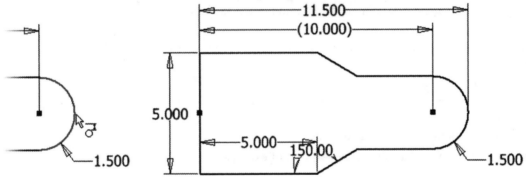

Figure 2-75

21. Edit the value of some of the sketch dimensions by double-clicking on the dimension's value and type in a new value and then press ENTER on the keyboard or click the green check mark in the Edit Dimension dialog box, and examine how the sketch changes. The arc should always be in the middle of the vertical line. Notice how the driven dimension changes when the horizontal, angle or radial dimension values changes.

22. Delete the horizontal constraint between the center of the arc and the midpoint of the vertical line by selecting the center point of the arc, select the horizontal constrain above the center point, right-click and click Delete from the menu as shown in the following image.

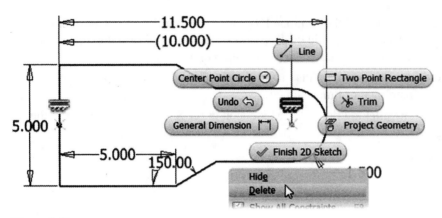

Figure 2-76

23. Turn relax mode off by clicking the Relax Mode icon in the Status Bar, as shown in the following image.

Figure 2-77

24. Display the visibility of all of the constraints by window selecting all of the geometry.

25. Click in a blank area in the graphics window and the constraints will disappear.

26. In the Status Bar click the Show All Constraints command, as shown in the following image, and practice deleting and adding other constraints.

Figure 2-78

27. Practice adding and deleting dimensions.

28. Close the file. Do not save changes. End of exercise.

INSERTING AUTOCAD FILES

You may have legacy AutoCAD files or receive AutoCAD files that you need to convert into Inventor parts. In this section you learn how to insert AutoCAD data into a sketch. When importing a 2D DWG file into Autodesk Inventor, you can either copy the contents from the DWG file to the clipboard via Autodesk Inventor or AutoCAD and paste the contents into Autodesk Inventor, or use an import wizard that guides you through the process. In this section you learn how to insert AutoCAD 2D data into a sketch in an Inventor part file.

TIP: AutoCAD does not need to be installed to import AutoCAD geometry into Inventor.

Inserting 2D AutoCAD Data into a Sketch

In this section you learn how to insert AutoCAD 2D data into the active sketch in a part or drawing. To insert AutoCAD data into the active sketch, follow these steps:

1. Start a new Inventor part file or open an existing part file.

2. Create a new sketch or make an existing sketch active.

3. Click the Insert AutoCAD File command on the Sketch tab > Insert panel as shown in the following image.

Figure 2-79

4. The Open dialog box will appear. Browse to and either double-click the desired DWG file or click on the DWG file and then click Open.

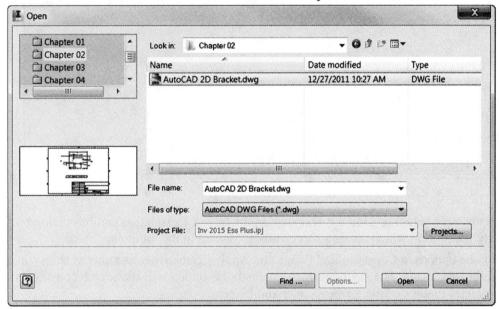

Figure 2-80

5. The Layers and Objects Import Options dialog box appears. In the Selective import section in the upper-left corner of the dialog box, uncheck the layer names you do not want data imported from as shown in the following image.

6. To select specific objects to insert, uncheck the All option, and then select the desired data in the preview window. In the preview window you can zoom and pan as needed.

7. You can change the background color of the preview image by clicking the black or white icon at the top-right corner of the dialog box.

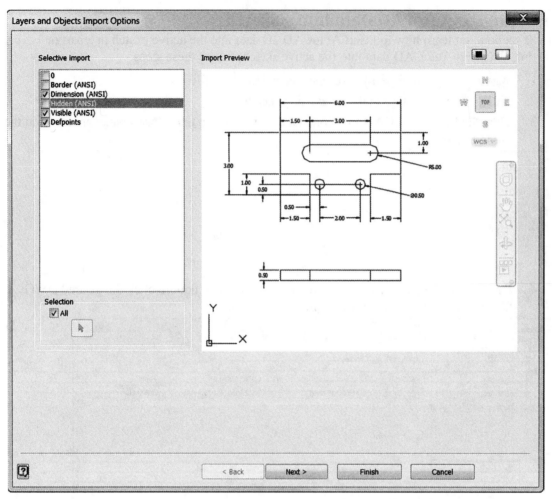

Figure 2-81

8. Click the Next button to go to the next step. In the Import Destination Options dialog box specify the units in which the data was created as shown in the following image.

9. Check the options to Constrain End Points and Apply geometric constraints as shown in the following image. The Apply geometric constraints option will add sketch constraints to geometry that is parallel, perpendicular and tangent.

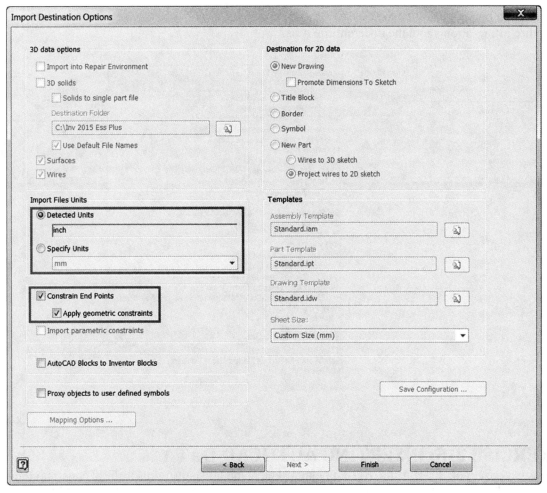

Figure 2-82

10. To import the data, click Finish.

11. Use the Zoom All command or double-click the wheel to see all the geometry.

12. Delete unnecessary geometry, constraints, and dimensions.

13. Add geometry (if needed), constraints, and dimensions to fully constrain the sketch.

OPEN OTHER FILE TYPES

Autodesk Inventor can also open parts and assemblies exported from other CAD systems. When files from other CAD systems are opened in Inventor they will be imported as solids or surface models depending upon the original file and the components will NOT have feature history and an assembly will NOT have any assembly constraints. You can add features to imported parts and edit the geometry by using Inventor's Direct Edit command. For files that are imported as an assembly, you can add assembly constraints. To open file types such as DXF, Alias, Catia, IDF Board Files, IGES, JT, Parasolids, PRO/E, SAT, STEP, SolidWorks, and Unigraphics NX, click the Inventor Application Menu > Open or click Open on the Quick Access toolbar. You can also use the Import DWG command from the Application Menu > Open; this command will import AutoCAD data into a new drawing, title block, border, symbol or part file without having to first create a new file.

In the Open dialog box, click the desired file format in the Files of type list. See the help system for more information about the different file types.

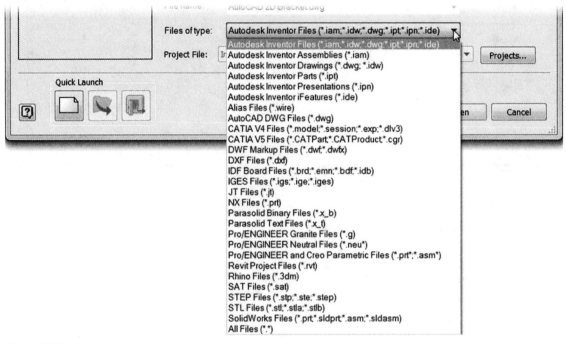

Figure 2-83

EXERCISE 2-5: INSERTING AUTOCAD DATA

In this exercise, you insert AutoCAD data into a sketch and add constraints to fully constrain the sketch.

1. Click the New command, click the English tab, and then double-click Standard (in).ipt, or if inch is the default unit; from the left side of the Quick Access toolbar you can click the down arrow of the New icon, and select Part.

2. Click the Start 2D Sketch command on the 3D Model tab > Sketch panel and then select the XY origin plane.

3. Click the Insert AutoCAD command from the Sketch tab > Insert panel.

4. From the Frequently Used Subfolder area (upper left corner of the dialog box) click the Chapter 02 subfolder and then in the file area double-click on the file *AutoCAD 2D Bracket.dwg*

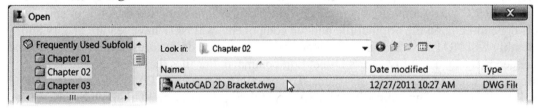

Figure 2-84

5. In the Layers and Objects Import Options dialog box you uncheck the layers that are not needed. In the upper left corner of the dialog box uncheck layers; 0, Border (ANSI) and Hidden (ANSI) as shown in the following image labeled (1).

6. In the Selection area near the bottom left corner of the dialog box uncheck All, labeled (2) in the following image.

7. Select the geometry and dimensions to insert, use the window selection (click and drag from the left to right) technique to select all of the geometry and dimensions in the top view labeled (3) in the following image.

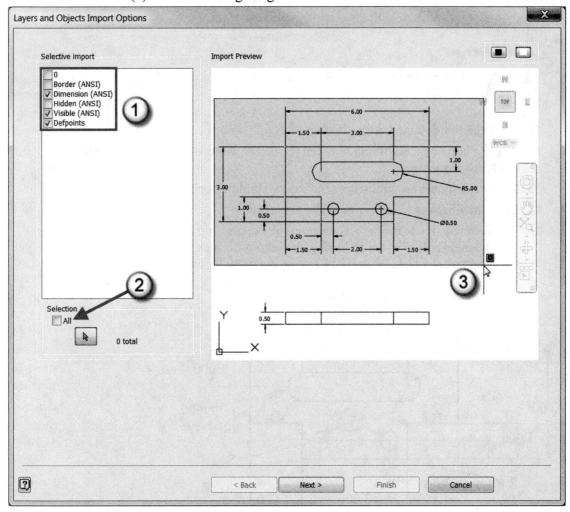

Figure 2-85

8. In the Selection area of the dialog box, verify that 27 total objects are selected as shown in the following image. If not, reselect all of the data in the top view.

Figure 2-86

9. Click the Next button on the bottom of the dialog box.

10. In the Import Destination Options dialog ensure inch is set as the detected unit and check the Constrain End Points and the Apply geometric constraints options as shown in the following image.

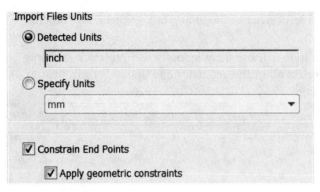

Figure 2-87

11. Click the Finish button on the bottom of the dialog box.

12. Apply a horizontal constraint between the center points of the two circles labeled (1) in the following image.

13. Apply a collinear constraint between the two middle horizontal lines labeled (2).

14. Press the ESC key twice to cancel the command.

15. The sketch is free to move. To constrain the sketch, drag the lower-left corner of the sketch labeled (3) in in the following image to the origin point of the sketch (0,0). Or you could add a coincident constraint between the origin point and the left point on the bottom line.

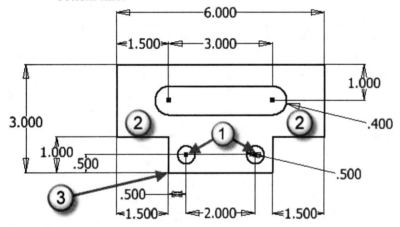

Figure 2-88

16. On the lower-right corner of the Status Bar, the text should state that "1 dimensions needed" to constrain the sketch.

17. Drag up the top-right endpoint of the top horizontal line up; the sketch will be rotated slightly as shown in the following image on the left.

18. Apply a horizontal constraint to the lower horizontal line, and this will fully constrain the sketch as shown in the following image on the right. The dimensions can be repositioned as needed.

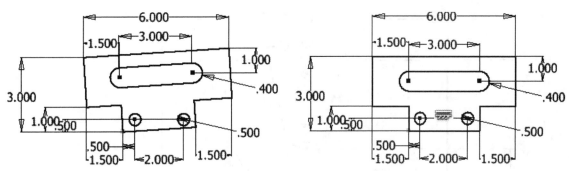

Figure 2-89

19. Press the F8 key to see all constraints.

20. Press the F9 key to hide all constraints.

21. The AutoCAD dimensions on the sketch are now parametric and can be edited. Practice editing the values of the dimensions by double-clicking on a dimension's value and enter a new value.

22. Close the file. Do not save changes. End of exercise.

APPLYING YOUR SKILLS

Skills Exercise 2-1

In this exercise, you create a sketch and then add geometric and dimensional constraints to control the size and shape of the sketch. Start a new part file based on the Standard (in).ipt, create a sketch on the XY plane, and create the fully constrained sketch as shown in the following image. Assume that the top and bottom horizontal lines are collinear, the center points of the arcs are aligned vertically, and the sketch is symmetric about the left and right sides. The bottom angled lines should be coincident with the center point of the lower arc (if the arc is drawn via the line command, the center point of the arc will automatically be coincident with the line it was drawn from). When done, close the file and do not save the changes.

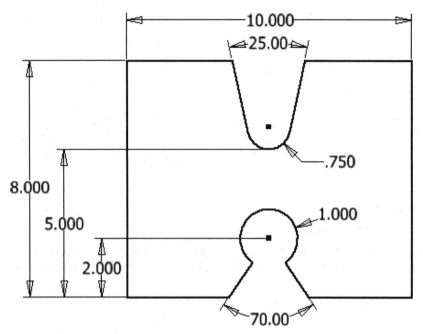

Figure 2-90

Skills Exercise 2-2

In this exercise, you create a sketch with linear and arc shapes, and then add geometric and dimensional constraints to fully constrain the sketch. Start a new part file based on the Standard (in).ipt template. Create a sketch on the XY plane, and create the fully constrained sketch as shown in the following image. First create the two circles and align their center points horizontally. Then create the two lines, and place a vertical constraint between the line endpoints on both ends. When done, close the file and do not save the changes.

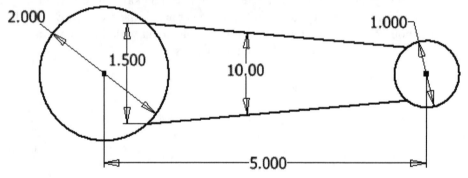

Figure 2-91

CHECKING YOUR SKILLS

Use these questions to test your knowledge of the material in this chapter.

1. True__ False__ While sketching, by default, geometric constraints are not applied to the sketch.

2. True__ False__ When you sketch and a point is inferred, a constraint is applied to represent that relationship.

3. True__ False__ It is recommended to never fully constrain a sketch.

4. True__ False__ When working on a millimeter part, you cannot input inch units.

5. True__ False__ After a sketch is fully constrained; you cannot change a dimension's value.

6. True__ False__ A driven dimension is another name for a parametric dimension.

7. True__ False__ Dimensions placed dynamically are not parametric.

8. True__ False__ You can only import 2D AutoCAD data into Autodesk Inventor.

9. Explain how to draw an arc while using the Line command.

10. Explain how to remove a geometric constraint from a sketch.

11. Explain how to change a vertical dimension to an aligned dimension while placing the dimension.

12. Explain how to create a dimension that is tangent to two arcs.

13. True__ False__ AutoCAD needs to be installed to insert AutoCAD geometry.

14. True__ False__ When a sketch is extruded that contains construction geometry, the construction geometry is deleted.

15. Explain how to change the unit type in a part file.

16. Explain where you would turn on Relax Mode.

17. True__ False__ When a pushpin appears in the Sketch entry in the browser, the sketch is fully constrained.

18. True__ False__ By default an arc length dimension can only be a driven dimension.

19. Explain how to draw a rectangle that is centered on the origin point.

20. True__ False__ When creating the first 2D sketch, you must select an origin plane to sketch on.

Chapter 3 – Creating and Editing Sketched Features

INTRODUCTION

After you have drawn, constrained, and dimensioned a sketch, your next step is to turn the sketch into a 3D part. This chapter takes you through the process to create and edit sketched features and to create features using primitive shapes.

OBJECTIVES

After completing this chapter, you will be able to perform the following:

- ☐ Describe what a feature is used for in the modeling process
- ☐ Describe the functions of Autodesk Inventor's browser
- ☐ Use direct manipulation techniques to create and edit a part
- ☐ Extrude a sketch into a part
- ☐ Revolve a sketch into a part
- ☐ Edit features of a part
- ☐ Edit the sketch of a feature
- ☐ Create a sketch on a plane
- ☐ Create sketched features using one of three operations: cut, join, or intersect
- ☐ Project edges of a part
- ☐ Create primitive features

FEATURES

After creating, constraining, and dimensioning a sketch, the next step in creating a model is to turn the sketch into a 3D feature. The first sketch of a part that is used to create a 3D feature is referred to as the base feature. In addition to the base feature, you can create secondary sketched features in which you draw a sketch on a planar face or work plane, and you can either add or subtract material to or from existing features in a part. Use the Extrude, Revolve, Sweep, or Loft commands to create sketched features in a part. Secondary features are covered later in this chapter. You can also create placed features such as fillets, chamfers, and holes by applying them to features that have been created. Placed features are covered in Chapter 4. Features are the building blocks of part creation.

A plate with a hole in it, for example, would have a base feature representing the plate and a hole feature representing the hole. As features are added to the part, they appear in the browser, and the history of the part or assembly, that is, the order in which the features are created or the parts are assembled. Features can be edited, deleted from, or reordered in the part as required.

Consumed and Unconsumed Sketches

You can use any sketch as a profile in feature creation. A sketch that has not yet been used in a feature is called an unconsumed sketch. When you turn a 2D sketched profile into a 3D feature, the feature consumes the sketch. The following image shows an unconsumed sketch in the browser on the left and a consumed sketch in the browser on the right. If desired, you can display more information in the browser about the features by clicking on the filter icon in the browser and click Show extended Names.

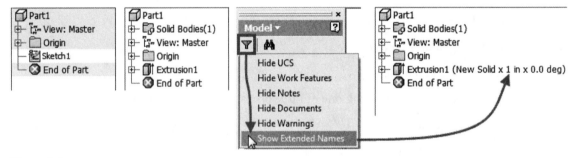

Figure 3-1

Although a consumed sketch is not visible as you view the 3D feature, you may need to access sketches and change their geometric or dimensional constraints in order to modify their associated features. A consumed sketch can be accessed from the browser by right-clicking and selecting Edit Sketch from the menu or by using the direct-manipulation mini-toolbar. The editing process will be covered later in this chapter. You can also edit the sketch by starting the Sketch command and selecting the sketch from the browser. The following image on the left shows the unconsumed sketch, and the image on the right shows the extruded solid that consumes the sketch.

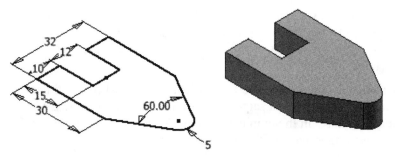

Figure 3-2

UNDERSTANDING THE BROWSER

The Autodesk Inventor browser, by default, is docked along the left side of the screen and displays the history of the file. In the browser you can create, edit, rename, copy, delete, and reorder features or parts. You can expand or collapse the browser to display the history of the features (the order in which the features were created) by clicking the + or the - on the left side of the feature or part name in the browser. An alternate method of expanding the browser is to place the cursor over a feature's icon (do not click) and the item in the browser automatically expands. To expand all the features, move the cursor into a blank area in the browser, right-click in a blank area in the browser and click Expand All from the menu.

The following image shows a browser with the features of a part file expanded.

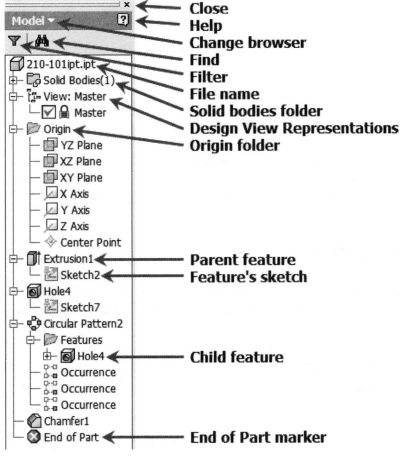

Figure 3-3

As you model a part it will grow in complexity, so will the information found in the browser. Dependent features are indented to show that they relate to the item listed above it. This is referred to as a parent-child relationship. If a hole is created in an extruded rectangle, for example, and the extrusion is deleted, the hole will also be deleted.

Each feature in the browser is given a default name. The first extrusion, for example, will be named Extrusion1, and the number in the name will sequence as you add similar features. The browser can also help you to locate features in the graphics window. To highlight a feature in the graphics window, simply move your cursor over the feature name in the browser.

To zoom in on a selected feature, right-click on the feature's name in the browser and select Find in Window on the menu or press the END key on your keyboard. The browser itself functions similarly to a toolbar except that you can resize it while it is docked. To close the browser, click the X in its upper-right corner. If the browser is not visible on the screen, you can toggle its visibility by clicking the View tab > Windows panel > User Interface > Browser as shown in the following image.

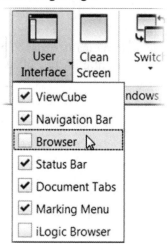

Figure 3-4

Specific functionality of the browser will be covered throughout this book in the pertinent sections. A basic rule to remember is to either right-click or double-click on the feature's name or icon in the browser to edit or perform a function on the feature.

SWITCHING ENVIRONMENTS

Up to this point, you have been working in the sketch environment where the work is done in 2D. The next step is to turn the sketch into a feature. To do so, you need to exit the sketch environment and enter the part environment. A number of methods can be used to accomplish this transition:

- Click the Finish Sketch command on the right side of the Sketch tab > Exit panel as shown in the following image on the left.
- In a blank area in the graphics window right-click and click Finish 2D Sketch from the marking menu as shown in the middle image.
- Press the S key on the keyboard.
- Click the 3D Model tab as shown in the image on the right and click on a command.
- Enter a shortcut key to initiate a feature creation command.

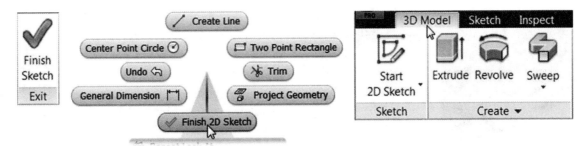

Figure 3-5

3D Modeling Commands

When you exit the sketch environment, the 3D Model tab is active. The following image shows the 3D Model tab. Many of these commands will be covered throughout this book.

Figure 3-6

DIRECT MANIPULATION

Direct manipulation allows you to start common commands and operations by clicking directly on the geometry in the graphics window. The direct manipulation tools appear as mini-toolbars or in-canvas buttons. Each direct manipulation option is explained next.

Mini-Toolbars

While not in a command you have different options depending upon what geometry is selected. After selecting the geometry click on the desired option. The different options will be explained throughout the book as they pertain to the topic.

Sketch

While not in a command, not in the sketch environment, and you select a sketch, the mini-toolbar appears and provides you the option of performing Extrude, Revolve, Hole, or Edit Sketch operations.

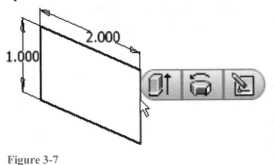

Figure 3-7

Face

While not in a command and you select a face, a mini-toolbar appears that allows you to quickly create a new sketch, edit an existing sketch, or edit a feature.

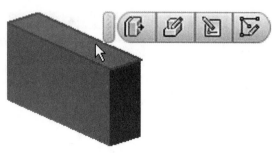

Figure 3-8

Edge
While not in a command and you select an edge, the mini-toolbar appears and provides you the option to fillet or chamfer the selected edge(s).

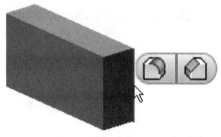

Figure 3-9

Mini-Toolbar–Command Options
After starting the Extrude, Revolve, Fillet, Chamfer, Hole, Face Draft and Shell modeling commands, a mini-toolbar will display command options in the graphics screen next to a selected object. The min-toolbar options are presented via buttons and selection tags display command options and prompts such as profile, face, and axis. The following image shows the min-toolbar buttons and the selection tag (profile) when extruding the first profile. You can move the mini-toolbar by clicking and dragging the vertical obround button in the upper left corner of the mini-toolbar. There are options to pin and fade the mini-toolbar by clicking on the options button on the bottom-right of the mini-toolbar. When the Pin Mini-Toolbar Position option is unchecked the mini-toolbar's position will move as the arrow on the face is dragged. When checked the mini-toolbar will stay in its current position even when the arrow on the face is dragged. The Fade option will fade the mini-toolbar when the cursor moves away from the mini-toolbar. The min-toolbar options are covered throughout the book where the command is covered.

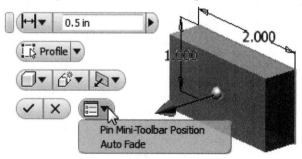

Figure 3-10

MINIMIZE DIALOG BOX
For commands that have a mini-toolbar, they also have a dialog and you have an option to minimize the dialog box. To minimize a dialog box, click the up arrow near the bottom of the

dialog box as shown in the following image on the left. The dialog box then displays only the horizontal title bar as shown in the image on the right. To maximize the dialog box, click the down arrow in the minimized dialog box as shown in the following image on the right. This option is set for each dialog box.

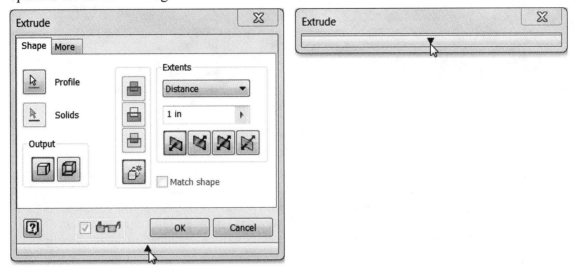

Figure 3-11

EXTRUDE A SKETCH

The most common method for creating a feature is to extrude a sketch and give it depth along the Z-axis. Before extruding, it is helpful to view the part in an isometric view. When you exit the first sketch the viewpoint will automatically change to the home view. Autodesk Inventor previews the extrusion depth and direction in the graphics window. To extrude a sketch follow one of these techniques:

- Finish the sketch, click the Extrude command on the 3D Model tab > Create panel as shown in the following image on the left.
- While not in a sketch, click on any geometry on the sketch and the mini-toolbar will appear, click the Create Extrude button as shown in the image in the middle
- Alternately, you can right-click in the graphics window and select Extrude on the marking menu as shown in the following image on the right.
- Press the shortcut key E.

Figure 3-12

After starting the Extrude command, the in-canvas display options will appear in the graphics window and the Extrude dialog box will appear. The following image on the left shows extrude options that are available when extruding the first sketch and the image on the right shows the operation buttons that are available when creating additional extrude features. You can either enter data in the mini-toolbar or in the dialog box. To access the button on the mini-toolbar click the down arrow next to each button to see more options and click and drag the arrow to change the distance or taper. The min-toolbar buttons will change depending upon what options are selected. If selection tags have a red arrow that command option needs to be satisfied before the command can be completed.

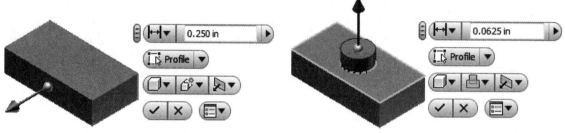

Figure 3-13

After you start the command, the Extrude dialog box also appears as shown in the following image. When you make changes in the dialog box, the change will also appear in the mini-toolbar and the shape of the sketch will change in the graphics window to represent these values and options. When you have entered the values and the options you need, click the OK button to create the extruded feature. The common extrude options will be explained in the next sections.

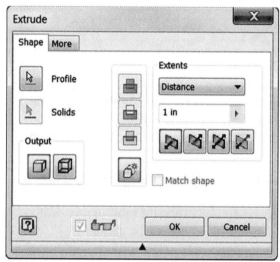

Figure 3-14

 TIP: When an arrow is red in a dialog box that prompts for profiles, faces, and axes, the color indicates that Inventor needs input from you to complete that function.

Shape

The Shape tab gives you options to specify the profile to use, operation, extents, and output type. The options are described below.

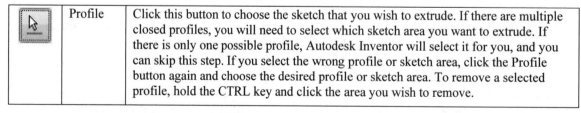

	Profile	Click this button to choose the sketch that you wish to extrude. If there are multiple closed profiles, you will need to select which sketch area you want to extrude. If there is only one possible profile, Autodesk Inventor will select it for you, and you can skip this step. If you select the wrong profile or sketch area, click the Profile button again and choose the desired profile or sketch area. To remove a selected profile, hold the CTRL key and click the area you wish to remove.

Operation

This is the unlabeled middle column of buttons. If this is the first sketch that you create a solid from, it is referred to as a base feature, and only the New Solid button is available. Once the base feature has been established, you can extrude a sketch, adding or removing material from the part by using the Join or Cut options, or you can retain the common volume between the existing part and the newly defined extrude operation using the Intersect option.

	Join	Adds material to the part.
	Cut	Removes material from the part.
	Intersect	Removes material, keeping what is common to the existing part feature(s) and the new feature.
	New Solid	Creates a new solid body. The first solid feature created uses this option by default. Select this option to create a new body in a part file that has an existing solid body.

Extents

The Extents option determines how the extruded sketch will be terminated. There are five options from which to choose as shown in the following image, but like the operation section, some options are not available until a base feature exists.

Figure 3-15

Distance

This option extrudes the profile a specified distance. With the Distance option you can either enter a value in the dialog box or in the graphics window where the profile will be extruded or click and drag the arrow in the graphics window as shown in the following image on the left. Another option is to click the arrow to the right where the distance value is displayed, click the Measure option as shown in the following image on the right to select two points to determine a value. Use the Show Dimensions option to display the dimensions of previously created features to select from, or select from the list of the recent values used. After a value is determined, a preview image appears in the graphics window to show how the extrusion will appear after creation.

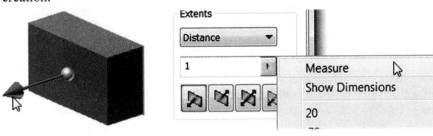

Figure 3-16

A preview image appears in the graphics window and the corresponding value appears in the distance area in the dialog box and in the mini-toolbar.

If values and units appear in red when you enter them, the defined distance is incorrect and should be corrected. For example, if you entered too many decimal places (e.g., 2.12.5) or an incorrect unit for the dimension value, the value will appear in red. You will need to correct the error before the extrusion can be created.

To Next

After selecting a profile, this option automatically extrudes the profile until it reaches a plane or face. The sketch must be fully enclosed in the area to which it is terminating; if it is not fully enclosed, use the To termination type with the Extend to Surface option. Click the Direction button to determine the extrusion direction.

To

This option extrudes the profile until it reaches a selected face, plane or point. To select a plane, face or point (midpoint or endpoint) to end the extrusion, click the Select Surface to end the feature creation button, as shown in the following image, and then select a face, plane or point at which the extrusion will terminate.

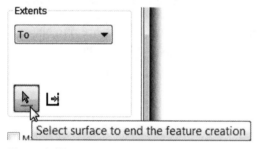

Figure 3-17

Between

This option extrudes the profile between two selected planes or faces. After selecting this option, the Select surface to start feature creation button is active as shown in the following image on the left, and then click the face or plane where the extrusion will start. Then click the Select surface to end the feature creation button, as shown in the following image on the right and then click the face or plane where the extrusion will terminate.

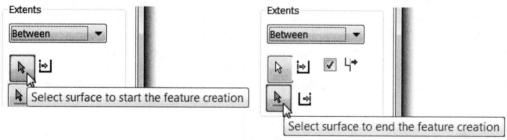

Figure 3-18

All

This option extrudes the profile all the way through the part in one or both directions.

Direction

There are four buttons from which to choose for determining the direction. Choose from the first two to flip the extrusion direction, click the third button (symmetric) to have the extrusion go equal distances in the negative and positive directions (for example, if the extrusion distance is 2 inches, the extrusion will go 1 inch in both the negative and positive Z directions), and click the asymmetric option to define different distances for the negative and positive direction.

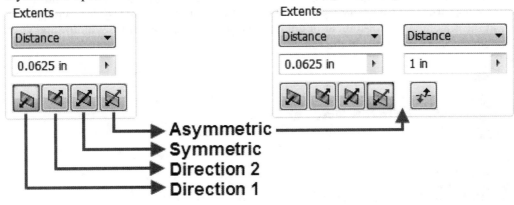

Figure 3-19

Output

Two options are available to define the type of output that the Extrude command can generate:

	Solid	Extrudes the sketch, and the result is a solid body.
	Surface	Extrudes the sketch, and the result is a surface.

More Tab

The More tab, as shown in the following image, contains additional options to refine the feature being created:

Alternate Solution

Alternate Solution terminates the feature on the most distant solution for the selected surface.

Minimum Solution

When checked, the Minimum Solution option terminates the feature on the first possible solution for the selected surface. An example is shown in the following image.

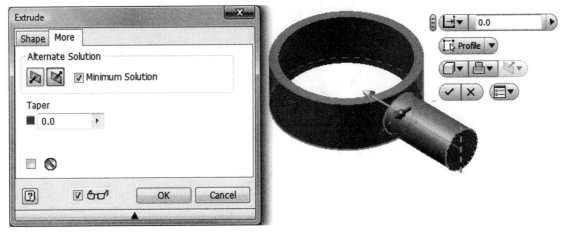

Figure 3-20

Taper

Taper extrudes the sketch and applies a taper angle to the feature. To extend the taper angle from the part, give the taper angle a positive or negative number. A positive taper increases the volume while a negative value decreases the volume of the resulting extruded feature. To add a taper value in the dialog box, mini-toolbar or click on the sphere in the graphics window and drag the arrow or enter a value as shown in the following image.

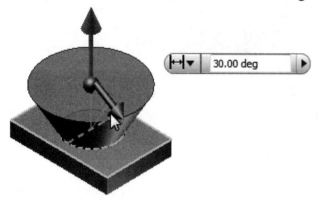

Figure 3-21

EXERCISE 3-1: EXTRUDING A SKETCH

In this exercise, you create a base feature by extruding an existing profile. You will examine the direction options available in the Extrude dialog box.

1. Open *ESS_E03_01.ipt* from the Chapter 03 subfolder.

2. From the 3D Model tab > Create panel click the Extrude command or click on the sketch and in the mini-toolbar click the Create Extrude button. Since there is only one closed profile, the profile is automatically selected.

3. In the Extrude dialog box, set the Distance to **.5** in (if needed expand the Extrude dialog box by clicking the down arrow at the bottom of the minimized Extrude dialog box).

4. In the graphics window select the arrow on the extrusion and drag the arrow until a distance of **1.000** is displayed in the value field of the Extrude dialog box and in the mini-toolbar as shown in the following image, and then release the mouse button.

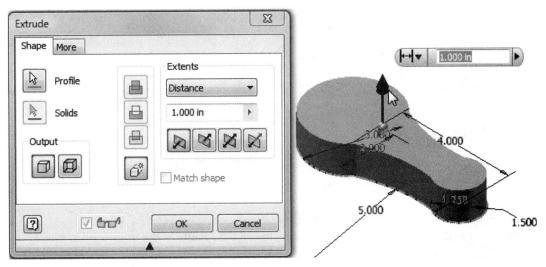

Figure 3-22

5. If needed, click the down arrow on the bottom of the dialog box and click the More tab in the Extrude dialog box.

6. Change the taper by typing **20.00 deg** in the Taper area.

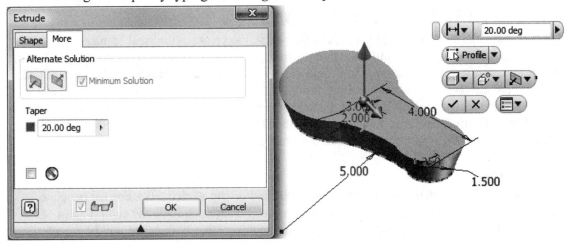

Figure 3-23

7. Adjust the taper by clicking and dragging the sphere to **10°** and then to **-10°**.

8. Click the Shape tab in the Extrude dialog box.

9. Flip the direction of the extrusion to go in the negative Y direction by selecting the Direction 2 button (second from the left button) on the direction area in the dialog box.

10. In the Extrude dialog box change the direction to Asymmetric (extrude different values in each direction) and enter different values for each direction.

11. In the min-toolbar change the extent to Symmetric as shown in the following image.

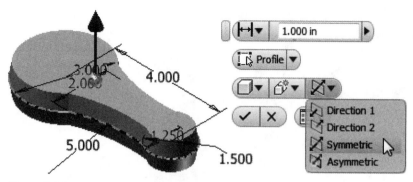

Figure 3-24

12. In the graphics window click and drag the arrow to different values.

13. Practice changing the values and directions to see the results in the mini-toolbar and in the Extrude dialog box. When done, click OK or click the green check mark in the mini-toolbar display area and the extrusion will be created. Later in this chapter you will learn how to edit features.

14. Close the file. Do not save changes. End of exercise.

LINEAR DIAMETER DIMENSIONS

Another method for creating a part is to revolve a sketch to create cylindrical features. To revolve a sketch, you follow similar steps that you did to extrude a sketch. You create the sketch, but the sketch is a quarter section of the completed feature. Add constraints and dimensions and then revolve the sketch about a centerline, straight edge or axis. To define the sketch you can use radial or diameter dimensions. To place diameter dimensions on a sketch you use a centerline or a normal line to define the linear diameter dimension. The following sections explain how to place a diameter dimension with a centerline and a normal line.

Centerline

To create a centerline, activate the Centerline command on the Sketch tab > Format panel, as shown in the following image on the left and then sketch a line. Click on the centerline to deactivate it. If the command is not deactivated, all geometry that is sketched will be a centerline. Or you can change an existing sketch entity to a centerline by selecting an existing sketched entity and then select the Centerline command. To create a linear diameter dimension by using a centerline, follow these steps:

1. Draw a sketch that represents a quarter section of the finished feature or part.

2. If needed draw a line that will be used as the centerline to revolve about or use a line in the sketch that the sketch will be revolved around.

3. Change an existing line into a centerline that the sketch will be revolved around by clicking the Centerline command on the Sketch tab > Format panel. The centerline will be treated as a normal line and can be used to define a closed profile.

4. Start the Dimension command.

5. Click the centerline, and a point or edge to be dimensioned. It does not matter the order that the entities are selected; however, one of the selections needs to be the centerline not just an endpoint of the centerline.

6. Move the cursor until the diameter dimension is in the correct location and click.

7. The following image on the right shows the linear diameter dimension created using the centerline to define the axis of revolution.

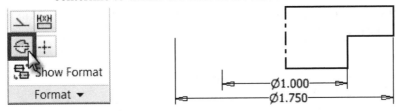

Figure 3-25

Normal Line

When a normal line is used to revolve the sketch around, you can create linear diameter (diametric) dimensions for sketches that represent a quarter outline of a revolved part. To create a linear diameter dimension, follow these steps:

1. Draw a sketch that represents a quarter section of the finished feature or part.

2. Draw a line that will be used as the centerline to revolve about or use a line in the sketch that the sketch will be revolved around.

3. Start the Dimension command.

4. Click the line (not an endpoint) that the sketch will be revolved around (axis of rotation).

5. Click the other point or line to be dimensioned.

6. Right-click and select Linear Diameter from the menu as shown in the following image on the left.

7. Move the cursor until the diameter dimension is in the correct location and click. The following image on the right shows a sketch that represents a quarter section of a part with a linear diameter dimension placed.

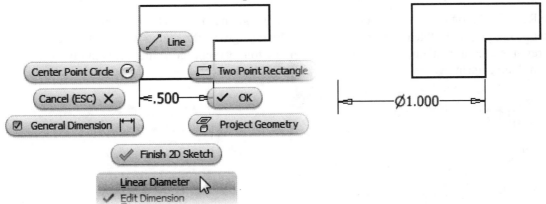

Figure 3-26

REVOLVE A SKETCH

After defining the sketch that will be revolved, use one of the following techniques to create a revolve feature:

• Click the Revolve command on the 3D Model tab > Create panel as shown in the following image on the left.

- While not in a sketch, click on the sketch geometry and the mini-toolbar will appear, click the Create Revolve button, as shown in the middle image.
- Right-click in the graphics window and click Revolve on the marking menu as shown in the following image on the right.
- Press the R key.

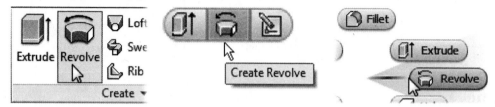

Figure 3-27

After starting the Revolve command, the mini-toolbar will appear in the graphics window and the Revolve dialog box will appear. The following image on the left shows the constrained sketch with a centerline and the image on the right shows the revolve mini-toolbar with the options that are available when revolving the first sketch. You can enter data in the Revolve dialog box or via the mini-toolbar and drag the arrow to revolve an angle other than a full 360 degrees.

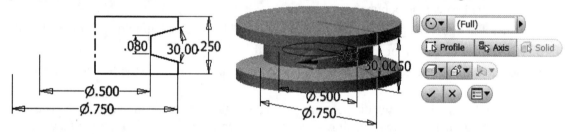

Figure 3-28

The Revolve dialog box, as shown in the following image, has five sections: Shape, Operation, Extents, Output, and Match Shape. When you make changes in the dialog box, the preview for the revolved feature changes in the graphics window to represent the values and options selected. When done entering values and options, click the OK button.

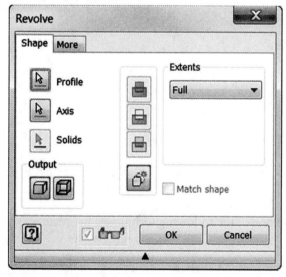

Figure 3-29

Shape

This section has three options: Profile, Axis and Solids.

	Profile	Click this button to choose the profile to revolve. If the Profile button is shown depressed, this is telling you that a profile or sketch needs to be selected. If there are multiple closed profiles, you will need to select the profile that you want to revolve. If there is only one possible profile, Autodesk Inventor will select it for you, and you can skip this step. If the wrong profile or sketch area is selected, click the Profile button, and choose the new profile or sketch area. To remove a selected profile, hold the CTRL key and click the profile to remove.
	Axis	Click a straight edge, centerline, work axis, or origin axis about which the profile(s) should be revolved. See the previous section on how to create a centerline and diametric dimensions.
	Solids	If there are multiple solid bodies in the part file, click this button to choose the solid body(ies) to participate in the operation.

Operation

This is the unlabeled middle column of buttons. If this is the first sketch that you create a solid from, it is referred to as a base feature, and only the bottom button is available. The operation defaults to New Solid (the bottom button). Once the base feature has been established, you can then revolve a sketch, adding or removing material from the part using the Join or Cut options, or you can keep what is common between the existing part and the completed revolve operation using the Intersect option.

	Join	Adds material to the part.
	Cut	Removes material from the part.
	Intersect	Removes material, keeping what is common to the existing part feature(s) and the new feature.
	New Solid	Creates a new solid body. The first solid feature created uses this option by default. Select this option to create a new body in a part file that has an existing solid body.

Extents

The Extents determines if the sketch will be revolved 360°, a specified angle, stop at a specific plane, or start and stop at specific planes.

Figure 3-30

Angle

This option revolves a profile a specified angle. You can enter a value in the Revolve dialog box, mini-toolbar or drag the arrow in the graphics window. With the angle option there are four buttons from which to choose for determining the direction as shown in the following image.

Select from the first two to flip the angle direction, click the third button (symmetric) to have the revolution go equal distances in the negative and positive directions, and click the asymmetric option to define different angles for the negative and positive direction. With the symmetric option, if the angle is 90 degrees, for example, the angle will go 45 degrees in both the negative and positive Z directions.

Figure 3-31

To Next

After selecting a profile, this option automatically revolves the profile until it reaches a plane or face. With this option the sketch must be fully enclosed in the area to which it is projecting; if it is not fully enclosed, use the To termination with the Extend to Surface option.

To

This option revolves the profile until it reaches a selected face, plane, or point. After the profile is selected, click the Select Surface button and select a plane, face, or point to terminate the revolve feature on.

Between

This option revolves a profile between two selected planes or faces. Click the Select surface to start the feature creation button, and then select two faces or planes that the revolve feature will start and terminate between.

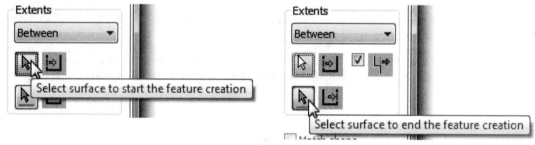

Figure 3-32

Full

Full is the default option and revolves a profile 360° about a centerline or selected edge or axis.

Output

Two options are available to select the type of output that the Revolve command can generate.

	Solid	Revolves the sketch, and the result is a solid body.
	Surface	Revolves the sketch, and the result is a surface.

More Tab

The More tab, as shown in the following image, contains additional options to refine the feature being created.

Alternate Solution

Alternate Solution terminates the feature on the face or plane that is further away. An example is shown in the following image, where the revolve feature continues past the first solution it finds on the selected face and terminates on the second solution of the selected face.

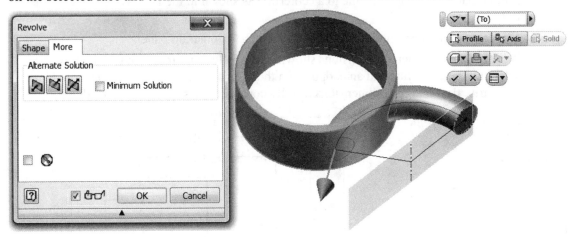

Figure 3-33

Minimum Solution

Minimum Solution terminates the feature on the first possible solution for the selected surface. An example is shown in the following image where the revolve feature terminates at the first solution of the selected face.

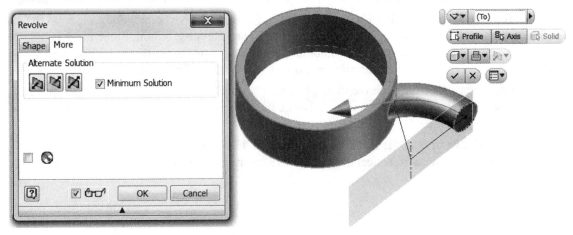

Figure 3-34

EXERCISE 3-2: REVOLVING A SKETCH

In this exercise, you create a sketch and then create a revolved feature to complete a part. This exercise demonstrates how to revolve sketched geometry about an axis to create a revolved feature.

1. Click the New command on the Quick Access toolbar, click the English tab, and then double-click Standard (in).ipt, or if inch is the default unit; from the left side of the Quick Access toolbar you can click the down arrow on the New icon, and click Part.

2. Click the Start 2D Sketch command on the 3D Model tab Sketch panel and then select the XY origin plane in the graphics window.

3. Create the sketch geometry as shown. Locate the lower endpoint of the geometry on the origin point. Select the left vertical line and then click the Centerline command on the Format panel to change the line to a centerline as shown in the following image on the left.

4. Click the Dimension command on the Sketch tab > Constrain panel.

5. Add the linear diameter dimensions shown in the following image on the right by selecting the centerline and an endpoint on the sketch. Then place the dimension. Note, for clarity the remaining dimensions to fully constrain the sketch were not added.

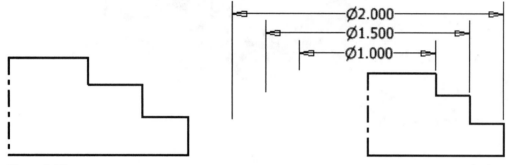

Figure 3-35

Figure 3-36

6. Right-click in the graphics window, and click Finish 2D Sketch from the marking menu.

7. From the 3D Model tab > Create panel bar, click the Revolve command or click on the sketch and then on the mini-toolbar click the Create Revolve button. Since there is only one closed profile, the profile is automatically selected as the profile and since there is only one centerline, the centerline is automatically selected as the axis.

8. If needed expand the Revolve dialog box by clicking the down arrow at the bottom the minimized Revolve dialog box and change the Extents to Angle as shown in the following image.

9. Enter **45 deg** or drag the arrow on the part until **45.00 deg** is displayed. The preview of the revolve updates to reflect the change as shown in the following image.

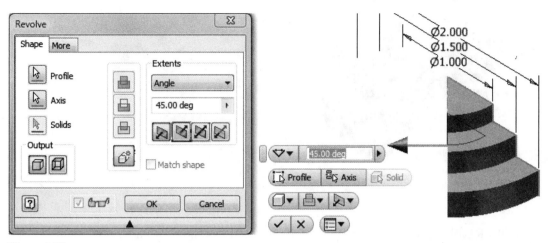

Figure 3-37

10. Change the direction of the revolve to go counter clockwise by selecting the left Direction 2 button in the dialog box or click and drag the arrow in the graphics window to go **45.00 deg** in the opposite direction. The preview image will reverse the direction counterclockwise.

11. Set the revolve direction to Symmetric; in the Revolve dialog box it's the third button from the left in the Direction area.

12. Enter **90 deg** for the angle. The preview should resemble the following image.

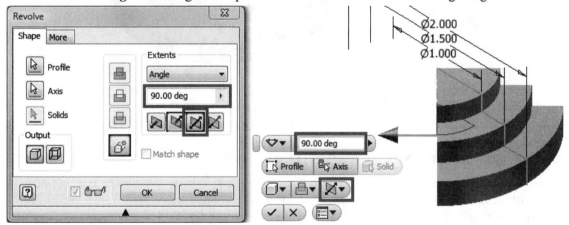

Figure 3-38

13. In the mini-toolbar change the Extents to Asymmetric.

14. In the graphics window click and drag the arrows to different values, similar to what is shown in the following image.

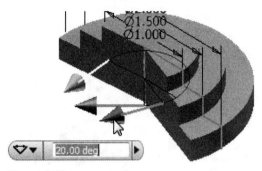

Figure 3-39

Figure 3-40

15. In the Revolve dialog box change the Extents to Full as shown in the following image in the left.

16. Click the OK button or click the green check mark in the mini-toolbar to create the feature. Your part should resemble the image on the right.

Figure 3-41

17. Close the file. Do not save changes. End of exercise.

PRIMITIVE SHAPES/FEATURES

A method to quickly create basic shapes is to use one of the primitive commands; box, cylinder, sphere or torus as shown in the following image. Primitive shapes are created from a sketch and are extruded (for box and cylinder) or revolved (for sphere and torus). The advantage to using the primitive commands is they combine these operations to reduce clicks.

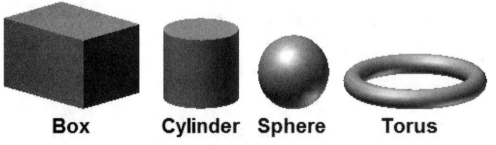

Figure 3-42

To create a primitive shape/feature, follow these steps.

First turn on the Primitive panel by selecting the Primitive panel visibility option from the drop down arrow on the right side of the panels as shown in the following image on the left. Then click one of the Primitive commands from the 3D Model tab > Primitives panel as shown in the following image on the right.

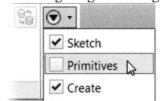

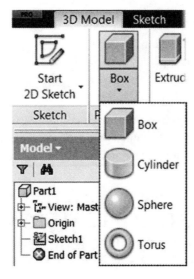

Figure 3-43

1. Select a plane to locate the primitive, the plane can be an origin plane, planar face on the part or a work plane.
2. Depending on the primitive that you are creating you will do the following.

Box
1. Select a point to locate center of the rectangle
2. Enter a value for the horizontal size
3. Press the Tab key
4. Enter a value for the vertical size
5. Press ENTER to extrude the rectangle
6. Enter a value for the extrusion distance
7. Click OK to create the feature

Cylinder
1. Select a point to locate the center of the circle
2. Enter a value for the diameter of the circle
3. Press ENTER to extrude the circle
4. Enter a value for the extrusion distance
5. Click OK to create the feature

Sphere
1. Select a point to locate the center of the circle
2. Enter a value for the diameter of the circle
3. Press ENTER to revolve the circle
4. Click OK to create the feature

Torus
1. Select a point to locate the center of the torus

2. Enter a value and then either press ENTER or click a point to define the radius of the torus

3. Enter a value for the diameter of the circle

4. Press ENTER to revolve the circle

5. Click OK to create the feature

TIP: Features created from the Primitive commands can be edited like any other feature. If a primitive command is a secondary feature you will need to edit its sketch to locate it. Editing a feature and a feature's sketch will be covered later in this chapter.

SECONDARY 2D SKETCHED FEATURES

A secondary 2D sketched feature is created from a sketch that you create on a planar face on a part or work plane and then add or remove material from the part. The basic steps to create a 2D sketch feature are as follows:

1. Create a new 2D sketch on a planar face on the part or on a work plane.

2. Draw geometry to define the outline of the profile.

3. Add constraints and dimensions.

4. Use the Extrude, Revolve, Sweep, or Loft commands to perform a Boolean operation; add material, remove material, or keep what is common between the part and the feature that is being created. The following image shows a part (cylinder) and a sketch (circle) on the left and the affect the three Boolean operations would have on the part.

Figure 3-44

5. Use the Extents options in the Extrude or Revolve commands to control how the feature will terminate. For more information about Extents refer back to the Extents section in the Extrude a Sketch and the Revolve a Sketch section that were covered earlier in this chapter.

There are no limits to the number of sketched features that can be added to a part. Each sketched feature is created on its own plane, and multiple features can reference the same plane. You sketch geometry, apply constraints and dimensions exactly as you did with the first sketch. In addition to constraining and dimensioning the new sketch, you can also constrain and dimension the new sketch to the edges on the part. The edges you dimension to do not need to lie on the active sketch plane; the dimensions will be placed on the current sketch plane but reference the selected edge.

In the following section, you learn how to create a sketch on a plane and create a feature from the sketch.

Create a new 2D Sketch

As stated previously, each 2D sketch must exist on its own plane and only one sketch can be active. The active sketch has a plane on which the sketch is drawn. A sketch must be created on a planar face, a work plane, or an origin plane. The planar face on the part does not need to have a straight edge. For example a cylinder has two planar faces, one on the top and the other on the bottom of the part. Neither has a straight edge, but a sketch can be placed on either planar face.

To make a sketch active, use one of the following methods:

- Click the Start 2D Sketch command from the 3D Model tab > Sketch panel as shown in the following image on the left, and then select the plane where you want to create the sketch.
- While not in the middle of an operation, right-click in the graphics window, and click New Sketch from the marking menu as shown in the middle of the following image. Then click a planar face, or a work plane.
- While not in a sketch, click on the planar face or work plane that you want to create the active sketch on. Then click the Create Sketch button from the mini-toolbar as shown in the image on the right.
- Press the S key, and then click the plane where you want to place the sketch.

Once you have created a sketch, it appears in the browser with the name Sketch#, and sketch commands appear in the Sketch tab. In the browser, the Sketch number will sequence for each new sketch that is created. When you create a new sketch or make a sketch active, by default the view will automatically change so you are looking straight at the sketch. This is controlled by the Application Option > Sketch tab > Look at sketch plane on sketch creation and edit. To manually adjust the viewpoint to look straight at a plane, click the Look At command on the Navigation Bar and then select the plane.

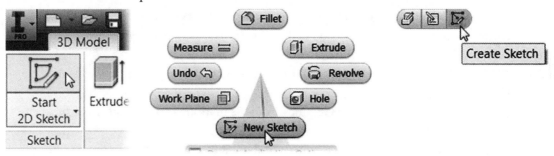

Figure 3-45

SELECT OTHER-FACE CYCLING

Autodesk Inventor has dynamic face highlighting that helps you to select the correct face, edge, part etc. to activate and to select objects. As you move the cursor over a given face, the edges of the face are highlighted. If you continue to move the cursor, different faces are highlighted as the cursor passes over them.

To cycle to a face that is behind another one, start a command and then move the cursor over the face that is in front of one that you want to select and hold the cursor still for two seconds. The Select Other tool appears, as shown in the following image on the left. Select the drop down arrow and move the cursor over the available objects in the list until the correct face is highlighted and then click. The number of objects that appear in the list will depend upon the geometry and the location of the cursor. You can also access the Select Other command by right-clicking while on the desired location in the graphics window and click Select Other from the marking menu as shown in the middle image.

You can specify the amount of time before the Select Other option will appear; click Tools tab > Options panel > Application Options > General tab and in the Selection area set the "Select Other" delay (sec) as shown in the image on the right. If you do not want the Select Other command to open automatically, type OFF in the field. The default value is 2.0 second.

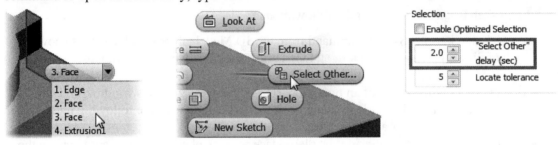

Figure 3-46

SLICE GRAPHICS

While creating parts, you may need to sketch on a plane that is difficult to see because features are obscuring the view. The Slice Graphics option will temporarily remove the portion of the part that obscures the active sketch plane on which you want to sketch. The following image on the left shows a revolved part with an origin plane visible and the Slice Graphics menu. The image on the right shows the graphics sliced and the origin plane visibility turned off. To temporarily slice the graphics screen, follow these steps:

1. Create a sketch or make a sketch active where the graphics need to be sliced.

2. Rotate the model so the correct side will be sliced. The side that faces out will be sliced away.

3. With the sketch active start the Slice Graphics command by performing one of the following:

   a. Right-click and select Slice Graphics from the marking menu as shown in the following image on the left

   b. Click Slice Graphics from the bottom of the Status Bar as shown in the middle image.

   c. Press the F7 key

   d. Click Slice Graphics on the View tab > Appearance panel.

4. The graphics will be sliced on the active sketch as shown in the following image on the right.

5. Use sketch commands from the Sketch tab to create geometry on the active sketch.

6. To exit the sliced graphics environment, right-click and select Slice Graphics from the marking menu, click Slice Graphics from the bottom of the Status Bar, press the F7 key or click the Finish Sketch button on the Sketch tab > Exit panel.

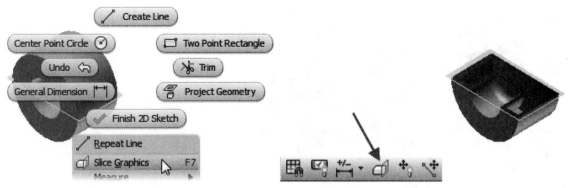

Figure 3-47

EXERCISE 3-3: SKETCH FEATURES

In this exercise, you create a sketch on the angled face of a part and then create an oblong on the new sketch plane.

1. Open *ESS_E03_03.ipt* from the Chapter 03 folder.

2. Create a sketch by selecting the top-inside angled face and click the Create Sketch button on the mini-toolbar as shown in the following image on the left.

3. The view should change so you are looking straight at the sketch, if not click the Look At command from the Navigation Bar, and then select the top angled plane.

4. Next you create a center-to-center slot. Start the command from the Sketch tab > Create panel > Center to Center Slot (it may be under the Two Point Rectangle command) as shown in the middle image. While creating the slot enter values of **1.500** for the center-to-center distance and **1.000** for the diameter as shown in the image on the right.

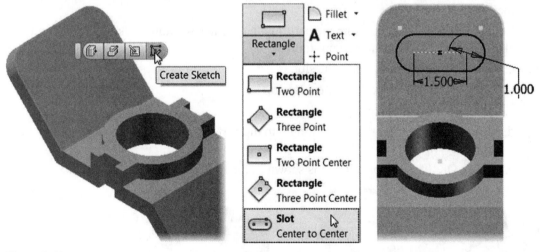

Figure 3-48

5. Next you center the slot, click the Horizontal constraint command on the Constrain panel as shown in the following image on the left.

6. Select the midpoint of the center point of the slot and the midpoint of the top horizontal edge of the part as shown in the following image on the right.

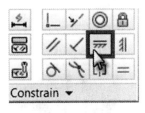

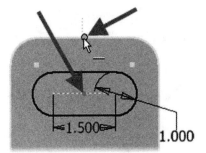

Figure 3-49

TIP: The horizontal and vertical direction is based on the sketch's coordinate system that is automatically aligned to the selected face when a sketch is created.

7. To fully constrain the slot place a **1.500** vertical dimension as shown in the following image.

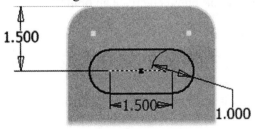

Figure 3-50

8. Click the Finish Sketch command on the Exit panel.

9. If the view did not automatically change to the home view press the F6 key to change to the Home View.

10. Next you remove material from the part. In the graphics window click on the slot and click Create Extrude from the mini-toolbar.

    a. For the profile, click inside the slot.

    b. In the mini-tool click the Cut operation.

    c. Change the Extents to All.

    d. Ensure that the direction is pointing into the part as shown in the following image on the left.

    e. Click OK. The completed part is shown in the following image on the right.

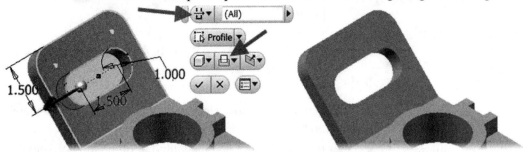

Figure 3-51

11. Practice creating sketched features and try different options.

12. Close the file. Do not save changes. End of exercise.

EDITING A FEATURE AND SKETCH

After you create a feature, the feature consumes all of the dimensions that were visible in the sketch. If you need to change a feature's options and values such as operation, extents, distance, taper etc. you edit the feature. You can also edit the feature's sketch and change the values of the dimensions or add or remove geometry.

Edit Feature Command

To change a feature's options, you need to edit the feature. There are multiple methods that you can use to edit the feature. There is no preferred method; use the method that works best for your workflow.

- While not in a sketch, move the cursor over the feature in the graphics window and click. Click the Edit "Feature Name" button from the mini-toolbar. The following image on the left shows the mini-toolbar button for editing an extrusion.
- Double-click on the features icon in the browser
- In the browser, right-click the feature's name and click Edit Feature from the menu as shown in the image on the right.

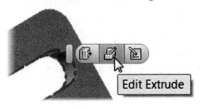
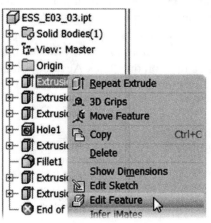

Figure 3-52

When editing a feature, the dialog box and mini-toolbar will appear that was used to create the feature. While editing, you can change the feature's values and its options except the join operation on a base feature (first feature in the browser) and the output (solid or surface).

Editing a Feature's Sketch

In the last section, you learned how to edit the values and the settings in which the feature was created. In this section, you learn how to add and delete constraints, dimensions, and geometry in the original 2D sketch. To edit the 2D sketch of a feature, while not in a sketch, do one of the following:

- Click on the feature in the graphics window whose sketch you want to edit. Then click the Edit Sketch button from the mini-toolbar as shown in the following image on the left.
- In the browser, right-click the name of the feature and click Edit Sketch from the menu as shown in the middle image.

- In the browser, expand the feature and right-click on the sketch entry under the feature and click Edit Sketch from the menu as shown in the image on the right.
- In the browser, expand the feature and double-click on the sketch icon.

Figure 3-53

While editing the sketch, you can add or remove objects. You can add geometry lines, arcs, circles, and splines to the sketch. To delete an object, right-click it and select Delete from the menu, or press the DELETE key. If you delete an object from the sketch that has dimensions associated with it, the dimensions are no longer valid for the sketch, and they will also be deleted. You can also delete the entire sketch and replace it with an entirely new sketch. When replacing entire sketches, you should first delete other features that would be consumed by the new objects and re-create them.

You can also add or delete constraints and dimensions. When the dimensions are visible on the screen, double-click the dimension text that you want to edit. The Edit Dimension dialog box appears. Enter a new value, and then click the checkmark in the dialog box or press the ENTER key. Continue to edit the dimensions and when finished, click Finish Sketch from the ribbon or click the Local Update button on the Quick Access toolbar as shown in the following image. The sketch will be re-consumed by the feature and the new values will be used to regenerate the features.

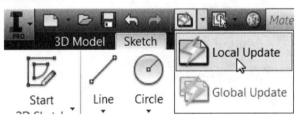

Figure 3-54

 TIP: If you receive an error after updating the feature, make sure that the sketch forms a closed profile. If the appended or edited sketch forms multiple closed profiles, you will need to edit the feature and reselect the profile area.

Renaming Features and Sketches
By default, each feature is given a name. These feature names may not help you when trying to locate a specific feature of a complex part, as they will not be descriptive to your design intent. The first extrusion, for example, is given the name Extrusion1 by default, whereas the design intent may be that the extrusion is the thickness of a plate. To rename a feature, slowly double-click the feature name and enter a new name. Spaces are allowed.

Deleting a Feature
You may choose to delete a feature after it has been placed. To delete a feature, right-click the feature name in the browser, and select Delete from the menu, as shown in the following image.

The Delete Features dialog box will then appear, and you should choose what you want to delete from the list. You can delete multiple features by holding down the CTRL or SHIFT key, clicking their names in the browser, right-clicking one of the names, and then selecting Delete from the menu. The Delete Features dialog box appears; it allows you to delete consumed and/or dependent sketches and features.

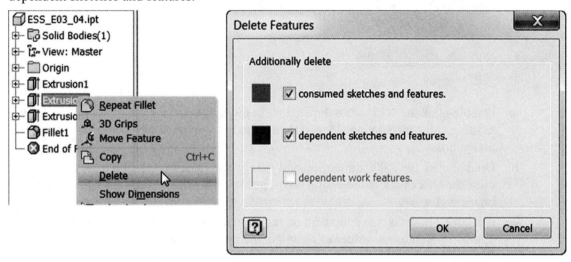

Figure 3-55

Failed Features

A failed feature has a red text for the feature name in the browser and has a yellow triangle with an explanation point displayed in front of the features icon as shown in the following image. After updating the part, this is an alert that the new values or settings were not regenerated successfully. To see what the feature looked like in its last successful state, move the cursor over the features name in the browser and it will highlight in the graphics window like what is shown in the following image on the left of the last good fillet feature. You can then edit the values, enter new values, or select different settings to define a valid solution. Once you define a valid solution, the feature should regenerate without error. When you try to create a fillet, chamfer, shell, or a thicken/offset feature that cannot be calculated, an error glyph will appear on the right side of the mini-toolbar as shown in the following image on the right.

Figure 3-56

EXERCISE 3-4: EDITING FEATURES AND SKETCHES

In this exercise, you will edit a consumed sketch in an extrusion and update the part. In the next section, you learn how to create sketched features that were created in this model.

1. Open *ESS_E03_04.ipt* from the Chapter 03 folder.

2. Edit the sketch of Extrusion1 by selecting the top planar face and then click Edit Sketch from the mini-toolbar as shown in the following image. You could have also right-clicked on Extrusion1 in the browser and clicked Edit Feature from the menu.

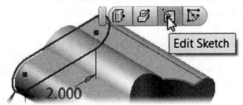

Figure 3-57

    a. Double-click the .375 radius dimension. In the Edit Dimension dialog box change the existing value by entering **.25**, and then press Enter or click the checkmark in the dialog box.

    b. Double-click the 2.000 dimension and change the value to **3** and then press Enter or click the checkmark in the dialog box. The sketch should resemble the following image on the left.

    c. Click the Finish Sketch command on the Sketch tab > Exit panel. The feature is updated with the new values as shown in the image on the right.

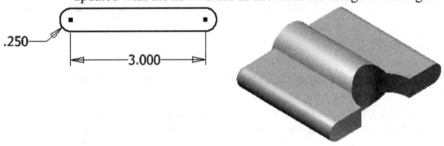

Figure 3-58

3. You now edit the extents that Extrusion2 was created with. In the graphics window click on the inside circular face and then click Edit Extrude on the mini-toolbar button as shown in the following image on the left, labeled (1). The Extrude dialog box and mini-toolbar buttons are displayed.

    a. Change the Operation to Join in the mini-toolbar as shown in the following image on the right labeled (2).

    b. Change the Extents option to To selected face/point option labeled (3) in the image on the right

    c. Select the bottom face labeled (4) in the image the right. The extrusion will then stop at this face no matter what dimension changes in the part.

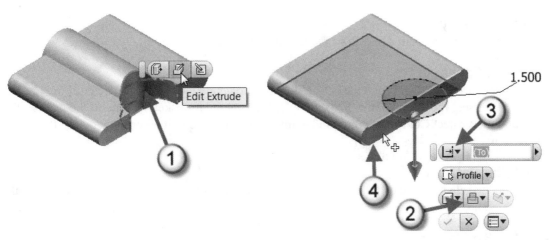

Figure 3-59

    d. Click the green check mark in the mini-toolbar display. The feature will update as shown in the following image on the left.

4. In the browser, right-click Extrusion3. Click Delete and then click OK in the dialog box to delete consumed sketches and features. When done, your part should resemble the following image on the right.

Figure 3-60

5. Practice editing the sketch dimensions and features.

6. Close the file. Do not save changes. End of exercise.

PROJECTING GEOMETRY

Modeling parts based partially on existing geometry is done often, and you will frequently need to reference existing faces, edges, or loops from features to create new features. The Project Geometry command is used to project an edge(s), face, point, or loop onto the active sketch. By default, projected geometry maintains an associative link to the original geometry that is projected. If you project the face of a feature onto another sketch, for example, and the parent sketch is modified, the projected geometry will update to reflect the changes.

Projecting Edges

In this section, you learn how to use the Project Geometry command that can project selected edges, vertices, work features, curves, the silhouette edges of another part in an assembly, or other features in the same part to the active sketch. There are four project commands available on the Sketch tab > Create panel: Project Geometry, Project Cut Edges, Project Flat Pattern and Project to 3D Sketch, as shown in the following image.

Project Geometry

Use to project geometry from a sketch or feature onto the active sketch.

Project Cut Edges

Use to project part edges that touch the active sketch. The geometry is only projected if the uncut part would intersect the sketch plane. For example, if a sphere has a sketch plane in the center of the part and the Project Cut Edges command is initialized, a circle will be projected onto the active sketch.

Project Flat Pattern

Use to project a selected face or faces of a sheet metal part flat pattern onto the active sheet metal part sketch plane.

Project to 3D Sketch

Use to project geometry from the active 2D sketch onto selected faces to create a 3D sketch.

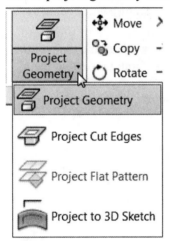

Figure 3-61

To project geometry, follow these steps:

1. Create a 2D sketch or make an existing 2D sketch active onto which the geometry will be projected.

2. Click the Project Geometry command on the Sketch tab > Create panel.

3. Select the geometry to be projected onto the active sketch or click a point in the middle of a face and all edges of the face will be projected onto the active sketch. If you want to project all edges that define the perimeter (a loop), use the Select Other / Face Cycling command to cycle through until they all appear highlighted, as shown in the following image on the left. The image on the right shows the projected geometry.

4. To exit the operation, right-click and click OK from the marking menu or press the ESC key or click another command.

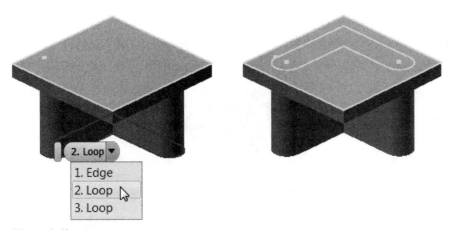

Figure 3-62

If you selected a loop to project, the sketch is updated to reflect the modification when the projected geometry changes. If a face is projected, the internal islands that are defined on the face are also projected and will update accordingly. For example, if the loop of edges or if the following image on the left is projected, the four lines that define the cutout will be projected and updated if the original feature is modified. To disassociate projected geometry from the original geometry, window select the profile or click the Show Constraints option on the Status Bar and then delete the reference constraints that are were created for each projected edge/curve.

Figure 3-63

EXERCISE 3-5: PROJECTING GEOMETRY

In this exercise, you will project geometry to create a feature, edit the original sketch and update the linked feature and then delete the sketch constraints that were created from the projected geometry.

1. Open *ESS_E03_05.ipt* from the Chapter 03 folder.
2. Change your viewpoint so it resembles the following image on the left.
3. Create a sketch on the back face of the cylinder (opposite side of Extrusion2 – the extruded square) as shown in the following image on the left.
4. Rotate your viewpoint so you can see the back of the part so it resembles the following image on the right.
5. Click the Project Geometry command on the Sketch tab > Create panel and select the front planar face of Extrusion2 (by selecting the inside the planar face, all of the edges that define the sketch will be projected) as shown in the following image on the right.

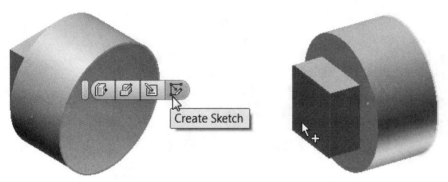

Figure 3-64

6. Rotate your viewpoint so you can see the back of the part. Notice that the edges of the front face have been projected onto the active sketch and the sketch is fully constrained.

7. Right-click and click Finish 2D Sketch from the marking-menu.

8. Click on one of the projected lines and click Create Extrude from the mini-toolbar and extrude the inside area of the projected geometry **.5 inches**, cutting material into the part as shown in the following image on the left.

9. In the browser right-click on Extrusion2 and click Edit Sketch from the menu (the original extruded square).

10. Double-click on the 1.000 dimension and type **.5** and press enter. The sketch should resemble the following image on the right. If needed you can rotate your viewpoint to better see the sketch.

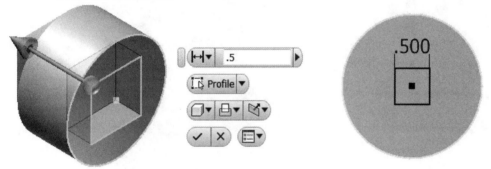

Figure 3-65

11. Click Finish Sketch from the Sketch tab > Exit panel and if needed rotate the viewpoint so you can see the back of the part. Notice that Extrusion3 has been updated to reflect the change to the projected geometry.

12. Edit the sketch of Extrusion 3 by clicking on one of the internal planar faces of the extrusion that removed material and click Edit Sketch from the mini-toolbar as shown in the following image.

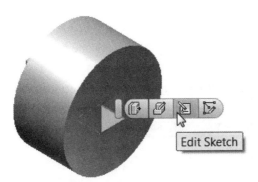

Figure 3-66

13. Next you will delete the reference constraints that were created when the geometry was projected. Press the ESC key twice to cancel any command and then select the square profile by dragging a window around the profile.

14. Delete the four reference constraints that surround the square (these constraints were automatically created when the geometry was projected onto this sketch), right-click in a blank area in the graphics window and click Delete Constrains from the menu as shown in the following image on the left.

15. Notice that only the four coincident constraints remain on the sketch and are displayed as yellow squares.

16. Click and drag the endpoints of the sketch and they will drag freely. Note that the sketch requires ten constraints or dimension to be fully constrained.

17. If desired, add constraints and dimensions or delete the four lines and sketch a new profile.

18. Finish the sketch and rotate the part so you see that Extrusion3 is a different size and shape than Extrusion2. The image on the rights shows an example of the new shape.

Figure 3-67

19. Close the file. Do not save changes. End of exercise.

PART MATERIAL, PROPERTIES AND APPEARANCE

When modeling parts you want to define the material and color so it correctly represents the manufactured part. The part material also affects the mass properties of the part.

Part Material

To change a part's physical properties and appearance to a specific material, follow one of these techniques:

Click the down arrow in the Material area of the Quick Access toolbar and select a material from the list as shown in the following image.

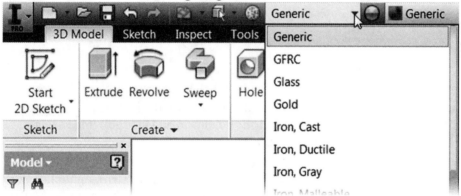

Figure 3-68

- Right-click on the part's name in the browser and click iProperties from the menu as shown in the following image on the left.
- Click the Inventor Application Menu > iProperties as shown in the image on the right.

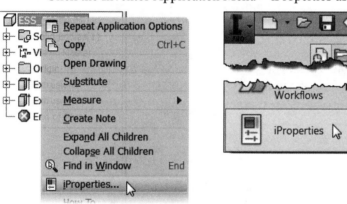

Figure 3-69

With the last two techniques, the iProperties dialog box will appear. In the dialog box click the Physical tab and select a material from the material drop-down list as shown in the following image on the left. To update the physical properties click the Update button in the iProperties dialog box. The image on the right shows updated physical properties. Note that the mass, area, volume and center of gravity are also displayed.

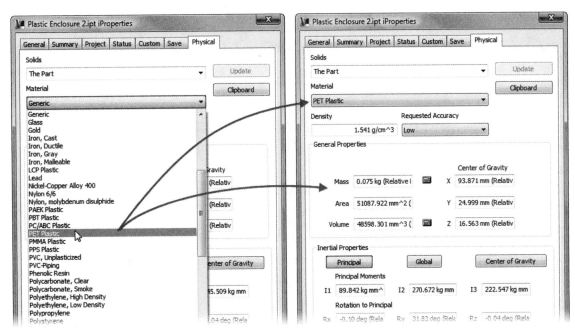

Figure 3-70

Click the OK button in the dialog box to complete the operation and the appearance of the part in the graphics window changes to reflect the selected material.

Appearance

After applying a material you may need to change the color / appearance of the part, for example if the part is to be painted red. You can override the appearance (color) of a part by clicking on the down arrow in the Appearance area of the Quick Access toolbar as shown in the following image. The appearance override only changes how the part appears and has no effect on the physical material or the mass of the part.

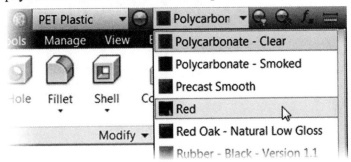

Figure 3-71

Additional Appearance Commands

While working with a part, you can also adjust shadows, reflections, lighting style, perspective viewpoint, ground plane, and easily change the visual style by using the commands found on the View tab > Appearance panel as shown in the following image. Following is brief description of each command.

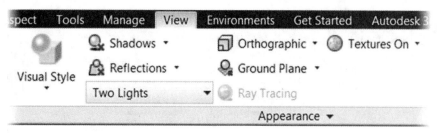

Figure 3-72

Visual Style

Set the appearance of model faces and edges in the graphics window. There are ten different styles to choose from as shown in the following image on the left. You can also add Visual Styles to the Navigation Bar and select a style from the list as show in the image on the right. The visual styles do not change the part's properties; they only change how the part is displayed. Combine visual styles with the other appearance options to display your part(s) differently.

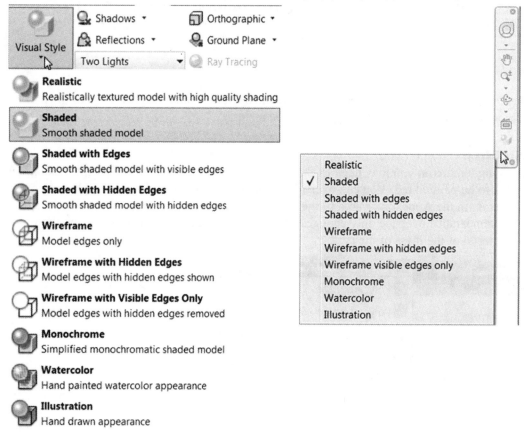

Figure 3-73

Shadows

To give your model a realistic look, you can choose different options for displaying shadows. By default shadows are turned off.

Reflections

Click the Reflections command to toggle reflections on / off. The reflection is displayed on the ground plane that is parallel to the Bottom plane of the ViewCube. You can change which plane is the top and bottom by adjusting the viewpoint with any of the navigation commands so the view is parallel to the bottom of the part that you want. Right-click on the ViewCube and click Set Current View as Top.

Lights
Select or set different lighting options. Under the Lights command, click the Settings option. From within the dialog box you can control the lights direction, color, add lights, and control brightness and ambience. Also from this dialog box you can turn on Image Lighting, which allows you to set a background image and set the scale of the image. With a scene image set, you can rotate your viewpoint 360 degrees. To move the image, select the Ground Plane Settings option, change the Position & Size option to Manual adjustment and a triad will appear. Select the arrows on the triad to move the image.

Orthographic / Perspective
Set the viewpoint to be orthographic or perspective. When set to orthographic, the viewpoint is parallel, meaning that lines are projected perpendicular to the plane of projection. When set to perspective, the geometry on the screen converges to a vanishing point similar to the way the human eye works. You can adjust the perspective by pressing down the CTRL and SHIFT key and spin the wheel on the mouse.

Ground Plane
Click the Ground Plane command to toggle the ground plane on and off. You can change which plane is the ground plane by adjusting the viewpoint with any of the navigation commands so the view is parallel to the bottom of the part that you want. Right-click on the ViewCube and click Set Current View as Top. You can adjust the ground plane's appearance by clicking the down arrow next to Ground Plane and click Settings.

Textures On / Textures Off
If you have a material or an appearance that is applied to a part and has a texture, you can toggle the texture on and off. This is a helpful option to increase graphics performance.

APPLYING YOUR SKILLS

Skills Exercise 3-1
In this exercise, you create a bracket from a number of extruded features. Assume that the part is symmetrical about the center of the horizontal slot.

1. Start a new part based on the English Standard (in).ipt template.
2. Create a sketch on the XY origin plane.
3. Sketch the outline for the base feature as shown in the following image.
4. Add geometric constraints and dimensions. Make sure that the sketch is fully constrained.
5. Extrude the base feature.
6. Create the three remaining features to complete the part.

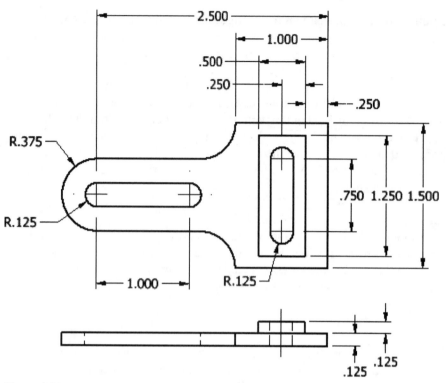

Figure 3-74

The completed part should resemble the following image. When done, close the file. Do not save changes. End of exercise.

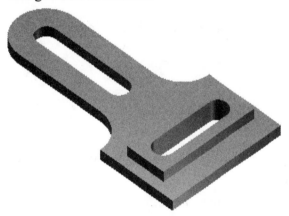

Figure 3-75

Skills Exercise 3-2

In this exercise, you create a connecting rod and add draft to extrusions during feature creation.

1. Start a new part based on the English Standard (in).ipt template.
2. Create a sketch on the XY origin plane.
3. Sketch the outside shape of the connecting rod as shown in the following image.
4. Add geometric constraints and dimensions to fully constrain the sketch.
5. Extrude the base feature using the Symmetric option, adding a **-10°** taper.
6. Create a separate feature for each pocket by projecting geometry. The sides of the pocket are parallel to the sides of the connecting rod.

Note that you could create half of the part and mirror it to create the other half. If desired, complete the exercise by projecting the geometry and repeat the exercise by modeling half the part and mirroring it. Consult Help for information on mirroring features.

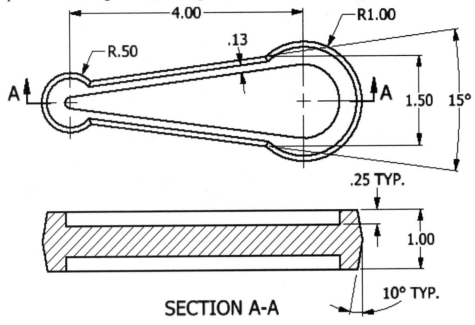

Figure 3-76

The completed part should resemble the following image. When done, close the file. Do not save changes. End of exercise.

Figure 3-77

Skills Exercise 3-3

In this exercise, you create a pulley using a revolved feature. Assume that the part is symmetric about the middle of the part vertically.

1. Start a new part based on the English Standard (in).ipt template.
2. Create a sketch on the XY origin plane.
3. Sketch the cross-section of the pulley as shown in the following image.

 TIP: To create a centerline, draw a line, select it, and then click the Centerline command on the Sketch tab > Format panel.

4. Apply appropriate sketch constraints.

5. Add dimensions.
6. Revolve the sketch using the Full Extents.

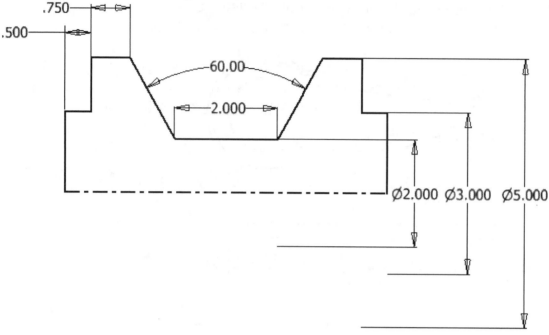

Figure 3-78

The completed part should resemble the following image. When done, close the file. Do not save changes. End of exercise.

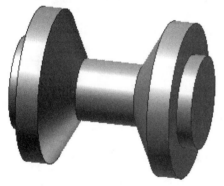

Figure 3-79

CHECKING YOUR SKILLS

Use these questions to test your knowledge of the material covered in this chapter.

1. What is a base feature?
2. True__ False__ When creating a feature with the Extrude or Revolve command, the options in the mini-toolbar only allow you to define the distance or angle.
3. When creating a revolve feature, which objects can be used as an axis of revolution?
4. Explain how to create a linear diameter (diametric) dimension in a sketch.
5. Name two ways to edit a feature.

6. True___ False___ Once a sketch becomes a base feature, you cannot delete or add constraints, dimensions, or objects to the sketch.

7. Name three operation types used to create sketched features.

8. True___ False___ A direct manipulation technique can only be started by clicking on a face of the part.

9. True___ False___ Once a sketched feature exists; its extents type cannot be changed.

10. True___ False___ By default, geometry that is projected from one face to a sketch will update automatically based on changes to the original projected geometry.

11. Explain what the asymmetric option does for the extrude and revolve commands.

12. Where do you set the physical material property of a part?

13. True___ False___ After setting a part's material properties, the Appearance setting in the Quick Access toolbar must be set to Color Matching for the appearance to match the material of the part.

14. True___ False___ The Project Geometry command is used to copy objects onto any selected face.

15. True___ False___ By default, when a feature is deleted, the feature's sketch will be maintained.

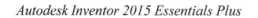

Chapter 4 – Creating Placed Features

INTRODUCTION

In Chapter 3, you learned how to create and edit base and sketched features. In this chapter, you will learn how to create placed features. Many of the placed features are predefined, except for specific values, and only need to be located. You can edit placed features in the browser like sketched features. When you edit a placed feature, either the dialog box and mini-toolbar that you used to create it will open or feature values will appear in the graphics window.

When creating a part, it is usually better to use placed features instead of sketched features wherever possible. For example, to make a through hole as a sketched feature, you can draw a circle profile, dimension it, and then extrude it with the cut operation. By creating a hole as a placed feature, you can select the type of hole, size it, and then place it using a dialog box. When drawing views are generated, the type and size of the hole are easy to annotate, and they automatically update if the hole type or values change. If a circle was extruded to represent the hole feature, the only information that you can retrieve in a drawing is the hole's diameter.

OBJECTIVES

After completing this chapter, you will be able to perform the following:

- ☐ Create fillets
- ☐ Create chamfers
- ☐ Create holes
- ☐ Shell a part
- ☐ Create work axes
- ☐ Create work points
- ☐ Create work planes
- ☐ Create a UCS
- ☐ Pattern features

FILLETS

While designing you will need to round a corner. This is accomplished with the Fillet command. Fillet features consist of fillets and rounds. Fillets add material to interior edges to create a smooth transition from one face to another. Rounds remove material from exterior edges. The following image shows a part without fillets on the left and the part with fillets on the right.

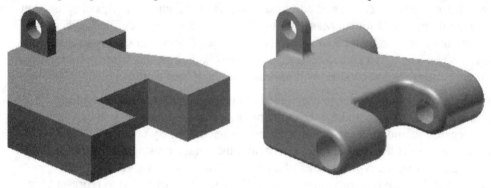

Figure 4-1

To create a fillet, you select an edge(s) that needs to be filleted and the fillet is created between the two faces that share the edge, or you can select two or three faces that a fillet will go between. When placing a fillet between two faces, the faces do not need to share a common edge. When creating a part, it is good practice to create fillets and chamfers as some of the last features in the part since fillets add complexity to the part, which in turn adds to the size of the file. They also remove edges that you may need to place other features from.

To create a fillet feature, click the Fillet command from the 3D Model tab > Modify panel, as shown in the following image on the left, while not in a sketch, click on an edge of a part and the mini-toolbar will appear click the Create Fillet button as shown in the image on the right or press the F key.

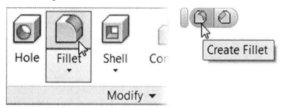

Figure 4-2

After you start the command, the Fillet dialog box appears as shown in the following image on the left labeled (1) and the mini-toolbar will appear as shown in the following image on the right labeled (2). Along the left side of the Fillet dialog box, there are three types of fillets: Edge, Face, and Full Round. When the Edge option is selected, you see three tabs: Constant, Variable, and Setbacks. Each tab creates a fillet along an edge(s) with different options. The options for each of the tabs and fillet types are described in the following sections. A preview of a fillet will appear on the part when the preview option on the bottom of the dialog box is checked and a valid fillet can be created from the values you input into the Fillet dialog box or the mini-toolbar.

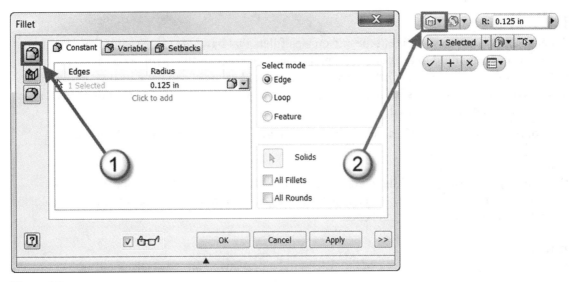

Figure 4-3

Each fillet feature can contain multiple selection sets, each having its own unique fillet value. There is no limit to the number of selection sets that can exist in a single instance of the feature. An edge, however, can only exist in one selection set. To create another selection set, in the dialog box click in the Click to add area and then select the edges that will be part of the selection set and change the radius as needed. If you change the value of a selection set, all of the fillets in that group will change.

To remove an edge or face that is part of a selection set, click the selection set that includes the edge or face, and the edges or faces will be highlighted. Hold down the CTRL key, and click the edge(s) or face(s) to be removed from the selection set. After the edges are selected, enter the desired values for the fillet. As changes are made in the dialog box, a representation of the fillet is previewed in the graphics window. Click OK or Apply to create the fillet.

To edit a fillet's type and radius, use one of the following methods to start the editing process:

- On the part, click on the face of the fillet and click the Edit Fillet button in the mini-toolbar.
- Right-click on the fillet's name in the browser and select Edit Feature from the menu.
- Double-click on the feature's name or icon in the browser.

TIP: If you get an error when creating or editing a fillet, a glyph will appear in the browser and in the mini-toolbar as shown in the following image. Try to create the fillet with a smaller radius, in a different sequence, or create the fillets as one feature.

Figure 4-4

Edge Fillet

An edge fillet is the default fillet type and creates fillets that have the same radius from beginning to end. There is no limit to the number of part edges that you can fillet with a constant fillet. You can select the edges as a single set or as multiple sets, and each set can have its own radius value. You need to select the edges individually that are to be filleted, the use of the window or crossing selection method is not allowed.

The following section describes the options that are available when creating an edge fillet.

Edges

By default, after issuing the Fillet command, you can click edges, and they appear in the first selection set. You can continue to select multiple edges. To remove an edge from the set, hold down the CTRL key and select the edge.

Radius

Enter a size for the fillet. The size of the fillet will be previewed on the selected edges.

Continuity

To adjust the continuity of the fillet, select either a tangent or smooth (G2) condition (continuous curvature), as shown in the following image in both the dialog box and in the mini-toolbar.

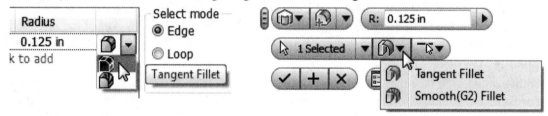

Figure 4-5

Select Mode

Edge

Edges and edges that are tangent to the selected edge will be filleted. This is the default option.

Loop

Click the Loop mode to have all of the edges that form a closed loop with the selected edge filleted.

Feature

Click the Feature mode to select all of the edges of a selected feature.

Solids

If multiple solid bodies exist, select the solid body option to apply All Fillets or All Rounds.

All Fillets

Click the All Fillets option to select all concave edges of a part that have not already been filleted. This operation adds material to the part. The following image in the middle shows an example of All Fillets applied to a part.

All Rounds

Click the All Rounds option to select all convex edges of a part that have not already been filleted. This operation removes material from the part. The following image on the right shows an example of All Rounds applied to a part.

No Fillets   **All Fillets (only)**   **All Rounds (only)**

Figure 4-6

When creating fillets on multiple edges and all the fillets cannot be created, a Create Fillet dialog box will appear as shown in the following image stating how many edges will not be filleted. After accepting the edges to be filleted, the edges that were not filleted will not be in the selection set of the fillet feature but the remaining edges will be filleted

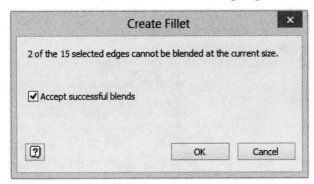

Figure 4-7

Click the More button >> on the lower-right corner of the Fillet dialog box to see more options as shown in the following image.

Figure 4-8

Roll along Sharp Edges

Click this option to adjust the specified radius, when necessary, to preserve the edges of adjacent faces.

Rolling Ball Where Possible

Click this option to create a fillet around a corner that looks as though a ball has been rolled along the edges that define a corner, as shown in the following image in the middle. When the Rolling ball where possible solution is possible, but it is not selected, a blended solution is used, as shown in the following image on the right.

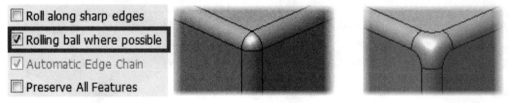

Figure 4-9

Automatic Edge Chain

Click this option to select tangent edges automatically when you click an edge.

Face Fillet

With the Face fillet type selected, as shown in the following image on the left labeled (1) and the mini-toolbar on the right labeled (2), the dialog box will change. Create a face fillet by selecting two or more faces; the faces do not need to be adjacent. If a feature exists that will be consumed by the fillet, the internal volume of the feature will be filled in by the fillet.

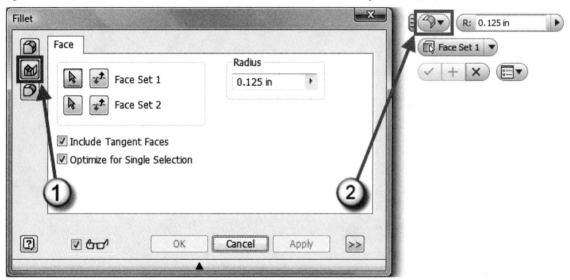

Figure 4-10

To create a face fillet, follow these steps:

1. Start the fillet command and click the Face Fillet option.

2. With the Face Set 1 button active, select one or more tangent contiguous faces on the part to which the fillet will be tangent.

3. With the Face Set 2 button active, select one or more tangent contiguous faces on the part to which the fillet will be tangent.

Check the Include Tangent Faces option to automatically chain all faces that are tangent to faces in the selection set.

The following image on the left shows a part that has a gap between the bottom and top extrusion. The middle image shows the preview of the face fillet. The image on the right shows the completed face fillet. Notice the rectangular extrusion on the top face is consumed by the fillet.

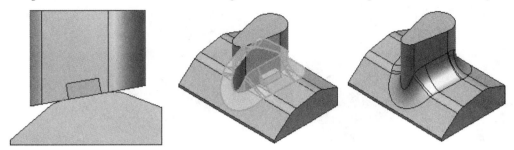

Figure 4-11

Full Round Fillet

Click the Full Round fillet type in the dialog box labeled (1) or in the mini-toolbar labeled (2) as shown in the following image. The full round fillet option creates a fillet that is tangent to three faces; the faces do not need to be adjacent.

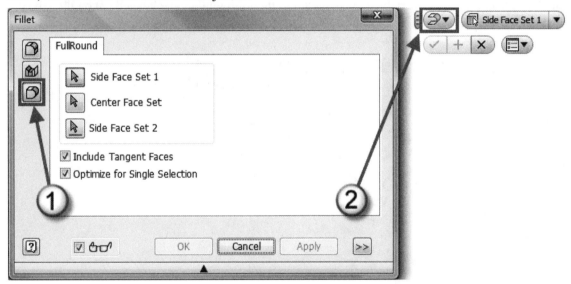

Figure 4-12

To create a Full Round fillet, follow these steps:

1. Start the fillet command and click the Full Round option.
2. With the Side Face Set 1 button active, select a face on the part that the fillet will start at and to which it will be tangent.
3. With the Center Face Set button active, select a face on the part that the middle of the fillet will be tangent.
4. With the Side Face Set 2 button active, select a face on the part that the fillet will end at and to which it will be tangent.

Check the Include Tangent Faces option to automatically chain all faces that are tangent to faces in the selection set.

Check the Optimize for Single Selection to automatically make the next selection set button active after selecting a face.

The following image shows two examples of three faces selected on the left and the resulting full round fillet on the right.

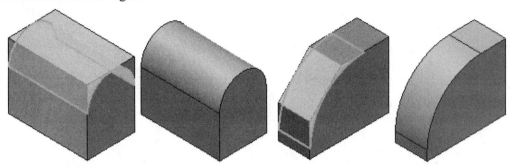

Figure 4-13

Variable Tab

You can also create a variable radius fillet that has a different starting and ending radius and/or a different radius between the starting and ending radius. To create a variable radius fillet, click the Edge Fillet option in the upper-left corner of the dialog box as shown in the following image labeled (1), and click the Variable tab, as shown in the following image labeled (2) on the left or click the Add Variable Radius Fillet Set option from the mini-toolbar, as shown on the right, labeled (2).

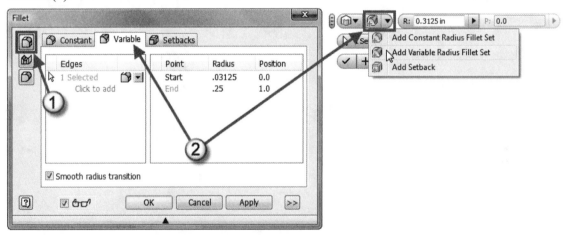

Figure 4-14

The following image on the left shows a variable fillet with the smooth option, and the image on the right shows a variable fillet blending in a straight line.

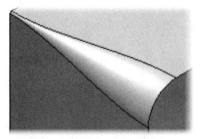

Figure 4-15

Setbacks Tab

You can specify the distance at which a fillet starts its transition from a vertex with the options on the Setbacks tab. Use this option when three or more edges converge and you need to control where the fillet will start its transition to the corner. The following image shows an example of a setback fillet. You can choose a different radius for each converging edge if needed. Click the minimal option to create a setback with the smallest possible fillet. You can only use setbacks where three or more filleted edges form a vertex. To create a fillet with a setback, follow these steps:

1. Start the fillet command.
2. In the graphics window, select three or more edges to fillet. The fillets must converge at a point.
3. Click the Setbacks tab.
4. In the graphics window, click the vertex point.
5. In the Fillet dialog box, specify the setback distance for each edge.

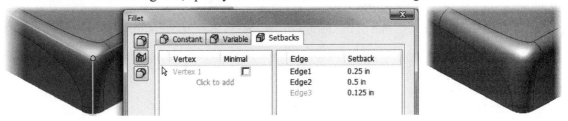

Figure 4-16

CHAMFERS

Chamfer features are used to bevel edges. When you create a chamfer on an interior edge, material is added to your model. When you create a chamfer on an exterior edge, material is removed from your model, as shown in the following image on the right.

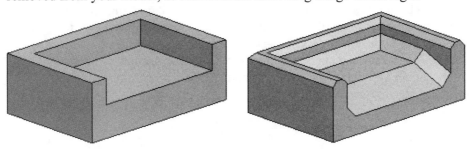

Figure 4-17

To create a chamfer feature, follow the same steps that you used to create fillet features. Click the common edge, and the chamfer is created between the two faces sharing the edge. To create a chamfer feature, click on the 3D Model tab > Modify panel and click the down arrow under Fillet and click Chamfer command as shown in the following image on the left, or while not in a sketch, click on an edge and the mini–toolbar will appear, then click the Create Chamfer button in the mini-toolbar, as shown in the image on the right.

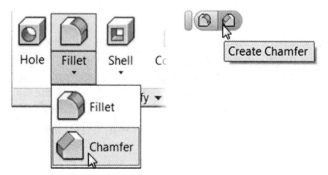

Figure 4-18

After you start the chamfer command, the Chamfer dialog box and mini-toolbar appears, select one of three methods to create chamfer features, the methods are described in the next section. As with fillet features, you can select multiple edges to be included in a single chamfer feature. From the dialog box or mini-toolbar, click a method, click the edge or edges to chamfer, enter a distance and/or angle, and then click OK.

To edit a chamfer feature use one of the following methods to start the editing

- In the graphics window select on the chamfered face (not the edge) to edit and click Edit Chamfer on the mini-toolbar.
- Double-click the chamfer's name or icon in the browser.
- Right-click the chamfer's name in the browser, and select Edit Feature from the menu.

Methods

There are three methods to create a chamfer feature; Distance, Distance and Angle, and Two Distances these options are on the left column of the Chamfer dialog box.

Distance

After starting the Chamfer command the Distance option is the default and creates a 45° chamfer on the selected edges. The Distance option in the Chamfer dialog box is shown in the following image on the left labeled (1) and the middle image shows the min-toolbar as shown in the middle image labeled (2). The image on the right illustrates the Distance option. You set the size of the chamfer by typing a distance in the dialog box. The value is the offset from the common edge of the two adjacent faces. You can select a single edge, multiple edges, or a chain of edges. A preview image of the chamfer appears on the part. If you select the wrong edge, hold down the CTRL key and select the edge to remove it.

Edges

Select an edge or edges to be chamfered.

Distance

Enter a distance to be used for the offset in both directions from the selected edge(s).

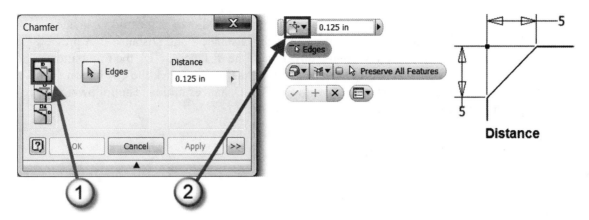

Figure 4-19

Distance and Angle

Click the Distance and Angle option to create a chamfer offset from a selected edge on a specified face, at the defined angle. In the Chamfer dialog box select the Distance and Angle option as shown in the following image on the left labeled (1) or in the mini-toolbar as shown in the middle image labeled (2), enter an angle and distance for the chamfer, then click the face to which the angle is applied and specify an edge to be chamfered. You can select one edge or multiple edges. The edges must lie on the selected face. A preview image of the chamfer appears on the part. If you have selected the wrong face or edge, click on the Edge or Face button, and choose a new face or edge. The following image on the right illustrates the use of the Distance and Angle option.

Edges

Select an edge or edges to be chamfered.

Face

Select a face on which the chamfer angle will be based.

Distance

Enter a distance to be used for the offset from the selected edge(s).

Angle

Enter a value that will be used for the chamfer.

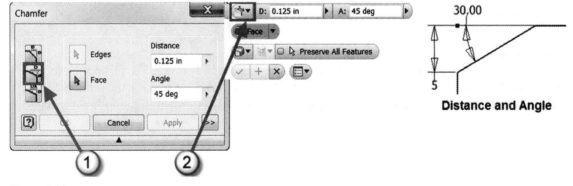

Figure 4-20

Two Distances

Click the Two Distances option to create a chamfer offset from two faces, each being the amount that you specify. In the Chamfer dialog box select the Distance and Angle option as shown in the following image on the left labeled (1) or in the mini-toolbar as shown in the middle image labeled (2). Click an edge first, and then enter values for Distance 1 and Distance 2. A preview image of the chamfer appears. To reverse the direction of the distances, click the Flip button. When the correct information about the chamfer is in the dialog box, click the OK button. You can only use a single edge or chained edges with the Two Distances option. The following image on the right illustrates the use of the Two Distances option.

Edge
Select an edge or edges to be chamfered.

Flip
Click the flip button to reverse the direction of the chamfer.

Distance1
Enter a distance to be used for the offset in one direction from the selected edge(s).

Distance2
Enter a distance to be used for the offset in one direction from the selected edge(s).

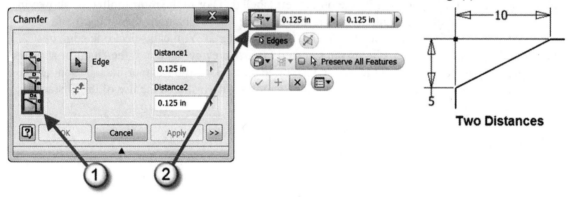

Figure 4-21

Click the More button >> on the lower-right corner of the Chamfer dialog box to see more options as shown in the following image. Below is a description of the options in this area.

Edge Chain
Click this option to include tangent edges in the selection set automatically, as shown in the following image.

Setback
When the Distance method is used and three chamfers meet at a vertex, click this option to have the intersection of the three chamfers form a flat edge (left button) or to have the intersection meet at a point as though the edges were milled (right button), as shown in the following image.

Figure 4-22

Preserve All Features

Click this option to check all features that intersect with the chamfer and to calculate their intersections during the chamfer operation. If the option's checkbox is clear, only the edges that are part of the chamfer operation are calculated during the operation.

EXERCISE 4-1: CREATING FILLETS AND CHAMFERS

In this exercise, you create constant radius fillets, full round fillets, face fillet, and chamfers.

1. Open *ESS_E04_01.ipt* in the Chapter 04 folder.

2. Click the Fillet command on the 3D Model tab > Modify panel and click the inside edge of the cutout or select the inside edge of the cutout first, and click Create Fillet from the mini-toolbar.

3. If needed expand the Fillet dialog box by clicking the down arrow at the bottom of the minimized Fillet dialog box. Click on the first entry in the Radius column, and type **.25** or in the mini-toolbar enter **.25** as shown in the following image.

Figure 4-23

4. Click Apply in the dialog box or click the plus symbol in the mini-toolbar to create the fillet.

5. Next, create a Full Round Fillet that will be tangent to the front three faces. In the Fillet dialog box, click the Full Round Fillet option in the left column, labeled (A) in the following image.

6. Click the front-inside face, then the left-front face, and then the back-vertical face of the part, as shown in the following image labeled (1), (2), and (3).

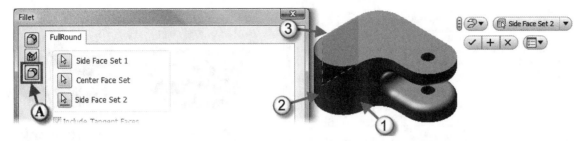

Figure 4-24

7. Click OK in the dialog box or click the check mark in the mini-toolbar to create the fillet.

8. In the browser, right-click on Extrusion4, and click Unsuppress Features.

9. Next, create a Face Fillet. Click the Fillet command in the Modify panel. In the Fillet dialog box, click the Face Fillet option in the left column as shown in the following image labeled (A).

10. Click the cylindrical face of Extrusion4 and then the full round fillet that you created in the last step, as shown in the following image labeled (1) and (2).

11. In the Fillet dialog box, type **.375** in in the Radius field, as shown in the following image.

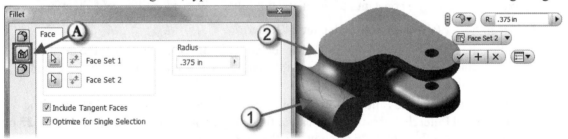

Figure 4-25

12. Click OK to create the fillet and rotate the viewpoint to examine the fillet features.

13. Move the cursor into a blank area in the graphics window, right-click, and click Repeat Fillet from the top of the menu.

14. Next you fillet two edges. Click the top and bottom edges of the model, as shown in the following image.

15. In the mini-toolbar input radius field, type **.125**, as shown in the following image.

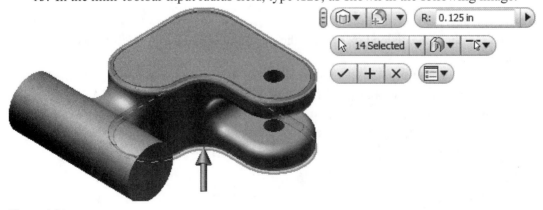

Figure 4-26

16. Click the green check mark (OK button) in the mini-toolbar to create the fillets.

17. Click the back cylindrical edge on Extrusion4 and click Create Chamfer from the mini-toolbar as shown in the following image on the left.

18. In the mini-toolbar's distance field, type **.25**, as shown in the following image on the right.

19. To create the chamfer and keep the dialog box open, click the green plus button in the mini-toolbar or click the Apply button in the Chamfer dialog box (if needed expand the Chamfer dialog box by clicking the down arrow at the bottom of the minimized Chamfer dialog box).

Figure 4-27

20. In the Chamfer dialog box or in the mini-toolbar, click the Distance and Angle option labeled (A) in the following image.

21. Click the front-circular face on Extrusion4 labeled (1) in the following image.

22. Click the front-circular edge of the same face labeled (2) in the following image.

23. In the Chamfer dialog box or in the mini-toolbar, enter **.25** in the Distance field and **60 deg** in the Angle field, as shown in the following image.

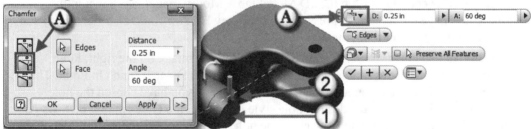

Figure 4-28

24. Click OK to create the chamfer. When done, your model should resemble the following image.

Figure 4-29

25. Practice editing and placing fillets and chamfers.

26. Close the file. Do not save changes. End of exercise.

HOLES

The Hole command lets you create drilled, counterbored, spotface, countersink, clearance, tapped, and taper tapped holes, as shown in the following image. You can place holes using sketch geometry or existing planes, points, or edges of a part. You can also specify the type of drill point and thread parameters.

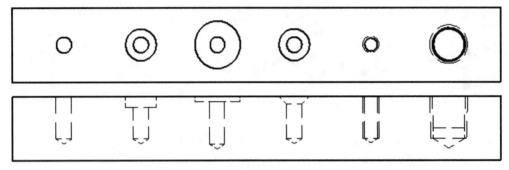

Figure 4-30

To create a hole feature, follow these steps:

1. Create a part that you want to place a hole on.

2. Click the Hole command from the 3D Model tab > Modify panel, as shown in the following image on the left, or press the shortcut key H. You could also right-click and click Hole from the marking menu.

3. The Hole dialog box appears, as shown in the following image on the right. Four placement options are available: From Sketch, Linear, Concentric, and On Point. The Placement options are covered in the next section. After you have chosen the hole placement options, select the desired hole style options in the Holes dialog box. As you change the options, the preview image of the hole(s) updates. When you are done making changes, click the Apply or the OK button to create the hole(s).

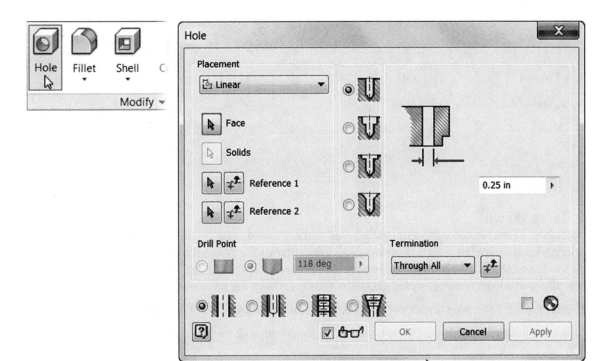

Figure 4-31

Editing Hole Features

To edit the type of hole feature, use one of the following methods:

- Click on the circular face of the hole that you want to edit and click Edit Hole from the mini-toolbar.
- Double-click the feature's name or icon in the browser.
- Right-click the hole's name or icon in the browser, and select Edit Feature from the menu.

Holes Dialog Box

In the Holes dialog box, you establish the placement method, type of hole, its termination, and additional options such as type of drill point, angle, and tapped properties.

Placement

Select the appropriate placement method. If you select From Sketch, a sketch that contains hole centers or any point, such as an endpoint of a line, must exist on the part. Hole centers are described in the next section. The Linear, Concentric, and On Point options do not require an unconsumed or shared sketch to exist in the model and are based on previously created features. Depending on the placement option you select, the input parameters will change, as shown in the following image.

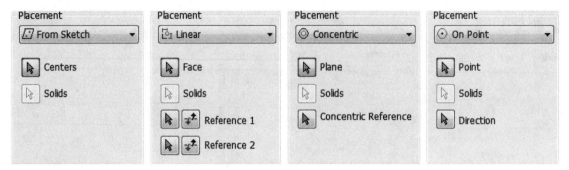

Figure 4-32

From Sketch

Select the From Sketch option to create holes that are based on a location defined within an unconsumed or shared sketch. You can base the center of the hole on a point/hole center or endpoints of sketched geometry like endpoints, centers of arcs and circles, and spline points. You can also use points from projected geometry that resides in the unconsumed or shared sketch.

Centers. Select the hole center point or sketch points where you want to create a hole.

Solids. If multiple solid bodies exist, select the solid body where you want to create a hole.

Linear

Select the Linear option to place the hole relative to two selected face edges.

Face. Select the face on the part where the hole will be created.

Solids. If multiple solid bodies exist, select the solid body where you want to create a hole.

Reference 1. Select a face edge as a positional reference for the center of the hole. When you select the edge, a dimension appears that can be edited to constrain the center of the hole dimensionally.

Reference 2. Select a face edge as a positional reference for the center of the hole. When you select the edge, a dimension appears that can be edited to constrain the center of the hole dimensionally.

Flip Side. Click this button to position the hole on the opposite side of the selected edge.

Concentric

Select the Concentric option to place the hole on a planar face and concentric to a circular or arc edge or a cylindrical face.

Plane. Select a planar face where you want to create the hole.

Solids. If multiple solid bodies exist, select the solid body where you want to create the hole.

Concentric Reference. Select a circular or arc model edge or cylindrical face to constrain the center of the hole to be concentric with the selected entity.

On Point

Select the On Point option to place the center of the hole on a work point. The work point must exist on the model prior to selecting this option.

Point. Select a work point to position the center of the hole.

Solids. If multiple solid bodies exist, select the solid body where you want to create the hole.

Direction. Select a plane, face, work axis, or model edge to specify the direction of the hole. When selecting a plane or face, the hole direction will be normal to the face or plane.

Hole Options

Click the type of hole that you want to create: drilled, counterbore, spotface, or countersink. To change the diameter, depth, countersink, counterbore diameter, countersink angle, or counterbore depth of the hole, click the dimension in the dialog box, and enter a desired value. The following image shows the counterbore options.

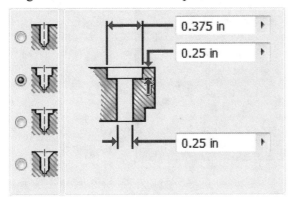

Figure 4-33

Termination

Select how the hole will terminate.

Distance

Specify a distance for the depth of the hole.

Through All

Choose to extend the hole through the entire part in one direction.

To

Select a plane at which the hole will terminate.

Flip

Reverse the direction in which the hole is drilled.

Drill Point

Select either a flat or angle drill point. If you select an angle drill point, you can specify the angle of the drill point.

Hole Type

Click the type of hole you want to create. There are four options: Simple Hole, Clearance Hole, Tapped Hole, and Taper Tapped Hole. The following image shows the tapped hole selected. After selecting the hole type, fill in the dialog box with the specific data for the hole you need to create.

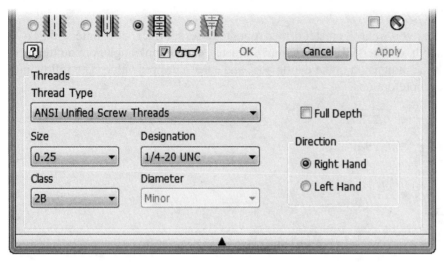

Figure 4-34

Simple Hole
Click the Simple Hole option to create a (drilled) hole feature with no thread features or properties.

Clearance Hole
Click the Clearance Hole option to create a simple hole feature that does not have threads.

Tapped Hole
Click the Tapped Hole option if the hole is threaded. Thread information appears in the dialog box so that you can specify the thread properties, as shown in the previous image.

Taper Tapped Hole
Click the Taper Tapped Hole option if the hole has a tapered thread. The taper tapped hole information appears in the dialog box area so you can specify the thread properties.

Center Points
Center points are sketched entities that can be used to locate hole features. To create a hole center, follow these steps:

1. Make a sketch active.
2. Click the Point, Center Point command in the Sketch tab Create panel as shown in the following image.
3. Click a point to locate the hole center where you want to place the hole.
4. Constrain and dimension the point as required.

When creating a hole(s) feature with the From Sketch option, all center points that reside in the sketch are automatically selected as centers for the hole feature. This can expedite the process of creating multiple holes, by creating them in a single hole feature. You can also select endpoints of lines, arcs, splines, center points of arcs and circles, or spline control points as hole centers. Points can be deselected or selected by holding down the CTRL or SHIFT key and then select the points individually or use a window or crossing section method.

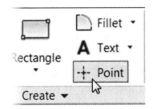

Figure 4-35

EXERCISE 4-2: CREATING HOLES

In this exercise, you add drilled, tapped, and counterbore holes to a part.

1. Open *ESS_E04_02.ipt* in the Chapter 04 folder.

2. The first hole you place is a linear hole. Click the Hole command in the 3D Model tab > Modify panel.

   a. For the Face, select the top planar face of the extruded rectangle (Extrusion2) labeled (1) in the following image.

   b. For Reference 1, select the left top vertical edge labeled (2) and enter a value **.375 inches**, do not press ENTER.

   c. Reference 2 will be current, select the horizontal edge labeled (3) and enter a value **.375 inches.**

   d. Verify that the Drilled hole option is selected labeled (4).

   e. Verify that the Termination is set to Through All, labeled (5).

   f. Change the hole's diameter to **.25 inches** labeled (6).

   g. Click OK to create the hole.

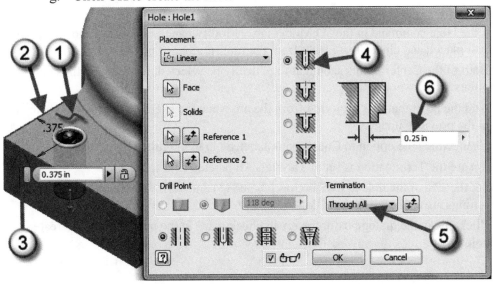

Figure 4-36

3. Next, you create multiple holes based on the Sketch option. Click the top planar face of Extrusion1 and click Create Sketch from the mini-toolbar as shown in the following image on the left.

4. Click the Point, Center Point command in the 3D Model tab > Sketch Panel, and place two points in the middle of the sketch labeled (1) and (2) in the following image on the right.

5. Add a horizontal constraint between the left point labeled (1) in the following image on the right and the center point that was automatically projected from the center of the right circular edges labeled (3) in the following image on the right. If the center point was not projected, use the Project Geometry tool to project the arc.

6. Add another horizontal constraint between the points labeled (2) and (3) in the following image on the right.

7. Add a **1.250 inch** and a **1.000 inch** horizontal dimension between the points as shown in the following image on the right.

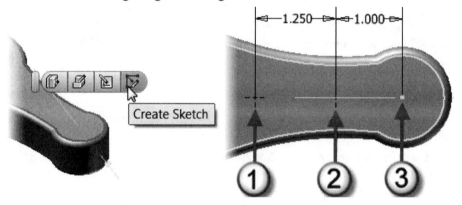

Figure 4-37

8. Right-click in the graphics window, click Finish 2D Sketch from the marking menu, the view should change to the home view. If not press the F6 key to change to the Home View.

9. Click the Hole command in the 3D Model tab > Modify panel, or select one of the points you just placed and click Create Hole from the mini-toolbar or press the H key.

   a. Both of the Center Points should automatically be selected, if not select the center-points.

   b. Add the point that was projected from the arc when the sketch was created labeled (3) in the previous image.

   c. Change the hole option to Countersink labeled (1) in the following image.

   d. Ensure the Termination is set to Through All labeled (2).

   e. Set the size of the hole to **0.25 inches** labeled (3) and verify the diameter and angle settings are as shown in the following image.

   f. Click OK in the dialog box or the green check mark in the mini-toolbar to create the holes.

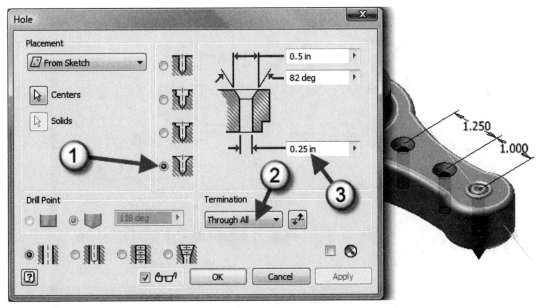

Figure 4-38

10. Next, you create a Taper Tapped hole that is concentric to the top of the left cylinder.

    a. Press the ENTER key to restart the Hole command.

    b. In the Hole dialog box change the Placement option to Concentric labeled (1).

    c. For the Plane, select the top face of the cylinder Extrusion3 labeled (2).

    d. For the Concentric Reference, select the top circular edge of the cylinder labeled (3).

    e. Change the hole option to Drilled labeled (4).

    f. Click the Taper Tapped Hole type labeled (5).

    g. Change the Thread Type to NPT labeled (6).

    h. Change the size to **1/2** labeled (7).

    i. Ensure that the Termination is set to Through All labeled (8)

    j. Click Apply in the Hole dialog box to create the hole.

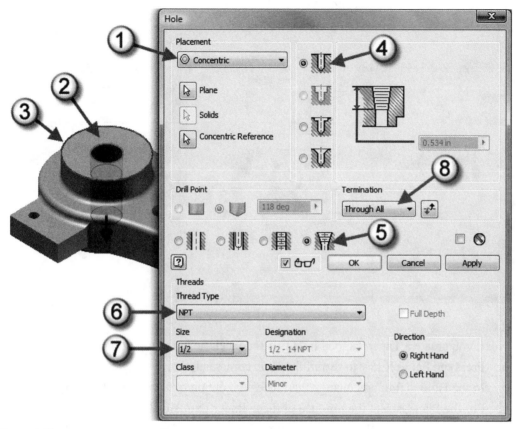

Figure 4-39

11. Lastly, you create a tapped hole that uses the work point and work axis that goes through the end of the part at an angle. Work point and work axis will be covered later in this chapter.

    a. Change the Placement option to On Point labeled (1) in the following image.

    b. For the Point, select the work point on the outside of the cylinder labeled (2).

    c. For the Direction, select the work axis that goes through the cylinder labeled (3).

    d. If needed click the Drilled Hole option labeled (4).

    e. Change the Thread Type to Tapped Hole labeled (5).

    f. Verify that the Thread Type is set to ANSI Unified Screw Threads labeled (6), if not make it current.

    g. Change the size to **0.25 inches** labeled (7).

    h. Change the Termination to Distance labeled (8).

    i. For the Thread, check the Full Depth option labeled (9).

    j. Change the distance value to **0.75 inches** labeled (10).

    k. Click OK to create the hole.

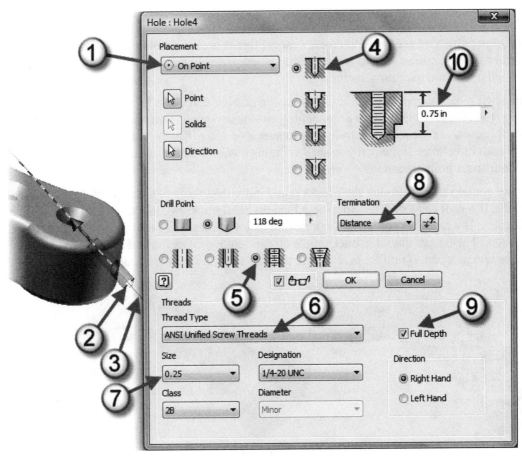

Figure 4-40

12. The completed part is shown in the following image (for clarity the visibility of the work axis and work point have been turned off). Rotate the viewpoint and examine the holes.

Figure 4-41

13. Practice editing the holes and placing new holes.

14. Close the file. Do not save changes. End of exercise.

SHELLING

As you design parts, you may need to create a model that is made with thin walls but is not a sheet metal part. The easiest way to create a thin-walled part is to create the main shape and then use the Shell command to remove material.

The term shell refers to giving a wall thickness to the outside shape of a part and removing the remaining material. Essentially, you are scooping out the inside of a part and leaving the walls a specified thickness, as shown in the following image. You can offset the wall thickness in, out, or evenly in both directions. If the part you shell contains a void, such as a hole, the feature will have the thickness built around it.

A part may contain more than one shell feature, and individual faces of the part can have different thicknesses. If a wall has a different thickness than the shell thickness, it is referred to as a unique face thickness. If a face that you select for a unique face thickness has faces that are tangent to it, those faces will also have the same thickness. You can remove faces from being shelled, and these faces remain open. If no face is removed, the part is hollow on the inside.

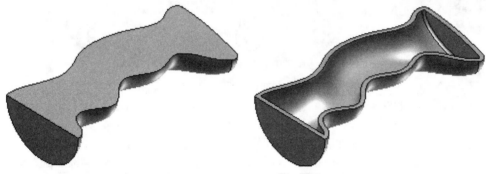

Figure 4-42

To create a shell feature, follow these steps:

1. Create a part that will be shelled.

2. Start the Shell command from the 3D Model tab > Modify panel, as shown following image on the left.

3. The Shell dialog box and the mini-toolbar appear, as shown in the middle and right of the following image (the dialog box is shown expanded).

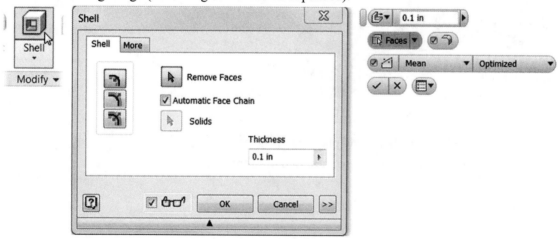

Figure 4-43

4. In the dialog box, select the direction for the shell, remove faces, and enter a thickness value and then click OK, and the part is shelled.

To edit a shell feature, use one of the following methods:

- In the graphics window select a face on the shell feature and click Edit Shell on the mini-toolbar.
- Right-click the name of the shell feature in the browser, and select Edit Feature from the menu. Alternately, you can double-click the feature's name or icon in the browser.

The following explains the Shell command options.

Direction
In this area you set the direction that the shell thickness will go.

Inside
Click this button to offset the wall thickness into the part by the given value.

Outside
Click this button to offset the wall thickness out of the part by the given value.

Both
Click this button to offset the wall thickness evenly into and out of the part by the given value.

Remove Faces
Click the Remove Faces button, and then click the face or faces to be left open. To deselect a face, click the Remove Faces button, and hold down the CTRL key while you click the face.

Automatic Face Chain
When you are removing faces and this option is checked, faces that are tangent to the selected face are automatically selected. Uncheck this option to select only the selected face.

Solids
If multiple solid bodies exist, select the solid body to shell.

Thickness
Enter a value or select a previously used value from the drop-down list to be used for the shell thickness.

Unique Face Thickness
Unique face thickness is available by clicking the More >> button that is located on the lower-right corner of the dialog box, as shown in the following image on the left.

To give a specific face a thickness, click on Click to add, select the face, and enter a value. A part may contain multiple faces that have different unique thicknesses. The image on the right shows a unique thickness applied to the left face.

Figure 4-44

EXERCISE 4-3: SHELLING A PART

In this exercise, you will use the Shell command to create a shell on a part.

1. Open *ESS_E04_03.ipt* in the Chapter 04 folder.
2. Click the Shell command on the 3D Model tab > Modify panel.
3. Remove the top face by selecting the top face of the part as shown in the following image.
4. Type a thickness of **.0625** inches.

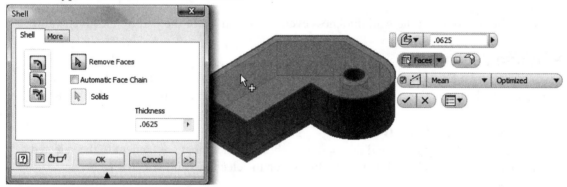

Figure 4-45

5. Click OK to create the shell feature.
6. Rotate the viewpoint and examine the shell. Only the top face should have been removed.
7. Change to the Home View by clicking the Home icon above the ViewCube.
8. Edit the Shell feature that you just created. Click on one of the inside faces of the shell and from the mini-toolbar click Edit Shell as shown in the following image.

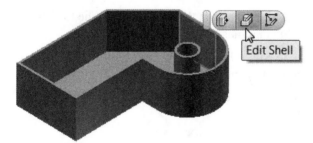

Figure 4-46

9. Click the More >> button on the bottom-right corner of the Shell dialog box, click in the "Click to add" area, and select the left outside-vertical face.

10. Enter a value of .5, as shown in the following image.

Figure 4-47

11. Click OK to update the shell. Your part should resemble the following image.

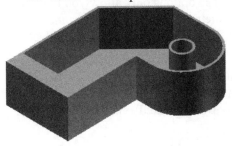

Figure 4-48

12. Practice editing the shell feature. Change the thickness direction, thickness, and delete the unique thickness by selecting the unique thickness entry in the dialog box and then press the Delete key.

13. Close the file without saving changes. End of exercise.

WORK FEATURES

When you create a parametric part, you define how the features of the part relate to one another. A change in one feature results in appropriate changes in all related features. Work features are special construction features that are attached parametrically to part geometry or other work features. You typically use work features to help you position and define new features in your model. There are three types of work features: work planes, work axes, and work points.

Use work features in the following situations:

- To position a sketch for new features when a planar part face is not available.
- To establish an intermediate position that is required to define other work features. You can create a work plane at an angle to an existing face, for example, and then create another work plane at an offset value from that plane.
- To establish a plane or edge from which you can place parametric dimensions and constraints.
- To provide an axis or point of rotation for revolved features and patterns.

- To provide an external feature termination plane off the part, such as a beveled extrusion edge, or an internal feature termination plane in cases where there are no existing surfaces.

Creating a Work Axis

A work axis is a feature that acts like a construction line. You can use a work axis to create work planes, work points, and subsequent part features. You can also use work axes as an Axis of rotation for the revolve command, axes of rotation for polar arrays, or to constrain parts in an assembly using assembly constraints. Their length always extends beyond the part—as the part changes size, the work axis also changes size. A work axis is tied parametrically to the part. As changes occur to the part, the work axis will maintain its relationship to the points, edge, or cylindrical face from which you created it. To create a work axis, use the Work Axis command on the 3D Model tab > Work Features panel or press the key / (forward slash). The Axis command will allow you to select all geometry in the graphics window to create an axis. Another option is to click the down arrow in the lower right corner of the Axis button and select an option for creating an axis using only certain types of geometry. These options only allow you to select geometry that is allowed for the active command; other geometry is filtered out and cannot be selected. For example, if the Through Two Points option is selected, only points can be selected in the graphics window.

You can also create a work axis when using the Work Plane or Work Point commands; right-click and select Create Axis when one of these work feature commands is active. Then, after the work axis is created, the command you were running will be active. The created axis will be indented as a child of the work axis or the work plane in the browser.

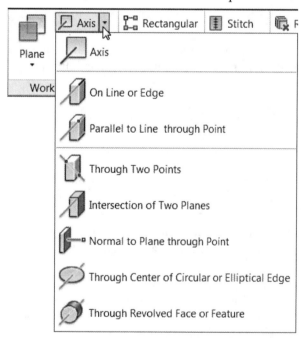

Figure 4-49

Use one of the following methods to create a work axis:

Axis Type	Process
Axis	Select geometry to create a work axis that is dependent upon the selected

---

	geometry, no geometry is filtered.
On Line or Edge	Select a line or a linear edge and a work axis is created that is collinear to the selected line or linear edge.
Parallel to Line through Point	Select a linear edge or sketch line and an endpoint, midpoint, sketch point, or work point and a work axis is created that is parallel to the selected line or linear edge and through the selected point.
Through Two Points	Select two endpoints, intersections, midpoints, sketch points, or work points and a work axis is created that goes through the two points.
Intersection of Two Planes	Select two nonparallel work planes or planar faces and the work axis is created coincident at the intersection of two planes.
Normal to Plane through Point	Select a planar face or work plane and an endpoint, midpoint, sketch point, or work point and a work axis is created that is perpendicular to the plane and point.
Through Center of Circular or Elliptical Edge	Select a circular edge, elliptical edge or an edge of a fillet and a work axis is created through the center point and perpendicular to the edge.
Through Revolved Face or Feature	Select a circular face and a work axis is created that goes through the center of the circular face.

EXERCISE 4-4: CREATING WORK AXES

In this exercise, you create a work axis to position a circular pattern. Circular patterns are covered later in this chapter.

1. Open *ESS_E04_04.ipt* in the Chapter 04 folder.
2. Select the inside angled planar face and click Create Sketch from the mini-toolbar as shown in the following image on the left.
3. If the view did not change and you are looking directly at the face, click the Look At command on the Navigation bar and then in the browser select Sketch5, the sketch that you just created.
4. Click the Point, Center Point command in the Sketch tab > Create panel, and place a point near the middle of the sketch.
5. Add a vertical constraint between the center point you just created and the midpoint on the top line.
6. Apply a horizontal constraint between the point and the midpoint of the edge on the right, as shown in the following image on the right.

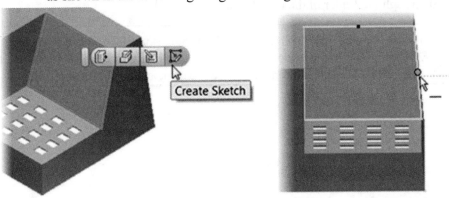

Figure 4-50

7. Finish the sketch by right-clicking in the graphics window and click Finish 2D Sketch on the marking-menu.

8. If the view did not automatically change to the home view, right-click in the graphics window, and then click Home View from the menu.

9. From the 3D Model tab > Work Features panel click the down arrow on the right of the Work Axis command and from the list click Normal to Plane through Point.

10. Select the angled planar face, and then select the center point. The work axis is created through this point and normal to the plane, as shown in the following image on the left.

 TIP: One use of a work axis is to use it as an axis of rotation when creating a circular pattern. The following image on the right shows a hole that was patterned around the work axis. Patterns are covered later in this chapter.

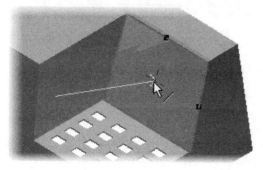 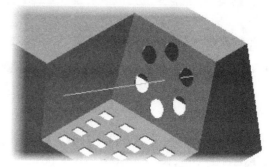

Figure 4-51

Figure 4-52

11. From the 3D Model tab > Work Features panel click the down arrow on the right of the Work Axis command and from the list click Through Center of Circular or Elliptical Edge.

12. Select the top circular edge on the back of the part as shown in the following image on the left. The axis is created through the center of the circular edge.

13. Undo the last work axis you just created. Click the Undo command from the Quick Access toolbar and the work axis will be removed.

14. From the 3D Model tab > Work Features panel click the down arrow on the right of the Work Axis command and from the list click Through Revolved Face or Feature.

15. Select the back circular face on the part as shown in the following image on the right. The axis is created through the center of the circular face.

 TIP: The results for the work axis in step 11 and 14 are the same. The Through Center of Circular or Elliptical Edge or the option Through Revolved Face or Feature create an identical work axis since both sets of geometry share the same centers.

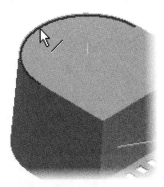 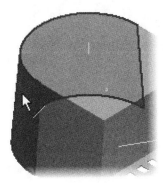

Figure 4-53

16. Practice creating work axes using different options.

17. Close the file. Do not save changes. End of exercise.

Creating Work Points

A work point is a feature that you can create on the active part or in 3D space and can be used to create other work features such as a work axis and work planes, place a hole using the On Point option and place 3D lines on the work points. Work points are created relative to selected geometry, if the selected geometry changes location; the work point will move to keep the relationship to the new location of the geometry. To create a work point, use the Point command on the 3D Model tab > Work Features panel or press the key (.) a period. The point command will allow you to select all geometry in the graphics window to create a work point. Another option is to click the down arrow in the lower right corner of the Point button and select an option for creating a work point using only filtered geometry type(s) as shown in the following image. These options allow you to select geometry that is filtered for the active command; other geometry is filtered out and cannot be selected. For example, if the Intersection of Three Planes option is selected, only planes can be selected in the graphics window.

You can also create a work point when using the Work Plane or Work Axis commands; right-click and select Create Point when one of these work feature commands is active. Then, after the work point is created, the command you were running will be active. The created point will be indented as a child of the work axis or the work plane in the browser.

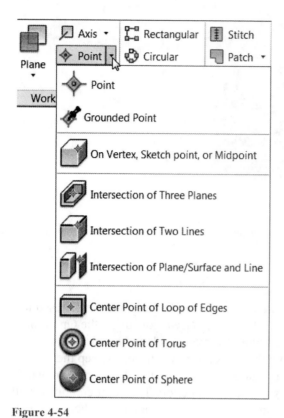

Figure 4-54

Use one of the following methods to create a work point:

Work Point Type	Process
Point	Select the desired geometry. No filters are applied.
Grounded Point	Select a work point, midpoint, or vertex. Grounded work points will be covered in the following section.
On Vertex, Sketch point, or Midpoint	Select a 2D or 3D sketch point, vertex, or the endpoint or midpoint of a line or linear edge.
Intersection of Three Planes	Select three work planes or planar faces or combination of work planes or planar faces.
Intersection of Two Lines	Select any two lines including linear edges, 2D or 3D sketch lines, or work axes.
Intersection of Plane/Surface and Line	Select a planar face, work plane, or surface and then select a work axis, sketch line, straight edge, or work axis. A work point will be created where the two selections intersect.
Center Point of Loop of Edges	Select an edge of a closed loop of edges and the work point will be created at the center of the loop or edge.
Center Point of Torus	Select a torus and a work point will be created at the center of the torus.
Center Point of Sphere	Select a sphere and a work point will be created at the center of the sphere.

Grounded Work Points

You can create grounded work points that are positioned in 3D space. Grounded work points are not associated with the part or any other work features, including the original locating geometry. When you modify surrounding geometry, the grounded work point remains in the specified location. To create a grounded work point, use the Grounded Work Point command on the 3D Model tab > Work Features panel and click the arrow next to the Point command, as shown in the following image, or press the hot key (;) a semicolon.

After starting the Grounded Point command, select a vertex, midpoint, sketch point, or work point on the model. When you have selected the vertex or point, a triad and a mini-toolbar will appear, as shown in the following image. The initial orientation of the triad matches the principle axes of the part. These colors represent the three axes: red X, green Y, and blue Z.

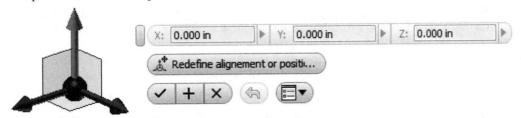

Figure 4-55

To precisely position the grounded work point relative to the selected point, enter values in the mini-toolbar. You can also select areas of the triad to move the triad and locate the grounded work point in the desired direction, as shown in the following image and as described in the following sections.

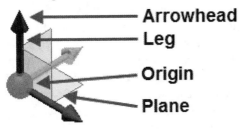

Figure 4-56

Arrowheads
Select an arrowhead to specify a position along a particular axis, and move the cursor or enter a value.

Legs
Select a leg to rotate about that axis, and move the cursor or enter an angle.

Origin
Click to move the triad freely in 3D space, move it to a selected vertex or point, or to enter X, Y, or Z coordinates.

Planes
Select a plane to restrict movement to the selected plane.

Once you position the triad, click Apply or OK in the mini-toolbar to create the grounded work point. By clicking Apply the mini-toolbar will remain open, allowing you to create another grounded work point. You can identify a grounded work point in the browser by the thumbtack icon that is placed on the work point. The following image shows a regular work point that is placed based on geometry (Work Point1) and a grounded work point based on values you enter (Work Point2) represented in the browser.

Figure 4-57

Creating Work Planes

Before introducing work planes, it is important that you understand when you need to create a work plane. You can use a work plane when you need to create a sketch and no planar face exists at the desired location, or if you want a feature to terminate at a plane and no face exists to select. If you want to apply an assembly constraint to a plane on a part and no part face exists, you will need to create a work plane. If a face exists in any of these scenarios, you should use it and not create a work plane. A new sketch can be created on a work plane.

A work plane looks like a rectangular plane. It is tied parametrically to the part. Though extents of the plane will appear slightly larger than the part, the plane is in fact infinite. If the part or related feature moves or resizes, the work plane will also move or resize. For example, if a work plane is tangent to the outside face of a 2 inch diameter cylinder and the cylinder diameter changes to 3 inches, the work plane moves with the outside face of the cylinder. You can create as many work planes on a part as needed, and you can use any work plane to create a new sketch. A work plane is a feature and is modified like any other feature.

Before creating a work plane, ask yourself where this work plane needs to exist and what you know about its location. You might want a plane to be tangent to a given face and parallel to another plane, for example, or to go through the center of two arcs. Once you know what you want, select the appropriate options and create a work plane. There are times when you may need to create an intermediate work plane before creating the final work plane. You may need to create a work plane, for example, that is at 30° and tangent to a cylindrical face. You should first create a work plane that is at a 30° angle and located at the center of the cylinder; then create a work plane parallel to the angled work plane that is also tangent to the cylinder.

You can also create a work plane while using the Work axis or Work Point commands; right-click and select Create Plane when one of these work feature commands is active. Then, after the work plane is created, the command you were running will be active. The created plane will be indented as a child of the work axis or the work point in the browser.

Work planes can also be associated to the Origin planes, axis and points that exist in every part. These origin entities initially have their visibility turned off, but you can make them visible by expanding the Origin folder in the browser, right-clicking on a plane or planes, and selecting Visibility from the menu. You can use the origin planes to create a new sketch or to create other work planes.

To create a work plane, click the Work Plane command on the 3D Model tab > Work Features panel, or press the hot key (]) an end bracket. The Work Plane command allows you to select all geometry types in the graphics window to create a work plane. Another option is to click the down arrow in the bottom of the Plane button and select an option for creating a work plane by only allowing you to select filtered geometry types as shown in the following image. These options will select predetermined geometry and will filter out all other types of geometry. For example if the Three Points option is selected, only points can be selected in the graphics window.

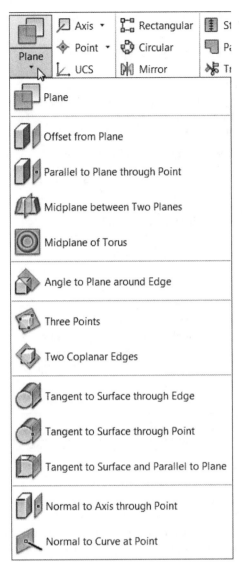

Figure 4-58

Use one of the following methods to create a work plane:

Work Plane Type	Process
Plane	Use this option to create a work plane that is dependent upon the selected geometry, no geometry is filtered.
Offset from Plane	Click a planar face and then drag the new work plane to a selected location. To specify the offset distance, enter a value in the input field.
Parallel to Plane through Point	Select a planar face or work plane and a point; order of selection does not matter. The work plane will be created that is parallel to the selected plane and at the point.
Midplane between Two Planes	Select planar faces or work planes. A work plane is created at the midplane of the two planes.
Midplane of Torus	Select a torus and a work plane is created that goes through the center / midplane, of the torus.
Angle to Plane around Edge	Select a planar face or a work plane and then select an edge or line that is parallel to the plane and enter the desired angle in the input field.
Three Points	Select a combination of three points. The points can be endpoints,

	intersections, midpoints, or work points. Once selected, a work plane is created that goes through the three points.
Two Coplanar Edges	Select two coplanar work axes, edges, or lines and a work plane is created that goes through the axis, edges or lines.
Tangent to Surface through Edge	Select a circular face and a linear edge and a work plane is created that passes through the linear edge and is tangent to the circular face.
Tangent to Surface through Point	Select a circular face and an endpoint, midpoint, or work point and a work plane is created that passes through a point and is tangent to the circular face.
Tangent to Surface and Parallel to Plane	Select a circular face and a planar face or work plane and a work plane is created that is parallel to a plane and tangent to the circular face.
Normal to Axis through Point	Select a linear edge or axis and a point and a work plane is created that is perpendicular to the edge or axis and passes through a point.
Normal to Curve at Point	Select a nonlinear edge or sketch arc, circle, ellipse, or spline and a vertex, edge midpoint, sketch point, or work point on the curve and a work plane is created that is normal to a circular edge and passes through a point.

When you are creating a work plane, and more than one solution is possible, the Select Other-Face Cycling command appears. Click the forward or reverse arrows from the Select Other command until you see the desired solution displayed. Click the checkmark in the selection box. If you clicked a midpoint on an edge, the resulting work plane links to the midpoint. If the selected edge's length changes, the location of the work plane will adjust to the new midpoint.

 TIP: The order in which points or planes are selected is irrelevant.

UCS—User Coordinate System

A User Coordinate System (UCS) is similar to the data in the origin folder; it contains three work planes, three axes, and a center point. Unlike the data in the origin folder you can create as many UCSs as required and position them as needed. The following list shows the common uses for a UCS.

- Create a UCS where it would be difficult to create a work plane, for example a compound angle.
- Locate a sketch on a UCS plane.
- Start and terminate features on UCS planes.
- A UCS axis can be used as a rotation axis to pattern features or parts.
- A UCS axis can be used to rotate parts.
- In an assembly, you can constrain UCSs of two parts.
- In a part or an assembly you can measure to the planes, axis or point in a UCS.
- Measure to the planes, axis or origin.

To start the UCS command, click 3D Model tab > Work Features panel UCS as shown in the following image.

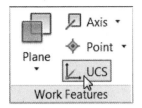

Figure 4-59

There are multiple methods to place a UCS:

- In a part file, a UCS can be placed on existing geometry.
- A UCS can be positioned using absolute coordinates in a part or an assembly file.

The first method to place a UCS is by selecting existing geometry:

1. Start the UCS command, click 3D Model tab > Work Features panel > UCS.
2. Select a point to locate the origin.
3. Select a point to define the direction of the X axis.
4. Select a point to define the direction of the Y axis.

When selecting points to locate or position a UCS valid inputs are: vertex of an edge, midpoint of an edge, sketch, work point origin, solid circular edge, or solid elliptical edge.

The following images show a UCS being placed at the top left vertex in the left image. The X axis is positioned by selecting a vertex as shown in the middle image, and the Y axis is positioned by selecting a vertex as shown in the image on the right. The midpoints of the edges could have also been used to align the UCS.

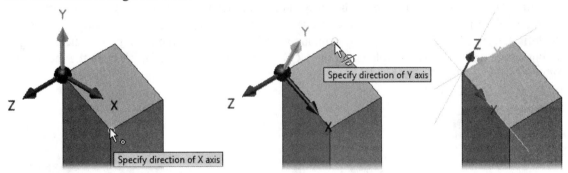

Figure 4-60

The second method to place a UCS is to enter absolute coordinates:

1. Start the UCS command, click 3D Model tab > Work Features panel > UCS.
2. Enter a value for the X, Y, and Z location. Press the Tab key to switch between the cells as shown in the following image.
3. After the three points are defined, press Enter or click in the graphics window.
4. To define the direction of the UCS, click on an arrow and enter a value.
5. To rotate the UCS about an axis on the UCS, click on the shaft of an arrow and enter a value.

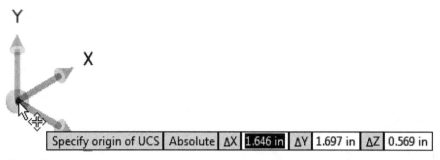

Figure 4-61

After creating a UCS, it will appear in the browser as shown in the following image. The UCS in the browser can be treated like the origin folder, turn the visibility on and off and measure to the planes, axis and center point.

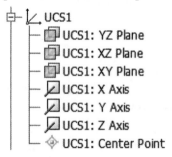

Figure 4-62

To edit a UCS, move the cursor over the UCS in the graphics window or in the browser and double-click or right-click, and then click Redefine Feature as shown in the following image on the left. Select on the desired UCS segment: arrow, leg, or origin, and enter a new value or drag to a new location. When done relocating the UCS, right-click and click Finish from the menu. Do NOT click Done [ESC] as this will cancel the operation. The image on the right shows the prompt to select a segment to edit.

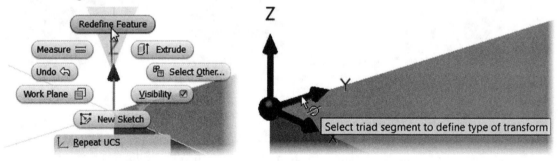

Figure 4-63

Feature Visibility

You can control the visibility of the origin planes, origin axes, origin point, user work planes, user work axes, user work points, and sketches by either right-clicking on them in the graphics window or on their name in the browser and selecting Visibility from the menu. You can also control the visibility for all origin planes, origin axes, origin point, user work planes, user work axes, user work points, sketches, solids, and UCS triad, planes, axis, and points from the View tab > Visibility panel > Object Visibility. Visibility can be checked to turn visibility on or cleared to turn it off, as shown in the following image.

Figure 4-64

EXERCISE 4-5: CREATING WORK PLANES AND A UCS

In this exercise, you create work planes in order to create a boss on a cylinder head and a slot in a shaft.

1. Open *ESS_E04_05-1.ipt* in the Chapter 04 folder.

2. From the 3D Model tab Work > Features panel click the down arrow on the lower-right corner of the Work Plane command and from the list click Angle to Plane around Edge.

3. Click the top rectangular face and the top-back left edge, and then enter a value of **-30** as shown in the following image on the left. Click the green checkmark in the mini-toolbar to create the work plane.

4. Create a sketch on the top face of the extrusion; do not select the work plane. Click on the top face of Extrusion1 and click Create Sketch command on the mini-toolbar as shown in the following image on the right.

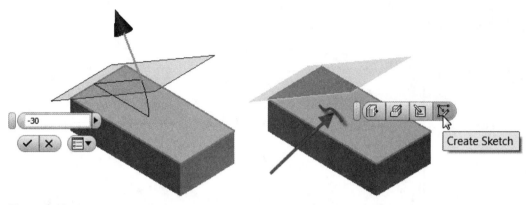

Figure 4-65

5. Create and dimension a **.5 inch** diameter circle and apply a horizontal constraint between the center of the circle and the midpoint of the left vertical edge as shown in the image on the right.

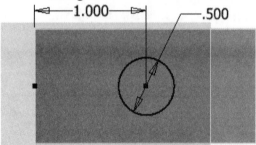

Figure 4-66

6. Fdinish the sketch.

7. Extrude the circle with the Extents set to To and select the work plane, as shown in the following image.

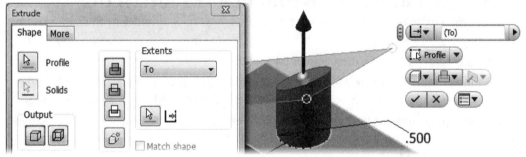

Figure 4-67

8. In the graphics window click on the work plane you created in step 3 click Edit Dimension from the mini-toolbar as shown in the following image and then enter **-40 degrees** and then click the green check mark in the mini-toolbar, if the part does not update, click the Update command on the Quick Access toolbar.

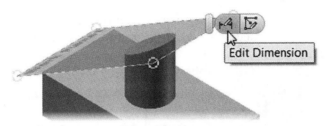

Figure 4-68

9. Change the angle of the work plane back to **-30 degrees**.

10. Turn off the visibility of the work plane by moving the cursor over an edge of the work plane in the graphics window, right-click, and click Visibility from the marking menu.

11. Another option to define a plane is to create a UCS. Click the UCS command on the 3D Model tab > Work Features panel.

   a. Align the UCS on the top face of Extrusion1 by selecting the three vertices in the order as shown in the following image on the left.

   b. Edit the UCS by double-clicking on one of the arrowheads on the UCS in the graphics window.

   c. Click the X leg of the UCS and enter a value of **-40** as shown in the following image on the right and press ENTER on the keyboard to see the change. To complete the edit, right-click and click Finish from the marking menu.

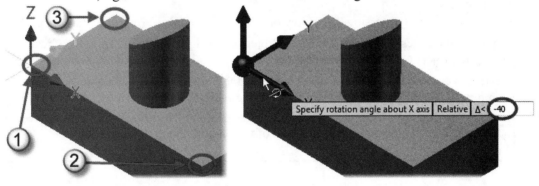

Figure 4-69

12. Reorder the UCS so it exists in the browser before Extrusion2. In the browser, click and drag the UCS entry so it is above Extrusion2 in the browser as shown in the following image.

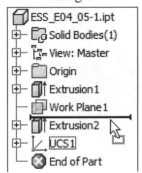

Figure 4-70

13. Edit Extrusion2 by clicking on a face of the circle that was extruded and click Edit Extrude from the mini-toolbar. In the Extrude dialog box click the arrow button for the option to Select surface to end the feature creation and in the browser expand the UCS1 entry and then click UCS1: XY Plane as shown in the following image on the left.

Figure 4-71

14. Click OK to complete the edit.

15. Create a work plane that is centered between two parallel planes. From the 3D Model tab > Work Features panel click the down arrow that is below the Plane command and from the list click Midplane between Two Planes.

16. Select the front-left planar face and then move the cursor near the back of the right-side planar face and right-click and click Select Other from the menu and select the back Face from the list as shown in the following image on the left.

17. Click one of the edges of the work plane you just created and click Create Sketch from the mini-toolbar.

18. Slice the graphics by pressing the F7 key or click Slice Graphics from the Status Bar.

19. To project the edges of the part, click the Project Cut Edges command from the Create panel (the Project Cut Edges command may be under the Project Geometry command).

20. Create and dimension a **.375 diameter** circle on the horizontal edge of the projected geometry as shown in the following image on the right.

TIP If the circle is placed at the midpoint of the projected edge, the horizontal dimension cannot be placed.

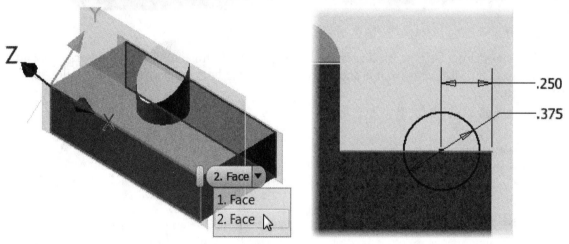

Figure 4-72

21. Finish the sketch by clicking Finish Sketch from the Sketch tab > Exit panel.

22. Extrude the circle **.5 inches** with the Symmetric option, as shown in the following image.

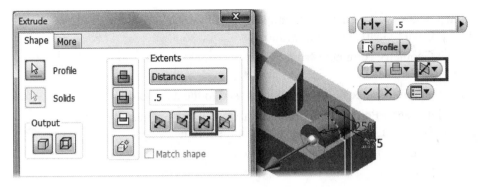

Figure 4-73

23. Turn off the visibility of the work plane and the UCS by moving the cursor over the work plane in the graphics window or in the browser and right-click and click Visibility from the marking menu and move the cursor over the UCS and right-click and click Visibility from the marking menu. Your screen should resemble the following image on the left.

24. To verify that the symmetric extrusion will be maintained in the center of the part if the width changes, edit Sketch1 of Extrusion1, and change the 1 inch vertical dimension to **1.5 inches.**

25. If needed click the Local Update command on the Quick Access toolbar. Your screen should resemble the following image on the right.

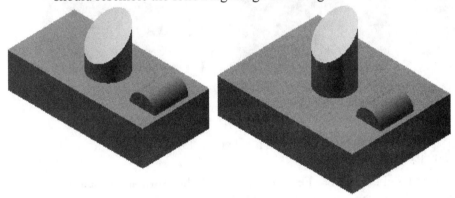

Figure 4-74

26. Use the Free Orbit command to view the part from different perspectives. Notice how Extrusion2 still terminates at the UCS XY plane and Extrusion3 is still in the middle of the part.

27. Close the file. Do not save changes.

In the next portion of the exercise, you place two holes on a cylinder.

28. Open *ESS_E04_05-2.ipt* from the Chapter 04 folder.

29. Create a work plane that is parallel to an origin plane and tangent to the cylinder.

    a. In the browser, expand the Origin folder.

    b. Create a work plane on the outside of the cylinder. From the 3D Model tab > Work Features panel click the down arrow below the Work Plane command and from the list click Tangent to Surface and Parallel to Plane.

    c. In the browser click the YZ plane under the Origin folder.

    d. Click a point to the front-right of the cylinder, as shown in the following image on the left.

30. Create a sketch on the work plane. In the graphics window select an edge of the work plane and click Create Sketch on the mini-toolbar.

31. Use the Project Geometry command from the Create panel to project the Z axis of the Origin folder onto the sketch.

32. Next you place a Point, Center Point that will be used to locate a hole.

    a. Place a Point, Center Point on the projected axis—this will center the point in the center of the cylinder horizontally as shown in the middle image.

    b. Add a **1.000 inch** vertical dimension, as shown in the middle image.

33. Finish the sketch.

34. Press H on the keyboard to start the Hole command and place a **.5 inch** Through All hole at the center point.

35. Turn off the visibility of the work plane and your screen should resemble the image on the right.

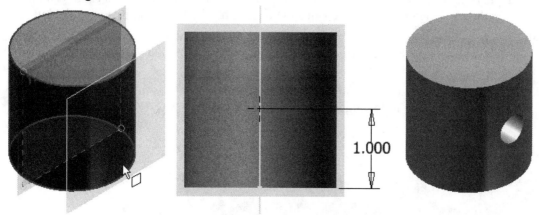

Figure 4-75

36. Next, you place a hole on the cylinder that is at an angle. First you create an angled work plane in the middle of the cylinder.

    a. From the 3D Model tab > Work Features panel click the down arrow below the Work Plane command and from the list click Angle to Plane around Edge.

    b. Select the plane to base the angle on from the browser, click the YZ plane under the Origin folder.

    c. Select the axis to rotate the plane about, in the browser, click the Z Axis under the Origin folder.

    d. In the Angle dialog box, enter **315 degrees** as shown in the following image on the left.

    e. Create the work plane by clicking the green check mark in the mini-toolbar.

37. Next, create a work plane that is parallel to an angled plane and tangent to the cylinder.

    a. From the 3D Model tab > Work Features panel click the arrow below the Plane command and from the list click Tangent to Surface and Parallel to Plane.

    b. In the graphics window click the angle work plane that you just created.

    c. Click a point near the front face of the cylinder, as shown in the following image on the right.

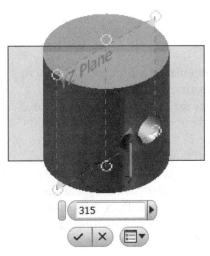
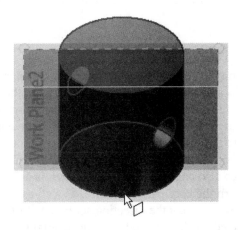

Figure 4-76

38. Turn off the visibility of the inside angled work planes. Move the cursor over the work plane. Right-click, and click Visibility from the marking menu.

39. Create a new sketch on the last work plane that you created.

40. Next you place another Point, Center Point that will be used to locate a hole.

    a. Place a Point, Center Point in the middle of the sketch.

    b. Apply a vertical constraint between the origin point that was automatically projected onto the sketch and the Point, Center Point labeled (1) as shown in the following image on the left.

    c. Apply a **1.5inch** vertical dimension as shown in the image on the left.

41. Finish the sketch.

42. Start the Hole command, and place a counterbore hole with the size of your choice at the center point.

43. Turn off the visibility of the work plane and your screen should resemble the image on the right.

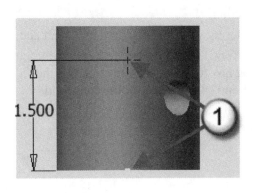

Figure 4-77

44. Next you change the angle of the plane that the hole is located. Expand Work Plane3 in the browser, double-click on Work Plane2, and enter a new value. Update the model to see the change.

45. Close the file. Do not save changes. End of exercise.

PATTERNS

There are two types of feature patterns that you can create; rectangular and circular. The pattern is represented as a single feature in the browser, and the original feature and individual feature occurrences are listed under the pattern feature. You can suppress the entire pattern or individual occurrences except for the first occurrence. Both rectangular and circular patterns have a child relationship to the parent feature(s) that you patterned. If the size of the parent feature changes, all of the child features will also change. If you patterned a hole, and the parent hole type changes, the child holes also change. Because a pattern is a feature, you can edit it like any other feature. You can pattern the base part or feature, as well as patterns. A rectangular pattern repeats the selected feature(s) along the direction set by one or two edges on the part or lines that reside in a sketch. These edges do not need to be horizontal or vertical, as shown in the following image. A circular pattern repeats the feature(s) around an axis, a cylindrical or conical face, or an edge.

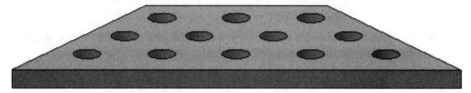

Figure 4-78

Rectangular Patterns

To create a rectangular pattern, follow these steps.

1. Click the Rectangular Pattern command on the 3D Model tab > Pattern panel, as shown in the following image on the left.

2. The Rectangular Pattern dialog box appears, as shown in the following image on the right.

3. Click one or more features to pattern.

4. Click the Direction 1 button in the dialog box to define the direction that the feature will travel.

5. Click an edge or line on a sketch to define the direction.

6. Define the count and the spacing or distance by entering values in the Column Count and Column Spacing cells in the dialog box.

7. If needed, click the Direction 2 button in the dialog box to define the direction that the feature will travel that is not parallel to Direction1 and enter values for the count and spacing.

8. As you enter values the pattern is previewed in the graphics window.

9. Click OK to create the pattern.

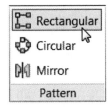

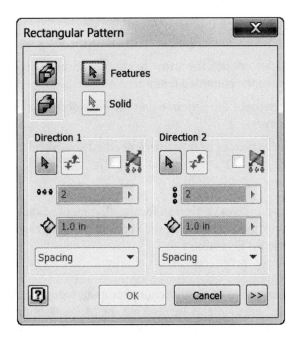

Figure 4-79

Rectangular Pattern Dialog Box

The following options are available in the Rectangular Pattern dialog box.

Pattern Individual Features

Click this button to pattern a feature or features. When you select this option, you activate a features button, as described below.

Pattern the Entire Solid

Click this button to pattern a solid body. When you select this option, you select the entire part as the item to pattern. You also have the Include Work Features option when patterning an entire solid.

Features

Click this button, and then click a feature or features to be patterned from either the graphics window or the browser. You can add or remove features to or from the selection set by holding down the CTRL key and clicking them.

Solid

If multiple solid bodies exist, select the solid body that you want the feature(s) patterned on.

Direction 1

In Direction 1, you define the first direction for the alignment of the pattern. It can be an edge, an axis, or a path.

Path. Click this arrow button, and then click an edge or sketch that defines the alignment along which you will pattern the feature.

Flip. If the preview image shows the pattern going in the wrong direction, click this button to reverse its direction.

Midplane. Check this option to have the occurrences patterned on both sides of the selected feature. The midplane option is independent for both Direction 1 and Direction 2.

Column Count. Enter a value or click the arrow to choose a previously used value that represents the number of feature(s) you will include in the pattern along the selected direction or path.

Column Spacing. Enter a value or click the arrow to choose a previously used value that represents the distance between the patterned features.

Distance. Define the occurrences of the pattern using the provided dimension as the total overall distance for the patterned features.

Curve Length. Create the occurrences of the pattern at equal spacing along the length of the selected curve.

Direction 2

In Direction 2, you can define a second direction for the alignment of the pattern. It can be an edge, an axis, or a path, but it cannot be parallel to Direction 1. The same options are available for Directions 2 that are available for Direction 1

More Options

More options to define the start point of the direction, compute type, and orientation method, as shown in the following image, are available by clicking the More >> button located in the bottom-right corner of the Rectangular Pattern dialog box.

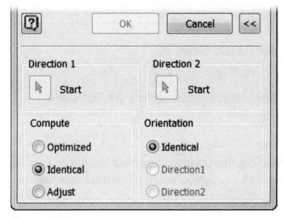

Figure 4-80

Start

Click the Start button to specify where the start point for the first occurrence of the pattern will be placed. The pattern can begin at any selectable point on the part. You can select the start points for both Direction 1 and Direction 2.

Compute

Optimized. Click this option to pattern the feature's faces instead of the feature(s) to calculate all of the occurrences in the pattern. This option is ideal when the occurrences you are creating do not intersect and are identical. It can improve the performance of pattern creation.

Identical. Click this option to use the same termination as that of the parent feature(s) for all of the occurrences in the pattern. This is the default option.

Adjust. Click this option to calculate the termination of each occurrence individually. Since each occurrence is calculated separately, the processing time can increase. You must use this option if a parent feature terminates to a face or plane.

Orientation

Identical. Click this option to orient all of the occurrences in the pattern the same as the parent feature(s). This is the default option.

Direction 1. Click this option to control the position of the patterned features by the selected direction. Each occurrence of the pattern is rotated to maintain proper orientation with the 2D tangent vector of the path.

Direction 2. Click this option to control the position of the patterned features by the selected direction. Each occurrence of the pattern is rotated to maintain proper orientation with the 2D tangent vector of the path.

EXERCISE 4-6: CREATING A RECTANGULAR PATTERN

In this exercise, you create a rectangular pattern of a hole in a cover plate.

1. Open *ESS_E04_06.ipt* in the Chapter 04 folder.

2. Click the Rectangular Pattern command in the 3D Model tab > Pattern panel.

   a. Click the small hole feature on the lower-left corner of the part as the feature to be patterned labeled (1) in the following image.

   b. In the Direction 1 area of the dialog box, click the Direction Path 1 Path button labeled (2), and then select the bottom horizontal edge of the part labeled (3). A preview of the pattern is displayed.

   c. If the pattern is previewed in the negative direction click the Flip button labeled (4).

   d. Enter **5** for the Count labeled (5) and **.625 inches** for the Spacing labeled (6).

   e. Click the Direction 2 Path button labeled (7), and select the vertical edge on the left side of the part labeled (8).

   f. Enter **4** for the Count labeled (9) and **.625 inches** for the Spacing labeled (10).

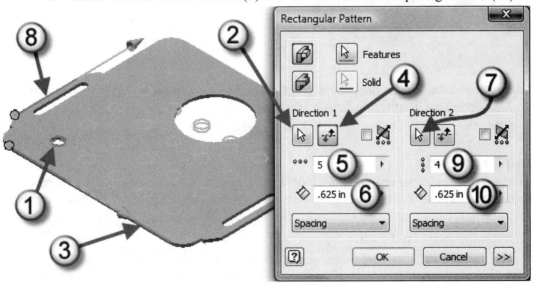

Figure 4-81

3. Click OK to create the pattern.

4. You now suppress three of the holes that are not required in the design. Expand the rectangular pattern feature in the browser to display the occurrences.

5. In the browser, move the cursor over an occurrence and it highlights in the graphics window. Hold down the CTRL key and click to select the three occurrences of the holes as shown in the following image.

6. Right-click on any one of the highlighted occurrences in the browser, and click Suppress, as shown in the following image.

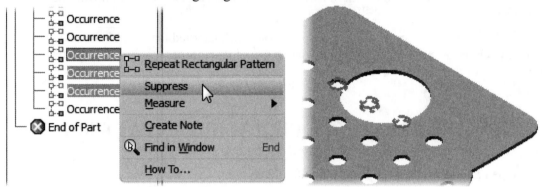

Figure 4-82

7. The holes are suppressed in the model, as shown in the following image.

Figure 4-83

8. Practice editing the feature pattern, and change the count and spacing for each direction. The suppressed occurrences remain suppressed.

9. Close the file. Do not save changes. End of exercise.

Circular Patterns

When creating a circular pattern, you must have a work axis, a part edge, or a cylindrical face about which the features will be patterned around. To create a circular pattern follow these steps:

1. Click the Circular Pattern command on the 3D Model tab > Pattern panel, as shown in the following image on the left.

2. The Circular Pattern dialog box appears, as shown in the following image on the right.

3. Click one or more features to pattern.

4. Click the Rotation Axis button in the dialog box to define the axis of rotation that the feature will be patterned around.

5. Click a work axis, an edge, or a cylindrical face (the centerline of the cylinder will be used) to define the axis.

6. Define the Occurrence Count and Occurrence Angle by entering values in the Occurrence Count and Occurrence Angle cells in the dialog box.

7. As you enter values the pattern is previewed in the graphics window.

8. Click OK to create the pattern.

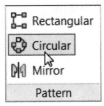

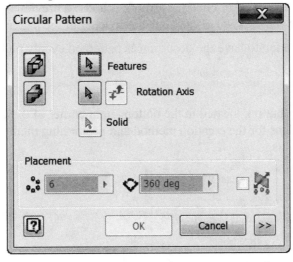

Figure 4-84

Circular Pattern Dialog Box

The following options are available in the Circular Pattern dialog box..

Pattern Individual Features

Click this button to pattern a feature or features. When you select this option, the features button is available and operates as described below.

Pattern the Entire Solid

Click this button to pattern a solid body. When you select this option, you select the entire part as the item to pattern. You also have the Include Work Features option when patterning an entire solid.

Features

Click this button, and then click a feature or features to be patterned. You can add or remove features to or from the selection set by holding down the CTRL key and clicking them.

Rotation Axis

Click the button and then click an edge, axis, or cylindrical face (center) that defines the axis about which the feature(s) will rotate.

Flip

If the preview image shows the pattern going in the wrong direction, click this button to reverse its direction.

Solid

If multiple solid bodies exist, select the solid body you want the feature(s) patterned on.

Placement

In the Placement section of the dialog box you define the number of occurrences and the angle.

Occurrence Count. Enter a value or click the arrow to choose a previously used value that represents the number of feature(s) that you will include in the pattern. A positive number will pattern the feature(s) in the clockwise direction; a negative number will pattern the feature in the counterclockwise direction.

Occurrence Angle. Enter a value or click the arrow to choose a previously used value that represents the angle that you will use to calculate the spacing of the patterned features.

Midplane. Check this option to have the occurrences patterned evenly on both sides of the selected feature.

More Options
By clicking the More >> button, located in the bottom-right corner of the Circular Pattern dialog box, you can access options for the creation method and positioning method of the feature, as shown in the following image.

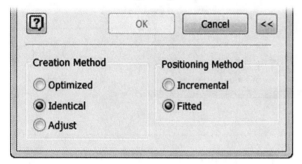

Figure 4-85

Creation Method
Optimized. Click this option to pattern the feature's faces instead of the feature(s) to calculate all of the occurrences in the pattern. This option is ideal when the occurrences you are creating do not intersect and are identical. It can improve the performance of pattern creation. This method is recommended when there are 50 or more occurrences.

Identical. Click this option to use the same termination as that of the parent feature(s) for all of the occurrences in the pattern. This is the default option.

Adjust. Click this option to calculate each occurrence termination individually. Because each occurrence is calculated separately, the processing time can increase. You must use this option if a parent feature terminates to a face or plane.

Positioning Method
Incremental. Click this option to separate each occurrence by the number of degrees specified in the Angle field in the dialog box.

Fitted. Click this option to space each occurrence evenly within the angle specified in the Angle field in the dialog box.

> **TIP:** For the axis of rotation you can use; a work axis, an edge, or a cylindrical face (the centerline of the circular face will be used).

EXERCISE 4-7: CREATING CIRCULAR PATTERN
In this exercise, you create a circular pattern of a counterbore hole.

1. Open *ESS_E04_07.ipt* in the Chapter 04 folder.
2. Edit the Hole1 feature to verify that the termination for the hole is Through All.
3. Click the Cancel button to close the Hole dialog box.
4. Click the Circular Pattern command in the 3D Model tab > Pattern panel.
5. Click the hole feature as the feature to pattern.
6. Click the Rotation Axis button in the Circular Pattern dialog box.
7. In the graphics window click the work axis to specify the rotation axis. A preview of the pattern is displayed in the graphics window.
8. Type **8** in the Occurrence Count field as shown in the following image.

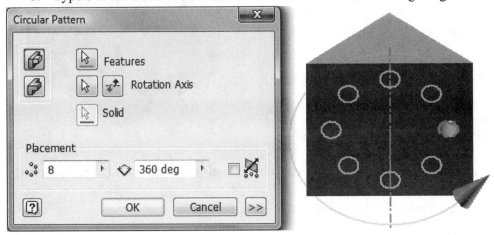

Figure 4-86

9. Click the OK button to create the pattern.
10. Rotate your viewpoint so you can see the back of the part, as shown in the following image. Notice that six holes do not go through because the Identical Creation Method was current when the pattern was created; that is, the patterned holes are identical to the original hole. If desired, change the visual style to Wireframe to verify that all the holes are identical.

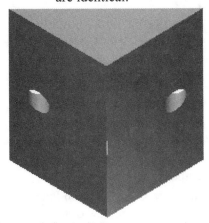

Figure 4-87

11. In the browser right-click on Circular Pattern1 and click Edit Feature from the menu or click on one of the circular faces of a patterned hole (not the original hole) and click Edit Circular Pattern from the mini-toolbar.

12. Click the More >> button.

13. Under Creation Method, select the Adjust option, as shown in the following image on the left.

14. Click OK to create the circular pattern. When done, your model should resemble the image on the right.

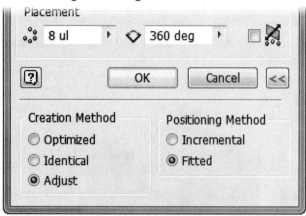

Figure 4-88

15. Edit the circular pattern, and try different combinations of count, angle, creation method, and positioning method.

16. Close the file. Do not save changes. End of exercise.

Linear Patterns—Pattern along a Path

You can also use the Rectangular Pattern command to pattern a feature about a path. You can define a path by a complete or partial ellipse, an open or closed spline, or a series of curves (lines, arcs, splines, etc.).

To pattern along a path, click the Path button, and use the options described above for rectangular patterns. The path you use can be either 2D or 3D.

EXERCISE 4-8: CREATING A PATTERN ALONG A NONLINEAR PATH

In this exercise, you pattern a boss and hole along a nonlinear path.

1. Open *ESS_E04_08.ipt* in the Chapter 04 folder. Note that the visibility of the sketch that the pattern will follow is on.

2. Click the Rectangular Pattern command in the 3D Model tab > Pattern panel.

3. For the features to pattern, in the browser or in the graphics window, click both the Extrusion2 and Hole2 features as shown in the following image on the left.

4. In the Direction 1 area in the Rectangular Pattern dialog box, click the Direction Path arrow button and then select a line or an arc in the visible sketch. A preview of the pattern is displayed, as shown in the following image on the right.

Figure 4-89

5. In Column Count cell enter **40**, and in Column Spacing cell enter **1.25 inches**. The preview shows 1.25 inches between each occurrence as shown in the following image.

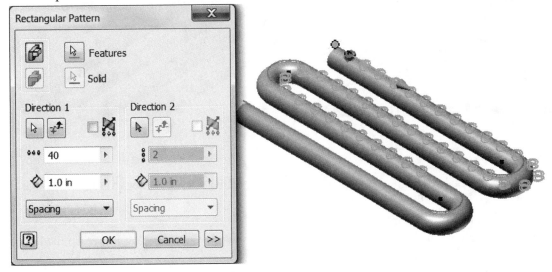

Figure 4-90

6. From the Spacing drop-down list, select Distance as shown in the following image. The preview shows 40 occurrences fit within 1.25 inches.

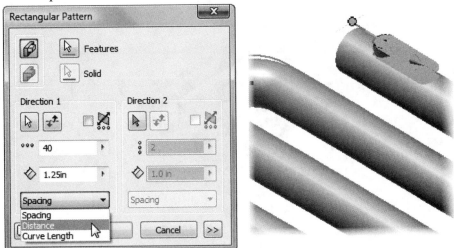

Figure 4-91

7. From the Distance drop-down list, select Curve Length. The preview shows the 40 occurrences fitting within the entire length of the path.

8. Rotate the model to verify that the occurrences on the right side are hanging off the model; this is because the first occurrence is spaced 1 inch away from the start of the path.

9. To solve the starting point issue, click the More >> button.

10. In the Direction 1 area in the bottom area of the dialog box click the Start button and then click the center point of the first hole, as shown in the following image on the left. The preview updates to show that all occurrences are now located on the part, as shown in the following image on the right. However, the last occurrence is on the back edge of the part.

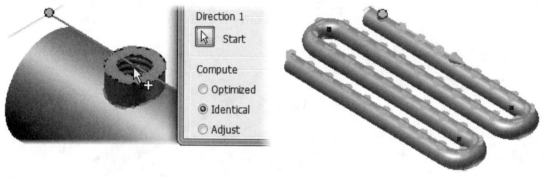

Figure 4-92

11. From the Curve Length drop-down list, select Distance. The curve length remains in the distance area but the value can be edited.

12. Click in the distance area and enter an equation that uses the current distance (56.425) and subtracts 1 inch. Enter **56.425 in – 1 in**, as shown in the following image on the left or enter a value of **55.425**.

13. Click OK to create the pattern.

14. In the browser, right-click on the entry Sketch, and uncheck Visibility from the menu. When done, your model should resemble the image on the right.

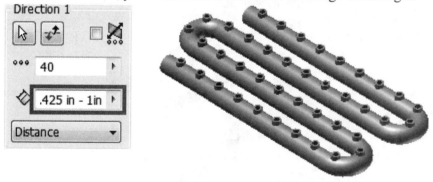

Figure 4-93

15. Edit the pattern trying different combinations.

16. Close the file. Do not save changes.

APPLYING YOUR SKILLS

Skills Exercise 4-1

In this exercise, you create a drain plate cover.

1. Start a new part based on the English Standard (in).ipt template.
2. Use the extrude, shell, hole, rectangular pattern, and the Fillet commands to create the part. Only fillet the inside vertical edges.

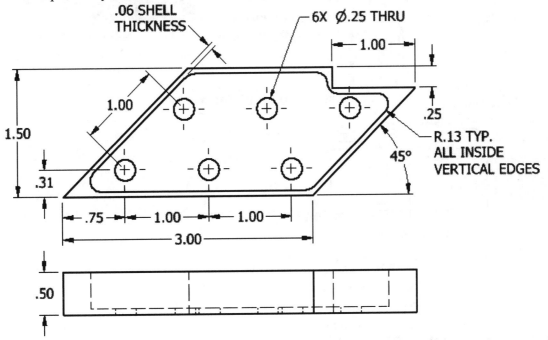

Figure 4-94

Skills Exercise 4-2

In this exercise, you create a connector.

1. Start a new part based on the English Standard (in).ipt template.
2. Use the revolve, work plane, hole, chamfer, fillet, and circular pattern commands to complete the part.

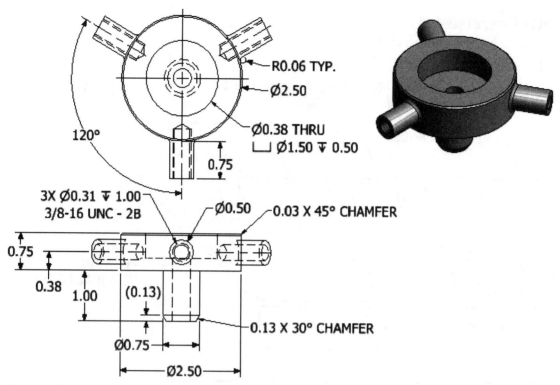

Figure 4-95

CHECKING YOUR SKILLS

Use these questions to test your knowledge of the material covered in this chapter.

1. True__ False__ When creating a fillet feature that has more than one selection set, each selection set appears as an individual feature in the browser.

2. When creating a fillet feature, what is a smooth radius transition?

3. True__ False__ When creating a fillet feature with the All Fillets option, material is removed from all concave edges.

4. True__ False__ When creating a chamfer feature with the Distance and Angle option, you can only chamfer one edge at a time.

5. True__ False__ When you are creating a hole feature, you must place points on a sketch.

6. What is a Point, Center Point used for?

7. True__ False__ When shelling a part you can only have one unique face thickness in the part.

8. True__ False__ The only method to create a work axis is by clicking a cylindrical face.

9. True__ False__ Every new sketch must be placed on a work plane.

10. Explain the steps to create an offset work plane.

11. True__ False__ A work plane is only used to create a sketch on.

12. True__ False__ You cannot create work planes from the origin planes.

13. True__ False__ A UCS can only be placed on existing geometry.

14. True__ False__ When you are creating a rectangular pattern, the directions along which the features are duplicated must be horizontal or vertical.

15. True__ False__ When creating a circular pattern, you can only use a work axis as the axis of rotation.

16. True__ False__ To start the Fillet command from a mini-toolbar, select two planes that define the location of the fillet.

17. True__ False__ Use the Fillet command with the Face option to create a fillet that is tangent to three faces.

18. While in the shell command, explain how to create a unique face thickness.

19. Explain three reasons why you would create a UCS.

20. True__ False__ Use the Linear Pattern command to pattern a feature along a selected path, consisting of multiple lines and arcs.

Chapter 5 – Creating and Editing Drawing Views

INTRODUCTION

After creating a part or assembly, the next step is to create 2D drawing views that represent that part or assembly. To create drawing views, start a new drawing file, select a 3D part or assembly on which to base the drawing views, project orthographic and isometric views from the part or assembly, and then add annotations to the views. You can create drawing views at any point after a part or assembly exists. The part or assembly does not need to be complete because the part and drawing views are associative in both directions (bidirectional). This means that if the part or assembly changes, the drawing views will automatically be updated. If a parametric dimension changes in a drawing view, the part will be updated before the drawing views get updated. This chapter will guide you through the steps for setting up styles, creating drawing views of a single part, editing dimensions, and adding annotations.

When creating drawings, you adhere to specific drawing standards that communicate information about designs in a consistent manner. There are many different drawing standards, such as ANSI and ISO. Each company usually adopts a drawing standard and modifies it to meet their requirements. This book follows the ANSI drawing standard. More information about drawing standards and best practices are covered throughout this chapter.

OBJECTIVES

After completing this chapter, you will be able to perform the following:

- ☐ Create base and projected drawing views from a part
- ☐ Create auxiliary, section, detail, and broken views
- ☐ Edit the properties and location of drawing views
- ☐ Retrieve and arrange model dimensions for use in drawing views
- ☐ Edit, move, and hide dimensions
- ☐ Add automated centerlines
- ☐ Add general, baseline, chain, and ordinate dimensions
- ☐ Add annotations such as text, leaders, Geometric Dimensioning & Tolerancing (GD&T), surface finish symbols, weld symbols, and datum identifiers
- ☐ Create hole notes
- ☐ Open a model from a drawing
- ☐ Open a drawing from a model
- ☐ Create a hole table

DRAWING OPTIONS

Before drawing views are created, the drawing options should be set to your preferences. To set the drawing options, click Application Options on the Tools panel. The Application Options dialog box will appear. Click the Drawing tab, your screen should resemble the following image. Make changes to the options before creating the drawing views, otherwise the changes may not affect drawing views that you have already created. A description of the common options follows. For more information about the Drawing Application Options consult the help system.

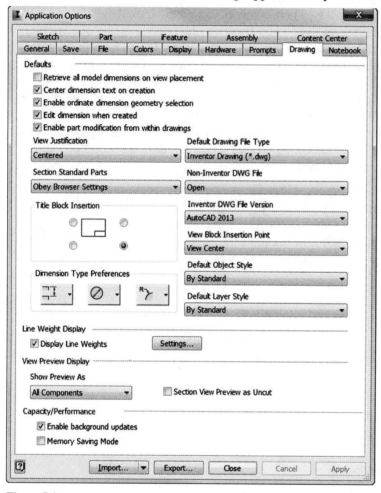

Figure 5-1

Retrieve All Model Dimensions on View Placement

Click this box to add applicable model dimensions to drawing views when they are placed. If the box is clear, no model dimensions will be placed automatically. You can override this setting by manually selecting the All Model Dimensions in the Drawing View dialog box when creating base views.

Center Dimension Text on Creation

Click this option to have dimension text centered as you create the dimension.

Edit Dimension When Created

Click this option to see the Edit Dimension dialog box every time a dimension is placed in a drawing.

Default Drawing File Type

In this section, select either Inventor drawing type, IDW or DWG, as the default file format. The IDW is a file format that can only be opened with Autodesk Inventor. When a drawing file is created from a DWG template, an Inventor DWG file is created and AutoCAD can open this file without translation. In AutoCAD, you can view, plot, and add annotations to the Inventor DWG file. You cannot edit the drawing views in AutoCAD as these are controlled by Inventor.

CREATING A DRAWING

The first step in creating a drawing from an existing part or assembly is to create a new drawing IDW or DWG file by using one of the following methods:

- From the Quick Access toolbar click the down arrow on the right side of the New icon and click Drawing from the drop list as shown in the following image on the left. This creates a new drawing file based on the default drawing file type (DWG or IDW that is set in the Application Options > Drawing tab.
- Click Drawing on the Home page as shown in the middle image.
- From the Inventor Application menu click New > Drawing as shown in the image on the right.

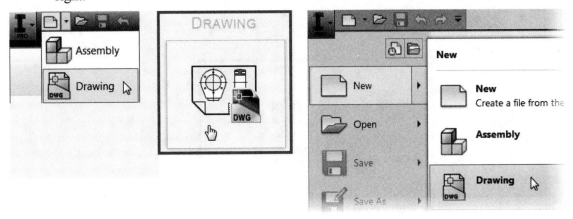

Figure 5-2

You can also create a drawing file from a template that is not the default by clicking the New file command from one of these areas:

- Quick Access toolbar as shown in the following image on the left
- Inventor Application menu, as shown in the image second on the left
- Get Started tab > Launch Panel as shown in the image, third from the left.
- On the Home page, as shown in the image, on the right.
- Or press CTRL + N.

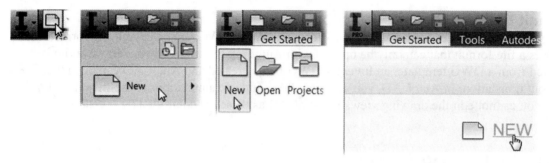

Figure 5-3

The Create New File dialog box appears. Then click the desired template folder on the left side of the dialog box, and in the Drawing - Create an annotated document area click the desired template file as shown in the following image.

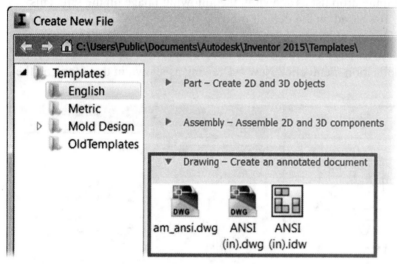

Figure 5-4

When the Metric template folder is selected there are seven drafting standards to select from, the drafting standards are:

- ANSI (American National Standards Institute)
- BSI (British Standards Institute)
- DIN (The German Institute for Standardization)
- GB (The Chinese National Standard)
- GOST (The Russian Standard)
- ISO (International Organization for Standardization)
- JIS (Japan Industrial Standard)

DRAWING SHEET PREPARATION

When you create a new drawing file using one of the provided template files, a drawing sheet with a default title block and border will appear. The template that is selected determines the default drawing sheet, title block, and border. The drawing sheet represents a blank piece of paper (sheet) on which you will add drawing views. If you need to create views that do not fit on a single sheet you can add sheets. To create a new sheet, click the New Sheet command from the Place Views tab Sheets panel as shown in the following image on the left. Alternately, you can right-click in the browser and click New Sheet from the menu as shown in the middle image, or on the current sheet in the graphics window right-click and click New Sheet from the menu as shown in the image on the right.

Figure 5-5

A new sheet will appear in the browser, and the new sheet will appear in the graphics window with the same size, border and title block of the active sheet. To edit the sheet's size right-click on the sheet name in the browser, and select Edit Sheet from the menu, as shown in the following image on the left. Then select a size from the list, as shown in the following image on the right. To use your own values, select Custom Size from the list, and enter values for the height and width. From the dialog box you can also change the sheet's name or slowly double-click on its name in the browser and then enter a new name.

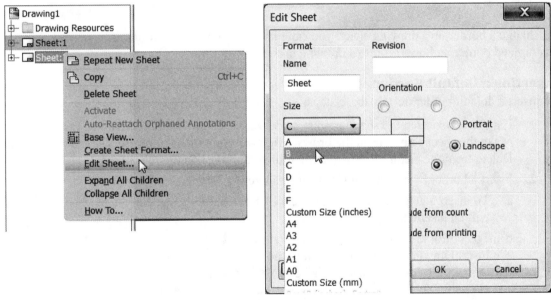

Figure 5-6

 TIP: The sheet size is inserted full scale (1:1) and should be plotted at 1:1. The drawing views will be scaled to fit the sheet size.

Title Block

To change a title block on a drawing sheet, you can either insert a default title block or construct a customized title block and insert it into a drawing sheet.

Inserting a Default Title Block

To insert a default title block, follow these steps:

1. If a title block exists in the sheet, it must be deleted before a new title block can be inserted.

2. Make the sheet active and in the browser right-click on the title block entry and click Delete from the menu as shown in the following image on the left.

3. Insert a title block by expanding Drawing Resources > Title Blocks in the browser.

4. Then either double-click on the title block's name or right-click on the title block's name and click Insert from the menu, as shown in the image on the right.

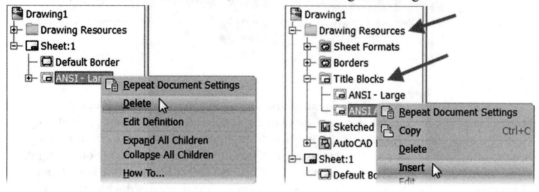

Figure 5-7

Border

To change a border on a drawing sheet, you can either insert a default border or construct a customized border and insert it into a drawing sheet.

Inserting a Default Border

To insert a default border, follow these steps:

1. If a border exists in the sheet, it must be deleted before a new border can be inserted. Make the sheet active, from the browser right-click on the Default Border entry and click Delete from the menu as shown in the following image on the left.

2. Insert a border by expanding Drawing Resources > Borders in the browser.

   a. To insert a generic border double-click on the border's name and a generic border will be inserted.

   b. To control the border's appearance right-click on Borders Default Border and click Insert Drawing Border, as shown in the following image in the middle. The Default Drawing Border Parameters dialog box will appear, modify the options as needed, click the More >> button to control text and layer data as well as the sheet's margin as shown in the following image on the right.

   c. Consult the Help system to learn how to create a new border.

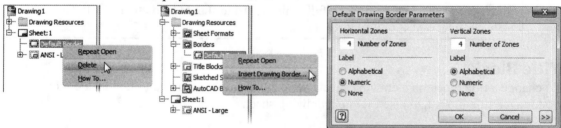

Figure 5-8

Edit Property Fields Dialog Box

The time will come when you will need to fill in title block information. Expanding the default title block in the browser and double-click or right-click on the Field Text entry and click Edit Field Text from the menu, as shown in the following image on the left, will display the Edit Property Fields dialog box. By default, the following information will already be filled in: Sheet Number, Number of Sheets, Author, Creation Date, and Sheet Size. To fill in other title block information such as Part Number, Company Name, Checked By, and so on, select the iProperties command button in the upper right corner of the Edit Property Fields dialog box, shown in the image in the middle. The Drawing iProperties dialog box will appear, as shown in the image on the right, and you can fill in the information as needed. You can find most title block information under the Summary, Project, and Status tabs.

Figure 5-9

Save Drawing to a Template

After getting a drawing setup, you can save the drawing to the template folder so you can create a new drawing that contains the changes. From the Application Menu click Save As > Save Copy As Template as shown in the following image. Save the file to the correct folder; Templates (the default location), English, Metric, or create a new folder. The location of the template files is set in the Application Options > File tab > Default templates field or overridden in the active project's Folder Options Templates.

Figure 5-10

CREATING DRAWING VIEWS

After you have set the drawing sheet format, border, and title block you can create drawing views from an existing part, assembly, or presentation file. The file from which you will create the views does not need to be open when a drawing view is created. It is suggested, however, that both the file and the associated drawing file be stored in the same directory and that the directory be referenced in the project file. When creating drawing views, you will find that there are many different types of views you can create. The following sections describe these view types.

Base View. This is the first drawing view of an existing part, assembly, or presentation file. It is typically used as a basis for generating the following dependent view types. You can create many base views in a given drawing file.

Projected View. This is a dependent orthographic or isometric view that is generated from an existing drawing view.

- Orthographic (Ortho View): A drawing view that is projected horizontally or vertically from another view.
- Isometric View: A drawing view that is projected at a 30° angle from a given view. An isometric view can be projected to any of four quadrants.

Auxiliary View. This is a dependent drawing view that is perpendicular to a selected edge of another view.

Section View. This is a dependent drawing view that represents the area defined by a slicing plane or planes through a part or assembly.

Detail View. This is a dependent drawing view in which a selected area of an existing view will be generated at a specified scale.

Broken View. This is a dependent drawing view that shows a section of the part removed while the ends remain. Any dimension that spans over the break will reflect the actual object length.

Break Out View. This is a drawing view that has a defined area of material removed in order to expose internal parts or features.

Crop View. This drawing view allows a view to be clipped based on a defined boundary.

Overlay View. This drawing view uses positional representations to show an assembly in multiple positions in a single view.

TIP: When you are creating drawing views, Inventor will place a temporary raster image for each view while precise views are being calculated. While a precise view is being calculated a small horizontal and a vertical line will appear in the corners of the view and two circular arrows are displayed in the browser in front of the views that are being calculated. While the view(s) are being calculated you can continue to work on the drawing.

Creating a Base View

A base view is the first view that you create from the selected part, assembly, or presentation file. When you create a base view, the scale is set in the dialog box, and from this view, you can project another drawing view. There is no limit to the number of base views you can create in a drawing based on different parts, assemblies, or presentation files. As you create a base view, you can select the orientation of that view from the Orientation list on the Component tab of the

Drawing View dialog box. By default there is an option to create projected views immediately after placing a base view.

To create a base view, follow these steps:

1. Click the Base View command on the Place Views tab > Create panel as shown in the following image on the top-left or right-click in the graphics window and click Base View from the marking menu as shown on the bottom-left image.

2. The Drawing View dialog box will appear, also shown in the following image on the right. On the Component tab, select an open document from the Select Document list labeled (1) click the Open an existing file icon labeled (2) to navigate to and select the part, assembly, or presentation file from which to create the base drawing view. After making the selection, a preview image will appear attached to your cursor in the graphics window. Do not place the view until the desired view options have been set.

3. If needed you can change the orientation of the base view by selecting a view from the Orientation list labeled (3).

4. If needed you can change the view orientation to a custom view by clicking on the Change view orientation button labeled (4).

5. Select the scale from the list or enter a scale for the view, labeled (5).

6. Select the style for the view labeled (6).

7. By default the option is on that allows you to create projected views immediately after placing a base view labeled (7).

8. If needed you can display the view's identifier (name) and the scale, labeled (8). You can also enter a new View Identifier.

9. Locate the base view by selecting a point in the graphics window. Move the cursor in the direction to place an orthographic or isometric view and click. Continue locating views and when done right-click and click Create from the marking menu.

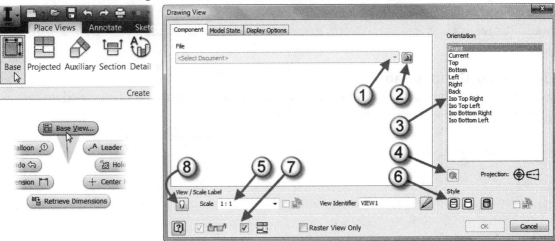

Figure 5-11

The Drawing View dialog box has three tabs: Component, Model State, and Display Options as shown in the previous image on the right.

The Component Tab

Use the options on this tab, as shown in the previous image, to select the file that the views will be created from and how the views will appear. Consult the Help system for more information on these options.

The Model State Tab

Use the options on this tab, as shown in the following image, to specify the state of the weldment or member state of an iAssembly or iPart to use in a drawing view. These options change based on the file that views are being created from.

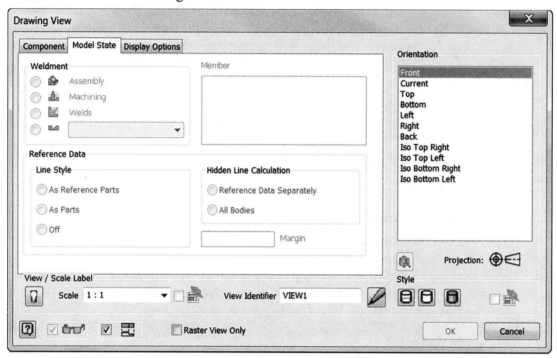

Figure 5-12

The Display Options Tab

Use the options on this tab, as shown in the following image, to control how tangent edges and features like threads and work features will be displayed.

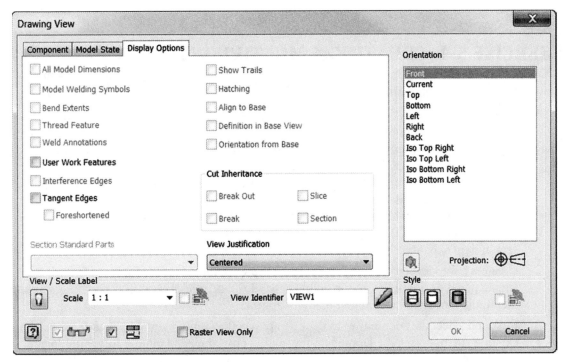

Figure 5-13

Creating Projected Views

A projected view can be an orthographic or isometric view that you project from a base view or any other existing view. When you create a projected view, a preview image will appear that shows the orientation of the view you will create as the cursor moves to a location on the drawing. There is no limit to the number of projected views you can create. To create a projected drawing view, follow these steps:

1. Click the Projected View command on the Place Views tab > Create panel as shown in the following image on the left. You could also right-click inside the bounding area of an existing view box, displayed as dashed lines when the cursor moves into the view, and click Projected View from the marking menu as shown in the following image on the right.

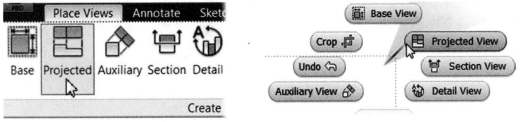

Figure 5-14

2. If you selected the Projected View command from the Create panel, click inside the desired view to project a view from.

3. Move the cursor horizontally, vertically, or at an angle (to create an isometric view) to get a preview image of the view you will generate. Keep moving the cursor until the preview matches the view that you want to create, and then press the left mouse button. Continue placing projected views.

4. When finished, right-click, and select Create from the marking menu.

EXERCISE 5-1: CREATING A MULTIVIEW DRAWING

In this exercise, you create a base view, and then you will add projected views to create a multi-view orthographic drawing. Finally, you will add an isometric view to the drawing.

1. Open the file *ESS_E05_01.idw* in the Chapter 05 folder. This drawing file contains a single sheet with a border and title block. In addition to the title block information, notice the numbers and letters present on the outside of the border. Use these as reference points to locate a specific detail, view, or dimension on a large sheet. Numbers are located horizontally along the top and bottom of the border. Letters are located vertically along the left and right border edges. A typical references example would be C2. Here, you would identify the C along the vertical portion of the border and the number 2 along the horizontal portion of the border. Where both of these two references intersect, your search item should be easily found.

2. Create a base view by clicking on the Base View command on the Place Views tab > Create panel or right-click in the graphics window and click Base View from the marking menu; the Drawing View dialog box will appear.

3. First you select the source file. In the File area on the Component tab, click the Open an existing file button in the Drawing View dialog box labeled (1) in the following image, and double-click the file *ESS_E05_01.ipt* in the Chapter 05 folder.

4. In the Orientation area, verify that Front (XY) is selected labeled (2).

5. In the Scale list, verify that 1:1 is current, labeled (3).

6. Verify that the Create projected views immediately after base view creation option is checked, labeled (4).

7. In Style, verify that the Hidden Line button in the lower right corner of the Drawing View dialog box is selected, labeled (5).

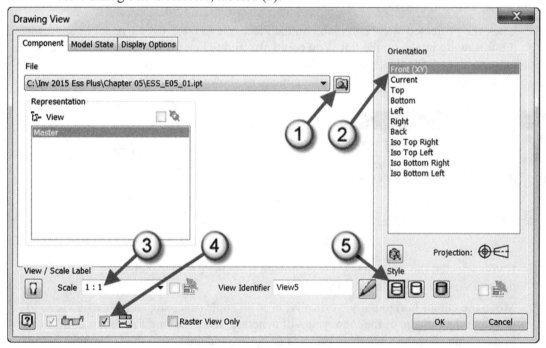

Figure 5-15

8. Position the view preview in the lower-left corner of the sheet (in zone C6), and then click to place the view as shown in the following image.

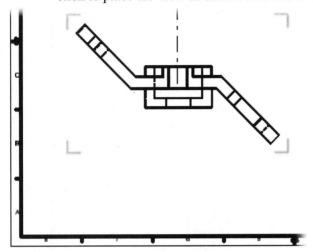

Figure 5-16

9. Next you place orthographic projected views. While still in the Base View command move the cursor to the right of the base view. Click in zone C2 to place the right-side view.

10. Move the cursor to the top of the base view. Click in zone E6 to place the top view.

11. Right-click, and click Create from the marking menu to create the views. When done your views should resemble the following image.

12. You could have created the right side and top view using the Projected View command.

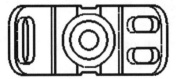

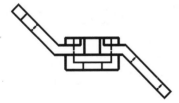

Figure 5-17

13. The views are crowded with a scale of 1:1. In the steps that follow, you will reduce the size of all drawing views by editing the base view scale to 1:2. The dependent views will update automatically. Edit the base view (front view) by either double-clicking in the base view or right-click in the base view and click Edit View from the marking menu.

TIP: To edit the view, right-click on the view border or inside the view. Do not right-click on the geometry.

14. When the Drawing View dialog box displays, select 1/2 from the Scale list, and click OK.

15. The scale of all views updates, as shown in the following image.

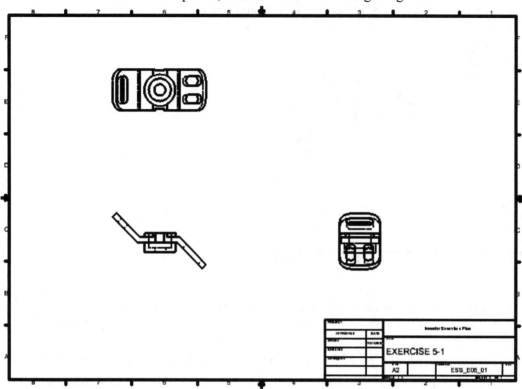

Figure 5-18

16. Next you change the drawing scale in the title block. If needed expand Sheet:1 in the browser by clicking to the left of the Sheet:1 entry in the browser.

17. From the browser, also expand the title block entry ANSI-Large under Sheet:1.

18. Right-click on the Field Text and click Edit Field Text from the menu.

19. The Edit Property Fields dialog box will display. In the SCALE cell, click on 1:1 and enter a new scale of 1:2 as shown in the following image on the left.

20. Click OK. The title block updates to the new scale, as shown in the image on the right.

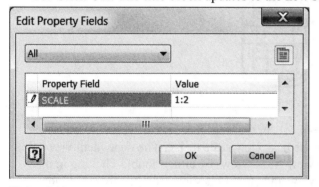

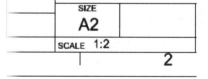

Figure 5-19

21. Next you create an isometric view. Begin by clicking the Projected View command on the Place Views tab > Create panel.

22. Click inside the base view (front view) and move your cursor to zone E3 and click to locate the isometric view, right-click and click create from the marking menu. Your drawing should resemble the following image.

Figure 5-20

23. Double-click the isometric view and click the Display Options tab.
24. Clear the check box for Tangent Edges as shown in the following image on the left.
25. In the Style area in the lower-right corner of the dialog box click the Shaded option as shown in the middle image and click OK to complete the edit. The isometric view should resemble the image on the right.

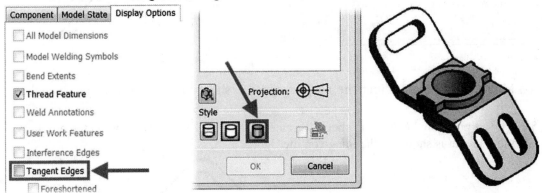

Figure 5-21

26. If desired practice editing and moving the drawing views.
27. Close all open files. Do not save changes. End of exercise.

Creating Auxiliary Views

An auxiliary view is a view that is projected perpendicular to a selected edge or line in a base view. It is designed primarily to view the true size and shape of a surface that appears foreshortened in other views.

To create an auxiliary drawing view, follow these steps:

1. Click the Auxiliary View command on the Place Views tab, as shown in the following image on the left. You can also right-click inside the bounding area of an existing view, shown as a dotted box when the cursor moves into the view, and then click Auxiliary View from the marking menu as shown in the image on the right.

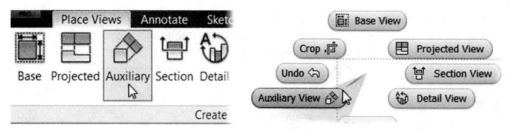

Figure 5-22

2. If you selected the Auxiliary View command from the Create panel, click inside the view from which the auxiliary view will be projected. The Auxiliary View dialog box will appear, as shown in the following image on the left. Type in a name for View Identifier and a value for the Scale of the view, and then select one of the Style options: Hidden, Hidden Line Removed, or Shaded.

3. In the drawing view, select a linear edge or line from which the auxiliary view will be projected perpendicularly, as shown in the following image on the right.

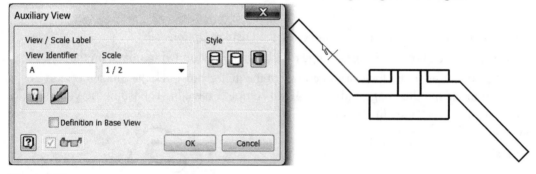

Figure 5-23

4. Move the cursor to position the auxiliary view, as shown in the following image on the left.

5. Click a point on the drawing sheet to create the auxiliary view. The completed auxiliary view layout is shown in the image on the right.

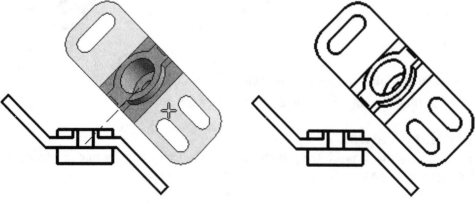

Figure 5-24

Creating Section Views

A section view is a view you create by defining a section line or multiple section lines that will represent the plane(s) that will be cut through a part or assembly. The view will represent the surface of the cut area and any geometry shown behind the cut face from the direction being viewed. When defining a section, you sketch line segments that are horizontal, vertical, or at an angle. You cannot use arcs, splines, or circles to define section lines. When you sketch the section line(s), geometric constraints will automatically be applied between the line being sketched and the geometry in the drawing view. You can also infer points by moving the cursor over (or scrubbing) certain geometry locations, such as centers of arcs, endpoints of lines, and so on, and then moving the cursor away to display a dotted line showing that you are inferring or tracking that point. To place a geometric constraint between the drawing view geometry and the section line, click in the drawing when a green circle appears; the glyph for the constraint will appear. If you do not want the section lines to have constraint(s) applied to them automatically when they are created, hold down the CTRL key when sketching the line(s). Because the area in the section view that is solid material appears with a hatch pattern by default, you may want to set the hatching style before creating a section view.

To create a section drawing view, follow these steps:

1. Click the Section View command on the Place Views tab > Create panel, as shown in the following image on the left. You can also right-click inside the bounding area of an existing view, displayed as a dotted box when the cursor moves into the view. You can then click Section View from the marking menu as shown in the middle image.

2. If you clicked the Section View command in the Create panel, click inside the view from which to create the section view.

3. Sketch a line or lines that define where and how you want the view to be cut. In the image on the right, a vertical line is sketched through the center of the object. When sketching and a green dot appears a coincident constraint will be applied.

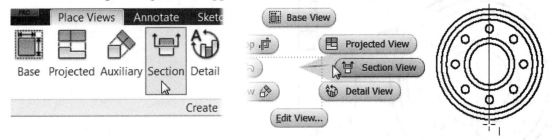

Figure 5-25

4. When you finish sketching the section line(s), right-click and select Continue from the marking menu as shown in the following image on the left.

5. The Section View dialog box will appear, as shown in the following image on the right. Fill in the information for how you want the label, scale, and style to appear in the drawing view. When the Include Slice option is checked, a section view will be created with some components sliced and some components sectioned, depending on their browser attribute settings. Placing a check in the box next to Slice The Whole Part will override any browser component settings and will slice all parts in the view according to the Section line geometry. Components that are not crossed by the Section Line will not be included in the section operation.

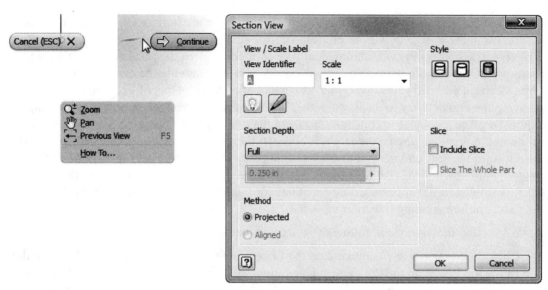

Figure 5-26

6. Move the cursor to position the section view (the section arrows will flip direction depending upon the location of the cursor), as shown in the following image and select a point to place the view.

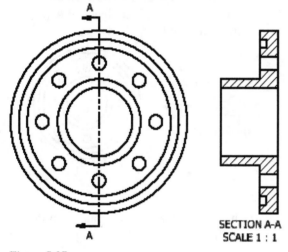

SECTION A-A
SCALE 1 : 1

Figure 5-27

Creating Aligned Sections

Aligned sections take into consideration the angular position of details or features of a drawing instead of projecting the section view perpendicular to the view, as shown in the following image on the left. As illustrated on the left, it is difficult to obtain the true size of the angled elements of the bottom area in the section view. In the Side view, they appear foreshortened or not to scale. Hidden lines were added as an attempt to better clarify the view.

An aligned section view creates a section view that is perpendicular to its section lines. This prevents objects in the section view from being distorted.

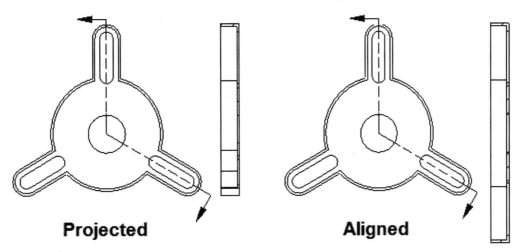

Projected   **Aligned**

Figure 5-28

To create an aligned section view, follow these steps:

1. Click the Section View command on the Place Views tab > Create panel. You can also right-click inside the bounding area of an existing view, shown as a dotted box when the cursor moves into the view. You can then select Section View from the menu.

2. If you started the Section View command from the Create panel, click inside the view from which to create the aligned section view.

3. Sketch the line or lines that define where you want the view to be cut. The following image on the left shows a vertical line drawn through the center of the part and an angle line through the middle of the slot feature. Note that when sketching a section line and a green dot appears, a coincident constraint will be applied.

4. When you finish sketching the section line(s), right-click and click Continue from the marking menu.

5. The Section View dialog box will appear, as shown in the following image on the right. Fill in the information for how you want the label, scale, and style to appear in the drawing view. Verify that the type of section being created is Aligned. Components that are not crossed by the Section Line will not be included in the slicing operation.

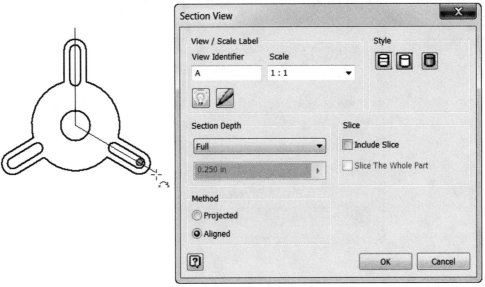

Figure 5-29

6. The completed aligned section is displayed in the following image. With the aligned section the view of the bottom-right slot is rotated so it is a full section (not truncated).

7. To edit the location of the section line(s) right-click on a section line and click Edit from the menu. The sketch environment will be current, add or delete constraints as needed. Dimensions can also be added between a section line and existing geometry. Before adding dimensions use the Project Geometry command to project the existing geometry onto the active sketch.

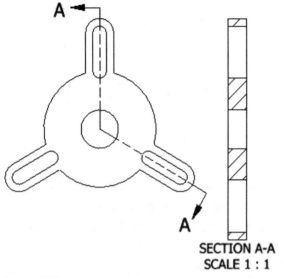

SECTION A-A
SCALE 1 : 1

Figure 5-30

Modifying Section View and a Hatch Pattern

You edit the section view by right-clicking on a section line and click Edit Section Properties as shown in the following image on the left. In the Edit Section dialog box as shown in the image on the right, you can change the section depth, to include a slice and change the method to Projected or Aligned if the view supports it.

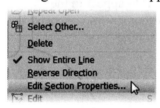
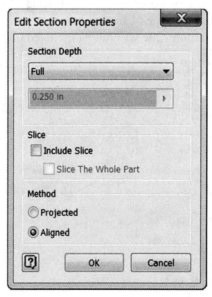

Figure 5-31

You can also edit the hatch pattern by right-clicking on the hatch pattern in the section view and selecting Edit from the menu as shown in the following image on the left and the Edit Hatch Pattern dialog box appears as shown in the image on the right. Make the desired changes in the Pattern, Angle, Scale, Line Weight, Shift (shifts the hatch pattern a specified distance, but still stays within the section boundary), Double, and Color areas. Click the OK button to reflect the changes in the drawing.

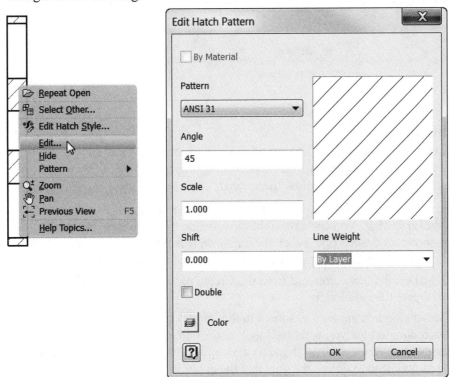

Figure 5-32

Hatching in Drawing Views

When the cross section view or an isometric view is projected from a section view, the hatch pattern will be displayed. You can also control the visibility of the hatch pattern in the section view or the projected isometric view by double-clicking in the view or right-click inside of the bounding box of the view, and click Edit View from the marking menu as shown in the image on the right.

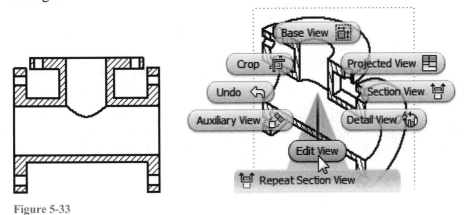

Figure 5-33

When the Drawing View dialog box appears, click on the Display Options tab. To see the hatch pattern, place a check in the box next to Hatching, as shown in the following image or uncheck it to turn off the hatch pattern.

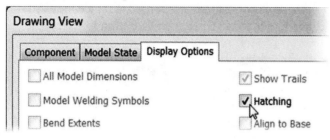

Figure 5-34

Creating a Detail View

A detail view is a drawing view that isolates an area of an existing drawing view and can reflect a specified scale. You define a detailed area by a circle or rectangle and can place it anywhere on the sheet. To create a detail drawing view, follow these steps:

1. Click the Detail View command on the Place Views tab > Create panel as shown in the following image on the left. You can also right-click inside the bounding area of an existing view, shown as dashed lines when the cursor moves into the view, right-click and click Detail View from the marking menu shown in the middle image.

2. If you started the Detail View command from the Create panel, click inside the view from which you will create the detail view.

3. The Detail View dialog box appears as shown in the image on the right. Fill in information according to how you want the label, scale, and style to appear in the detail view, and pick the desired view fence shape to define the view boundary. Do not click the OK button yet as you need to define the area that the detail view will be based on.

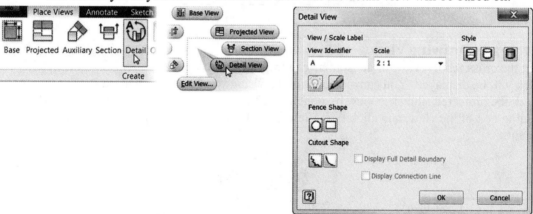

Figure 5-35

4. In the selected view, select a point to use as the center of the fence shape of the detail area. The following image on the left shows the icon that appears when creating a circular fence. The image on the right shows the icon used for creating a rectangular fence.

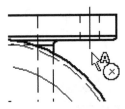

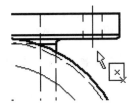

Figure 5-36

5. Click another point that will define the radius of the detail circle, as shown in the following image on the left, or corner of the rectangle, as shown in the image on the right. As you move the cursor, a preview of the boundary will appear.

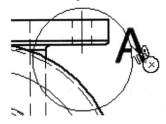

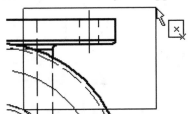

Figure 5-37

6. Select a point on the sheet where you want to place the view. The following image on the left shows the completed detail view based on a circular fence; a similar detail based on a rectangular fence is shown on the right.

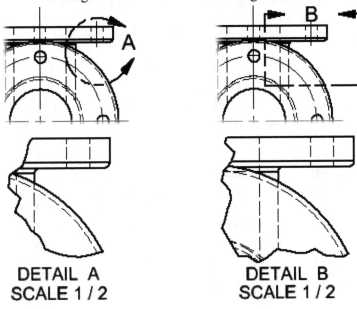

Figure 5-38

Modifying a Detail View

After a detail view is created, options are available to fine-tune the view. To access these options, right-click on the edge of the detail circle or rectangle and choose options, as shown in the following image. The three detail view options are explained below.

- **Smooth Cutout Shape.** Placing a check in this box will affect actual detail view. The following image shows a smooth cutout shape instead of ragged.
- **Full Detail Boundary.** This option displays a full detail boundary in the detail view when checked, as shown in the following image.

- **Connection Line.** This option will create a connection line between the main drawing and the detail view, as shown in the following image.

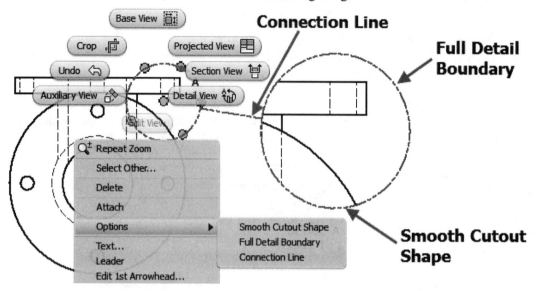

Figure 5-39

Once a connection line has been created in a detail view, you can add a new vertex by right-clicking the detail boundary or connection line and clicking Add Vertex from the menu. Picking a point on the connection line will allow you to add the vertex and then move the new vertex to the new position. You can even remove a vertex by right-clicking a vertex and choosing Delete Vertex from the menu.

Moving Drawing Views

To move a drawing view, move the cursor over the view until a bounding box consisting of dotted lines appears, as shown in the following image. Press and hold down the left mouse button, and move the view to its new location. Release the mouse button when you are finished. As you move the view, a rectangle will appear that represents the bounding box of the drawing view. If you move a base view, any projected children or dependent views will also move with it as required to maintain view alignment. If you move an orthographic or auxiliary view, you will only be able to move it along the axis in which it was projected from the part edge or face. You can move detail and isometric views anywhere in the drawing sheet.

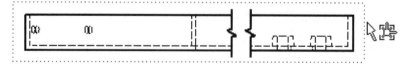

Figure 5-40

EXERCISE 5-2: CREATING AUXILIARY, SECTION, AND DETAIL VIEWS

In this exercise, you create a variety of drawing views from a model of a cover.

1. Open the file *ESS_E05_02.idw* from the Chapter 05 folder. Zoom in on the top view.

2. First you create an auxiliary view. Click the Auxiliary View command on the Place Views tab > Create panel.

   a. In the graphics window, click in the top view.

   b. Select the left-outside angled line, as shown in the following image on the left.

   c. Click in zone B3 to define the projection direction and place the view to the upper-left of the front view as shown in the image on the right.

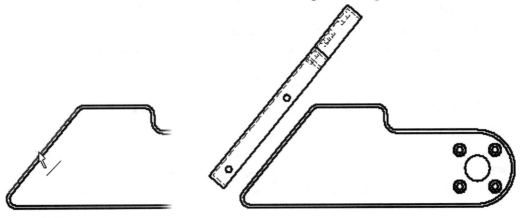

Figure 5-41

3. In the graphics window, select and drag on the border of the views to better fit them in the drawing.

4. Next create a section view. Click the Section View command on the Place Views tab > Create panel.

   a. In the graphics window, click in the top view.

   b. To define the first point of the section line, hover the cursor over the center hole until a green dot appears (do not click), move the cursor up and click a point directly above the hole (the dotted lines represent the inferred point), as shown in the following image on the left.

   c. Click a point below the geometry to create a vertical section line.

   d. Right-click and click Continue from the marking menu.

   e. Place the section view with the default settings to the right of the top view, as shown in the following image on the right.

   f. If the section view does not show the top portion of the part, drag the endpoints of the section line in the top view so it is above the view.

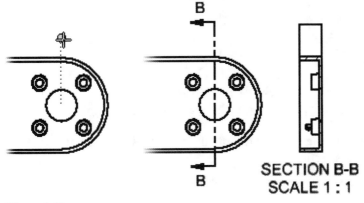

Figure 5-42

5. Try to drag the section line in the top view. If the section line can move follow these steps.

   a. Right-click on the section line and click Edit from the menu.

   b. Use the Project Geometry command and project the large circle that is concentric to the right side of the part.

   c. Apply a coincident constraint between the section line and the center point of the projected circle.

   d. Click the Finish Sketch command from the Exit panel.

TIP: If the section sketch line cannot move and you need to reposition it, edit the section line as described in the previous step 5, but delete the constraint that is holding the line in place.

6. If desired, project an isometric view from the section view.

7. Delete the section view by right-clicking in the section view and click Delete from the menu and then click OK to confirm that the view will be deleted.

8. Next you create an aligned section view. Click the Section View command on the Place Views tab > Create panel.

   a. In the graphics window, click in the top view.

   b. To define the first point of the section line, hover the cursor over the center hole until a green dot appears (do not click), move the cursor up and then click a point directly above the hole (the dotted lines represent the inferred point), as you did in step 4b.

   c. Click the center point of the center circle.

   d. Move the cursor over the center point of the lower-right circle (a green dot will appear) and then click a point outside of the geometry as shown in the following image on the left.

   e. Right-click and click Continue from the menu.

   f. Place the aligned section view with the default settings to the right of the top view, as shown in the image on the right.

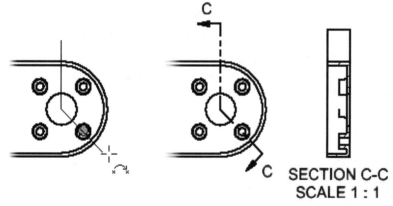

Figure 5-43

9. If the section view does not show the entire part, drag the endpoints of the section line in the top view so the entire part is sectioned.

10. Finally, create a detail view. Click the Detail View command from the Place Views tab > Create panel.

a. In the graphics window, click in the top view.

b. Select a point near the lower-left corner of the top view to define the center of the circular boundary of the detail view.

c. Drag the circular boundary to include the entire lower-left corner of the view geometry, as shown in the following image on the left.

d. Click to position the detail view below the break view. The image in the middle shows the completed detail in the top view and the image on the right shows the completed detail view.

 TIP: Your view identifier (letter) may be different than what is shown.

11. Reposition the drawing views as shown in the following image.

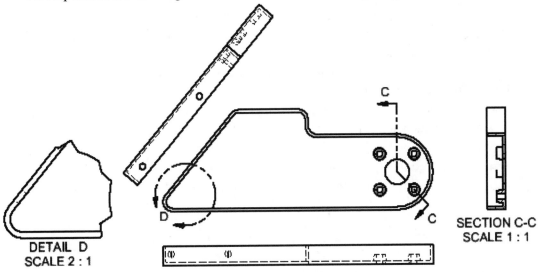

Figure 5-44

12. Close all open files. Do not save changes. End of exercise.

Creating Break Views

When creating drawing views of long parts, you may want to remove a section or multiple sections from the middle of the part in a drawing view and show just the ends. This type of view is referred to as a "break view." You may, for example, want to create a drawing view of a 2" x 2" x ¼" angle, as shown in the following image, which is 48 inches long and has only the ends chamfered. When you create a drawing view, the detail of the ends is small and difficult to see because the part is so long.

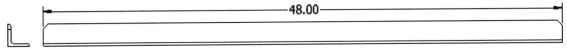

Figure 5-45

In this scenario, you can create a break view that removes the middle of the angle and leaves a small section on each end. When you place an overall length dimension that spans the break, it appears as 48 inches, and the dimension line shows a break symbol to note that it was based from a break view, as shown in the following image.

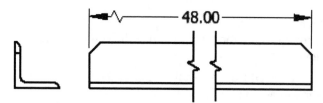

Figure 5-46

You create a break view by adding as many breaks to an existing drawing view as needed. The view types that can be changed into break views are as follows: part views, assembly views, projected views, isometric views, auxiliary views, section views, break out views, and detail views. After creating a break view, you can move the breaks dynamically to change what you see in the broken view.

To create a break view, follow these steps:

1. Create a base or projected view or one that will eventually be shown as broken.
2. Click the Break command on the Place Views tab > Modify panel, as shown in the following image on the left.
3. If you selected the Break command on the Place Views tab > Modify panel, click inside the view that you want to break.
4. The Break dialog box will appear, as shown in the following image on the right. Do not click the OK button at this time, as this will end the command.

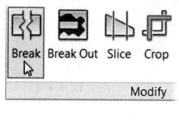
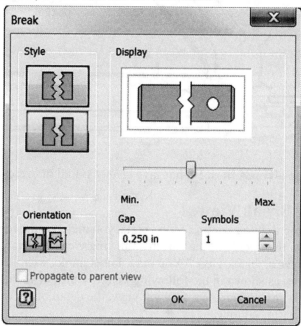

Figure 5-47

5. In the drawing view that will be broken, select a point where the break will begin, as shown in the following image.

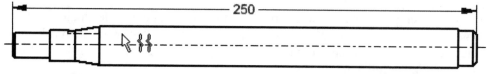

Figure 5-48

6. Select a second point to locate the second break, as shown in the following image. As you move the cursor, a preview image will appear to show the placement of the second break line.

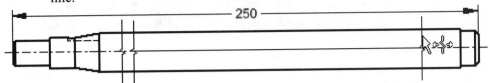

Figure 5-49

7. The following image illustrates the results of creating a broken view with a dimension added. Notice that the dimension line appears with a break symbol to signify that the view is broken.

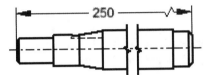

Figure 5-50

8. To edit the properties of the break view, move the cursor over the break lines, and a green circle will appear in the middle of the break. Right-click and select Edit Break from the menu. The same Break dialog box will appear. Edit the data as needed, and click the OK button to complete the edit.

9. To move the break lines, click on one of the break lines and, with the left mouse button pressed down, drag the break line to a new location, as shown in the following image. Drag the cursor away from the other break line to reduce the amount of geometry that is displayed, drag the cursor into the other break line to increase the amount of geometry that is displayed. In either case the other break line will follow to maintain the gap size.

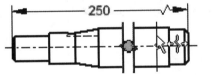

Figure 5-51

EXERCISE 5-3: CREATING BREAK VIEW

In this exercise, you create a break view and a break out view.

1. Open the file *ESS_E05_03.idw* in the Chapter 05 folder. This file has a base view and a side view that is too long to fit in the drawing.

2. Start the Break command from the Place Views tab > Modify panel.

3. In the graphics window, click in the right side view to specify that is the view that you want to break. With the Break dialog box open click start and end points between the two holes. The points specify the area that will be removed, as shown in the following image.

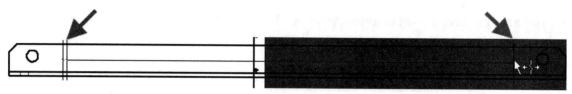

Figure 5-52

4. Move the right side view so it is next to the front view as shown in the following image.

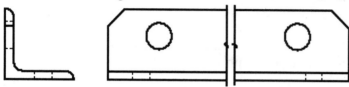

Figure 5-53

5. To edit the properties of the break view, move the cursor between the break lines, and a green circle will appear in the middle of the break. Right-click and select Edit Break from the menu as shown in the following image on the left.

6. In the Break dialog box move the Display slider to about 3/4, labeled (1) in the middle image and change the Gap to 0.50 inches labeled (2) in the middle image. Click the OK button to complete the edit.

7. To move the break lines, click on one of the break lines and with the left mouse button pressed down, drag the break line to a new location. Drag the cursor away from the other break line to reduce the amount of geometry that is displayed, drag the cursor into the other break line to increase the amount of geometry that is displayed. In either case the other break line will follow to maintain the gap size.

8. Next you will create a dimension. Press the D key on the keyboard and place the dimension on the two outside points. Click OK in the Edit Dimension dialog box. Notice the break symbol in the dimension as shown in the following image on the right. Dimensioning a drawing will be covered later in this chapter.

9. When done, your screen should resemble the image on the right.

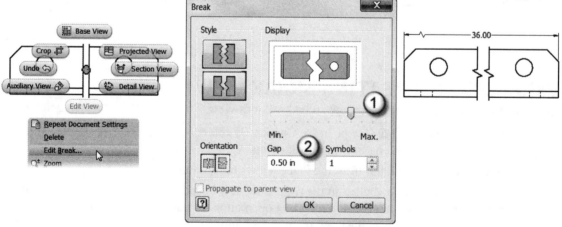

Figure 5-54

10. Close all open files. Do not save changes. End of exercise.

EDITING DRAWING VIEWS

After creating the drawing views, you may need to edit the properties of, delete a drawing view, or replace the component that a drawing references. The following sections discuss these options.

Editing Drawing View Properties

After creating a drawing view, you may need to change the label, scale, style, or hatching visibility, break the alignment constraint to its base view; or control the visibility of the view projection lines for a section or auxiliary view. To edit a drawing view, follow one of these steps:

- Double-click in the bounding area of the view.
- Double-click on the icon of the view you want to edit in the browser.
- Right-click in the drawing view's bounding area or on its name, and select Edit View from the marking menu, as shown in the following image.

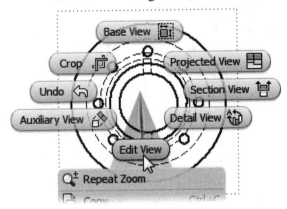

Figure 5-55

When you perform the operations listed above, the Drawing View dialog box will appear, as shown in the following image. This is the same dialog box used to create drawing views. Depending on the view that you selected, certain options may be grayed out from the dialog box. Make the necessary changes, and click the OK button to complete the edit. When you change the scale in the base view, all the dependent views will be scaled as well. You can also change the orientation of the base view; dependent views will then be updated to reflect the new orientation.

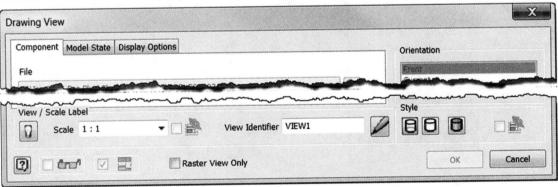

Figure 5-56

Deleting Drawing Views

To delete a drawing view, either right-click in the bounding area of the drawing view or on its name in the browser and select Delete from the menu. You can also click in the bounding area of the drawing view, and press the Delete key on the keyboard. A dialog box will appear, asking you to confirm the deletion of the view. If the selected view has a view that is dependent on it, you will be asked if the dependent views should also be deleted. By default, the dependent view(s) will be deleted. To exclude a dependent view from the delete operation, expand the dialog box by clicking on the >> button, and click on the Delete cell on the row of the view to change the option to No as shown in the following image.

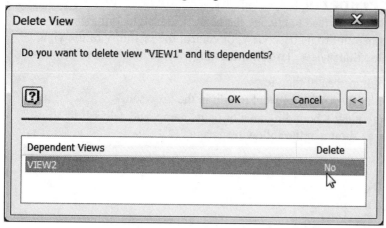

Figure 5-57

Break and Align Views

After creating or deleting drawing views you may need to move a view to a different location on the drawing, but the view can only move orthographically to its parent view. To break this relationship click the Break Alignment command on the Place Views tab > Modify panel as shown in the following image. To align a view to another view follow the same process but click Horizontal to align a view horizontally to a selected view, Vertical to align a view vertically to a selected view and In Position to keep a view near its current position in relation to a selected view.

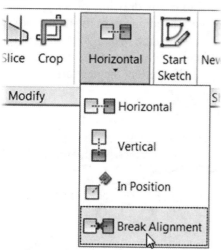

Figure 5-58

Replace Model Reference

While annotating a drawing you may want to change the component that the drawing references for the geometry. Parts, assemblies, and presentation files can be replaced, but they can only be replaced with the same type of file. The file replacing the existing file should be similar in shape and size otherwise dimensions may be orphaned. To replace a model that a drawing view references, follow these steps:

1. Click the Replace Model Reference command on the Manage tab > Modify panel as shown in the following image on the left.

2. The Replace Model Reference dialog box will appear as shown in the following image on the right. All the files that are referenced in the drawing will appear in the list. In the dialog box click on the file to replace.

3. In the dialog box click the Select new model button.

4. Browse to the new file and select it.

5. In the Open dialog box click Open.

6. Click Yes in the warning dialog box to replace the model.

7. In the Replace Model Reference dialog box click OK to complete the command.

8. Cleanup the drawing annotations and the view orientations as needed.

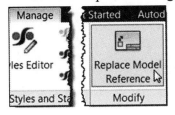
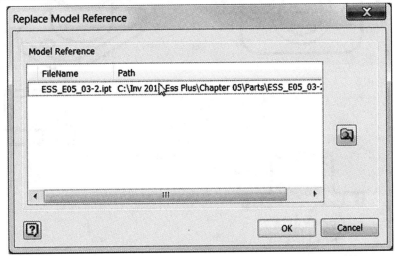

Figure 5-59

EXERCISE 5-4: EDITING DRAWING VIEWS

In this exercise, you will delete the base view while retaining its dependent views. The base view is not required to document the part, but its dependent views are. Next, you align the section view with the right-side view to maintain the proper orthographic relationship between the views. You also modify the hatch pattern of the section to better represent the material.

1. Open the drawing file *ESS_E05_04.idw* in the Chapter 05 folder. This drawing contains three orthographic views, an isometric view, and a section view.

2. Right-click on the front view (the middle view on the left side of the drawing, this is also the base view as shown in the following image, and choose Delete from the menu as shown in the following image on the left.

3. In the Delete View dialog box, notice that the projected views are highlighted on the drawing sheet. Select the More >> button in the dialog box.

4. Click on the word Yes in the Delete column for each dependent view to toggle each to No as shown in the following image on the right. This will delete the base view but keep the dependent views present on the drawing sheet.

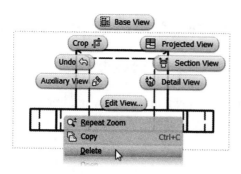
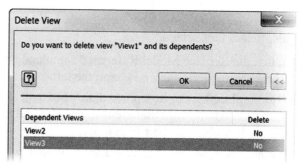

Figure 5-60

5. In the dialog box click OK to delete the base view and retain the two dependent views. Your drawing views should appear similar to the following image.

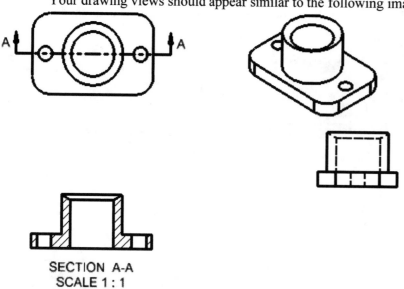

SECTION A-A
SCALE 1 : 1

Figure 5-61

6. With the front view deleted, the section view needs to be aligned with the right-side view. From the Place Views tab > Modify panel, click down arrow under the Break Alignment command and click Horizontal from the drop list.

7. Select in the right side view as the view to align and then click the section view as the base view.

8. Select on the border of the section view, and drag the section view vertically up to the area previously occupied by the front view. Notice how the right-side view is now aligned horizontally to the section view.

9. Click and drag the isometric view and the section view and notice the isometric view moves independently of the base view. Move the views back to their original locations.

10. From the Place Views tab > Modify panel, click down arrow under the Break Alignment command and click In Position.

11. Select in the isometric view as the view to position and then click the section view as the base view. Move the section view, and notice that the isometric view now moves with the section view. Move the isometric view and notice that the view can only move along the same angle. Your drawing should appear similar to the following image.

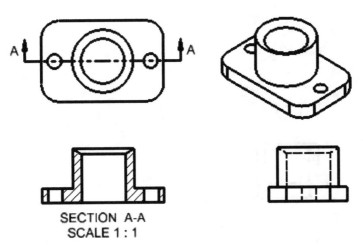

SECTION A-A
SCALE 1 : 1

Figure 5-62

12. You now edit the section view hatch pattern to represent the material as bronze using the ANSI 33 hatch pattern.

13. Right-click on the hatch pattern in the section view, and click Edit from the menu.

14. The Edit Hatch Pattern dialog box is displayed. Select ANSI 33 from the Pattern list, and click OK in the Edit Hatch Pattern dialog box. The hatch pattern changes, as shown in the following image.

Figure 5-63

15. Lastly, you replace the part with a similar part but the holes are in different locations. Click the Replace Model Reference command on the Manage tab > Modify panel.

16. In the Replace Model Reference dialog box click on the only file in the list.

17. In the Replace Model Reference dialog box click the Select new model button and browse to the Chapter 05 folder and select the file *ESS_E05_04-Replace.ipt* and then click Open in the dialog box.

18. In the warning dialog box click Yes to replace the model.

19. In the Replace Model Reference dialog box click OK to complete the command.

20. Notice that the views were updated to reflect the new part that has four holes centered on the fillets. Also notice that the hatch pattern and view alignment was maintained.

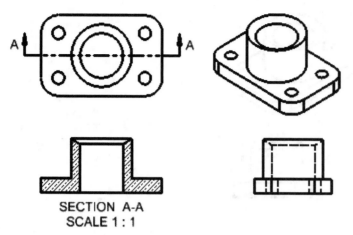

SECTION A-A
SCALE 1 : 1

Figure 5-64

21. Close all open files. Do not save changes. End of exercise.

ANNOTATIONS

To complete an engineering drawing, you must add annotations such as centerlines, dimensions, surface texture symbols, welding symbols, geometric tolerance symbols, text, bills of materials, and balloons. How these objects appear is defined by styles. Styles will be covered as the first topic in this section.

Drawing Standards and Styles

Each drawing is controlled by a drawing standard; the drawing standard controls overall drafting standards and which styles are available in a drawing. Only one standard can be active. Autodesk Inventor uses styles to control how objects appear. Styles control objects such as dimensions, centerlines, hole tables, and text. Styles are saved within an Autodesk Inventor file or to a project library location, and they can be saved to a network location so that many users can access the same styles. This section introduces you to styles. Once a style is used in a document, it is stored in the document. Changes made to a style are only saved in that document. The updated style library can be saved to the main style library but requires permission set in the local project file and rights of the folder that the styles are saved in. To help maintain standards, it is recommended that only a limited number of people have access to write to the style library. For more information on how to save styles to a style library consult the help system topic "Save styles to a style library".

Style Name/Value

Autodesk Inventor uses the style's name as the unique identifier of that style: only one name for the same style type can exist. For example, in a drawing, only one dimension style with a specific name "Default ANSI" can exist. An object can only be associated to one style.

Editing a Style

After dimensions have been placed, you may want to change how all of the dimensions appear. Instead of changing each dimension, you can alter the dimension style or create a new style. The easiest way to edit a dimension style is to move the cursor over a dimension whose style you want to change and right-click and click Edit Dimension Style from the menu as shown in the following image.

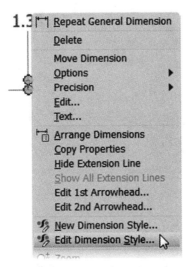

Figure 5-65

The Style and Standard Editor dialog box will appear as shown in the following image. Make changes to the style as needed and then click the Save button on the top of the dialog box.

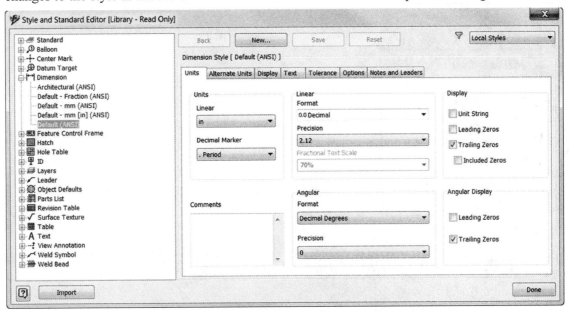

Figure 5-66

Creating a Style

Instead of editing a current dimension style, you can create a new style. To create a new style, follow these steps:

1. Click the Styles Editor command on the Manage tab > Styles and Standards panel.

2. Click and expand the style section for which you want to create a new style.

3. Right-click the style on which the new style will be based, and select New Style, as shown in the following image on the left. This image shows a new style being created from the Default (ANSI) dimension style.

4. The New Local Style dialog box will appear, as shown in the following image on the right. Enter a style name, and if you do not want the style to be used in the standard, uncheck Add to standard.

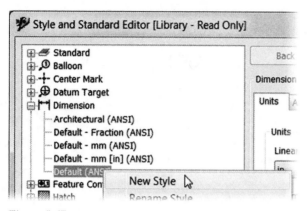

Figure 5-67

5. Make changes to the style, and save the changes.

6. To change existing objects to a different style, select the object or objects whose style you want to change (selected objects need to be the same object type, i.e., all dimensions), and then select a style from the Style area on the Annotate tab > Format panel as shown in the following image.

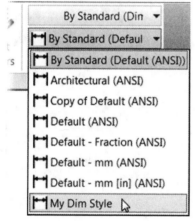

Figure 5-68

 TIP: Styles will be covered through the exercises in this chapter.

Centerlines and Center Marks

When you need to annotate the centers of holes, circular edges, or the middle (center axis) of two lines, four methods allow you to construct the needed centerlines. Use the Center Mark, Centerline, Centerline Bisector, and Centered Pattern commands under the Annotate tab, as shown in the following image. The centerlines are associated to the geometry that you select when you create them. If the geometry changes or moves, the centerlines update automatically to reflect the change. This section outlines the steps for creating the different types of centerlines.

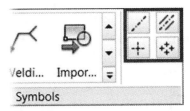

Figure 5-69

Centerline

To add a centerline, follow these steps and refer to the following image:

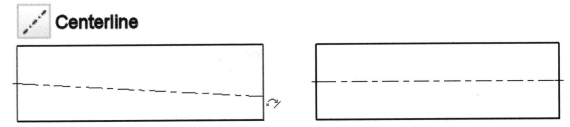

Figure 5-70

1. Click the Centerline command on the Annotate tab > Symbols panel.
2. In the graphics window, select a piece of geometry for the start of the centerline.
3. Click a second piece of geometry for the ending location. You can also select multiple circles or points. If multiple points or circles are selected whose center points fall on a circle, a circle with the centerline line type (often referred to as a bolt circle) will be created.
4. Continue placing centerlines by selecting geometry.
5. Right-click and click Create from the menu to create the centerline. The centerline will be attached to the midpoints of selected edges or center point of selected arcs and circles.

Centerline Bisector

To add a centerline bisector, follow the steps and refer to the following image:

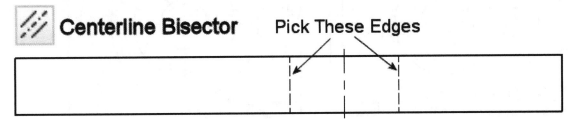

Figure 5-71

1. Click the Centerline Bisector command on the Annotate tab > Symbols panel.
2. In the graphics window, select two lines between which you want to place the centerline bisector. The lines do not need to be parallel to each other.
3. Continue placing centerline bisectors by selecting geometry.

Center Mark

To add a center mark, follow the steps and refer to the following image:

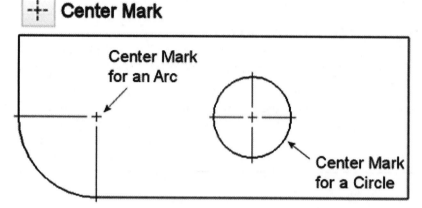

Figure 5-72

1. Click the Center Mark command on the Annotate tab > Symbols panel.
2. In the graphics window, select a center point of a circle or arc or select a circle or arc geometry in which you want to place a center mark.
3. Continue placing center marks by selecting arcs and circles.

Centered Pattern

To add a centered pattern, follow the steps and refer to the following image:

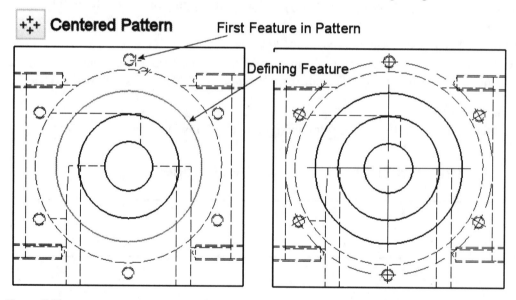

Figure 5-73

1. Click the Centered Pattern command on the Annotate tab > Symbols panel.
2. In the graphics window, select the circular face whose center point will be used as the center of the circle that a set of center marks will fall on, commonly referred to as a bolt circle.
3. Click the first feature of the pattern.

4. Continue selecting features in a clockwise or counter clockwise direction until all of the features are added to the selection set.

5. Right-click, and click Create from the menu to create the centered pattern.

Automated Centerlines for Drawing Views

Creating centerlines automatically can eliminate a considerable amount of work. You can control which features automatically get centerlines and marks and in which views these occur.

You can create automated centerlines for drawing views by right-clicking on the view boundary or hold down the Ctrl key and select multiple view boundaries and right-click to display the menu and click Automated Centerlines from the menu as shown in the following image on the left. The Automated Centerlines dialog box will appear as shown in the following image on the right. Use this dialog box to set the type of feature(s) to which you will apply automated centerlines, such as holes, fillets, cylindrical features, etc., and to choose the projection type (plan or profile). The following sections discuss these actions in greater detail.

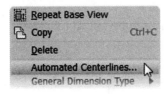
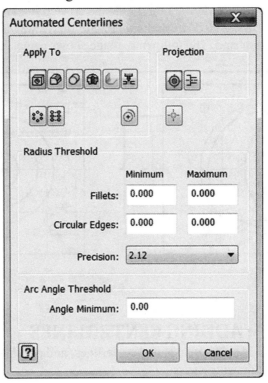

Figure 5-74

Apply To

This area controls the feature types to which you want to apply automated centerlines. Feature types include holes, fillets, cylindrical features, revolved features, circular patterns, rectangular patterns, sheet metal bends, punches, and circular sketched geometry. Click on the appropriate button to activate it, and automated centerlines will be applied to all features of that type in the drawing. You can click on multiple buttons to apply automated centerlines to multiple features. To disable centerlines in a feature, click on the feature button a second time.

Projection

Click on the projection buttons to apply automated centerlines to plan (axis normal) and/or profile (axis parallel) views.

Radius Threshold

Thresholds are minimum and maximum value settings and are provided for fillet features, arcs, and circles. Any object residing within a range should get the appropriate center mark. The values are based upon the model values, not the drawing values. This allows you to know what will or will not receive a centerline regardless of the view scale in the document. For example, if you set a minimum value of 0.50 for the fillet feature, a fillet that has a radius of 0.495 will not receive a center mark. A zero value on both threshold settings (min/max) denotes no restriction. This means that center marks will be placed on all fillets regardless of size.

Arc Angle Threshold

This option sets the minimum angle value for creating a center mark or centerline on circles, arcs, or ellipses.

TIP: Centerlines and center marks can be created in multiple views in one operation by holding down the CTRL key and selecting in the views and then starting the Automated Centerline command. The following image shows centerlines and centers marks added to two views.

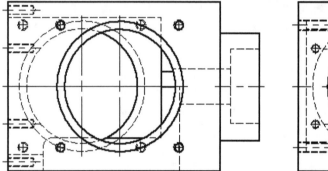 

Figure 5-75

EXERCISE 5-5: ADDING CENTERLINES

In this exercise, you add center marks, and centerlines, and use the Automated Centerlines command to annotate drawing views.

Both model dimensions and drawing dimensions are used to document feature size.

1. Open the drawing *ESS_E05_05.dwg* in the Chapter 05 folder. The drawing file contains four drawing views.

2. In this portion of the exercise you add centerlines and center marks to the top view. Zoom in on the top view.

3. Click the Center Mark command on the Annotate tab > Symbols panel.

4. Select the left outside arc as shown in the following image on the left. Then right-click and click OK from the marking menu.

5. Notice that the centerline does not extend beyond the center of the circle on the right side; this is because the arc is only on the left side. Click and drag on the right side of the centerline so it extends beyond the hidden line as shown in the middle image. A center

mark could have been placed on the hole on the left side and the centerlines extended as needed.

6. Click the Centerline command on the Annotate tab > Symbols panel.

7. Select the two arcs that define the center of the slot in the middle of the part as shown in the image on the right, then right-click and click Create from the marking menu.

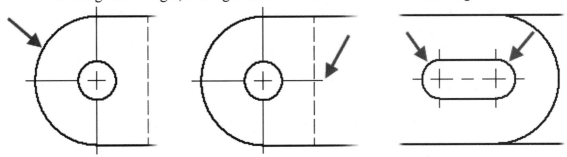

Figure 5-76

8. Next you create a centered pattern (bolt circle) on the right-side of the top view. Click the Centered Pattern command on the Annotate tab > Symbols panel.

9. First select the larger center circle labeled (1) in the following image on the left. The center of this circle will be the center of the centered pattern. Then select the six holes that surround the circle (you can click on the circle or on the circle's center point) and then right-click and click Create from the marking menu. The image on the right shows all the centerlines and center marks in the top view.

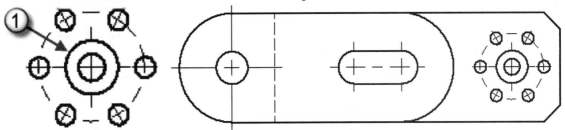

Figure 5-77

10. Pan your screen down so you can see the front view.

11. Click the Centerline Bisector command on the Annotate tab > Symbols panel.

12. In the front view, select the two hidden lines that represent the drilled hole on the left side and the center hole on the right side of the part. When done your screen should be similar to the following image.

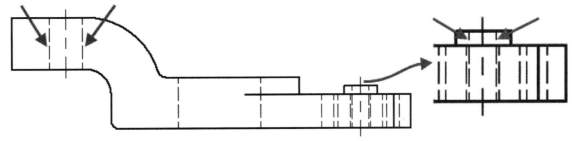

Figure 5-78

13. Close the drawing without saving the changes and reopen it, or undo or delete all the centerlines and center marks in the drawing. In the last portion of this exercise you create centerlines and center marks using the Automated Centerlines command.

14. Hold down the Ctrl key and click in the top, front, and side views and then right-click and click Automated Centerlines from the menu.

15. In the Automated Centerlines dialog box, make the following selections as shown in the following image on the left.

   a. In the Apply To area select; Hole Features, Fillet Features, Cylindrical Features, and Circular Patterned Features.

   b. In the Projection area select both the Objects in View, Axis Normal and the Objects in View, Axis Parallel.

   c. Click OK to create the centerlines. The image on the right shows the three views with the automatic centerlines.

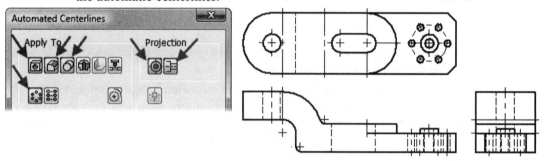

Figure 5-79

16. Zoom in and examine the centerlines that were created. If desired you can resize the centerlines by dragging their endpoints.

17. If the centerline and hidden lines do not display correctly you can adjust the global line scale. To adjust the global line scale, click the Styles Editor command from the Manage tab > Styles and Standards panel.

18. In the Styles and Standard Editor on the left side expand the Standard entry and click Default Standard (ANSI) (the bold text denotes that this is the active standard).

19. On the right side of the dialog box, enter a new value in the Global Line Scale area. To see the change in the centerlines and hidden lines in the graphics window, press Enter on the keyboard and then click the Save button on the top of the dialog box. Try different values, when finished, click Done on the lower right corner of the dialog box. Styles will be covered in later in this chapter.

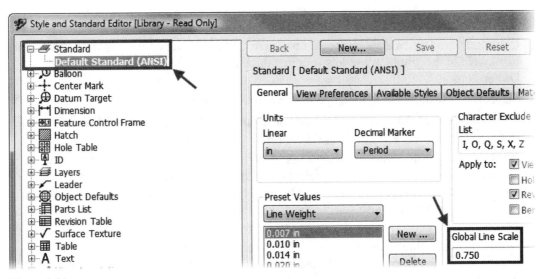

Figure 5-80

20. Close all open files. Do not save changes. End of exercise.

ADDING DIMENSIONS TO A DRAWING VIEW

Once you have created the drawing view(s) and centerlines you mostly likely will add dimensional annotations to the drawing. You may want to alter the model dimensions, hide certain dimensions, add drawing (general) dimensions, or move dimensions to a new location. The following sections describe these operations.

Retrieving Model Dimensions

Model dimensions may not appear automatically when you create a drawing view. You can use the Retrieve Dimensions command to select valid model dimensions for display in a drawing view. Only those dimensions that you placed in the model on a plane parallel to the view will appear.

To activate this command, use one of the following methods:

- Click on the Retrieve Dimensions command on the Annotate tab > Dimension panel as shown in the following image on the left.
- Right-click in a blank area in the graphics window (not in a drawing view), and click Retrieve Dimensions from the marking menu as shown in the image on the right.

The dimensions for the view that were used to create the part will appear.

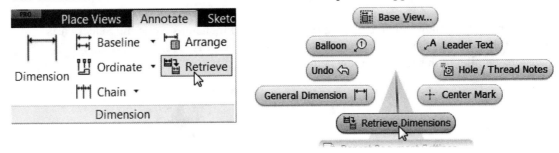

Figure 5-81

To retrieve model dimensions, follow these steps:

1. Click Retrieve Dimensions on the Annotate tab > Dimension panel or right-click in a blank area in the graphics window (not in a drawing view) and click Retrieve Dimensions.

2. Select the drawing view in which to retrieve model dimensions.

3. To retrieve model dimensions based on one or more features, click the Select Features radio button. Then select the desired features.

4. If you want to retrieve model dimensions based on the entire part in a drawing view, click the Select Parts radio button. Then select the desired part or parts. You can select multiple objects by selecting them simultaneously. It is not necessary to hold the SHIFT or CTRL keys. You can also select objects with a selection window or crossing selection box.

5. Or to see all the dimensions that are available in the view, click the Select Dimensions button. If the dimensions were selected with the Feature or the model dimensions appear in the drawing view in preview mode, click the Select Dimensions button, and select the desired dimensions to add to the view. The selected dimensions will be highlighted.

6. Click the Apply button to retrieve the model dimensions, and leave the dialog box active for further retrieval operations.

7. Click the OK button to retrieve the selected dimensions, and dismiss the Retrieve Dimensions dialog box.

The following image shows the effects of retrieving model dimensions using the Select Features mode. In this example, the large rectangle of the engine block was selected. This resulted in the horizontal and vertical model dimensions being retrieved.

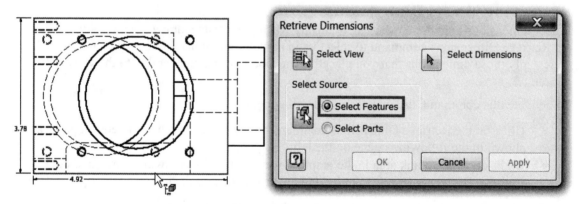

Figure 5-82

The following image shows the result of retrieving model dimensions using the Select Parts option. In this example, the entire engine block was selected. This resulted in all model dimensions parallel to this drawing view being retrieved.

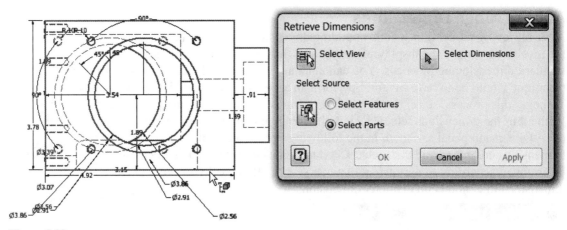

Figure 5-83

Selecting Dimensions – Additional Options

As you annotate a drawing you will need to select multiple dimensions. For example, you would select multiple dimensions to arrange them, or change their dimension styles. To select multiple dimensions you can use the same selection techniques, window, crossing, etc., that you learned about in the Selecting Objects section in Chapter 2. There are additional selection options available in a drawing. To use one of the selection options click the down arrow next to the current selection command on the Quick Access toolbar, as shown in the following image on the left, or press down the Shift key and right-click and click the desired selection option from the menu as shown in the image on the right.

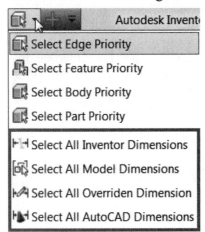
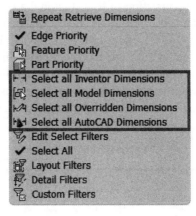

Figure 5-84

Following are explanations for the dimension selection options.

Select All Inventor Dimensions. This option selects all dimensions that are in the current sheet.

Select All Model Dimensions. This option selects all model dimensions that were retrieved in the current sheet.

Select All Overridden Dimensions. This option selects all dimensions whose values have been changed or values are hidden.

Select All AutoCAD Dimensions. This option is only available when working in a DWG file and selects all AutoCAD dimensions in the current sheet.

Auto Arrange Dimensions

After retrieving model dimensions or adding dimensions manually (covered in the next section), the results are usually the display of dimensions that need to be rearranged in order to conform to standard dimensioning practices. You can manually reposition the dimensions or a better technique would be to have Inventor perform an automatic arrangement of the linear dimensions. To begin this process, select the dimensions using any selection technique or selection option. With all of the dimensions selected, click the Arrange Dimensions command from the Annotate tab > Dimension panel as shown in the following image. You can also start the Arrange Dimensions command and then select the dimensions to arrange. The linear and dimensions will be arranged according to the current dimension style. If needed you can manually arrange dimensions like radial and diameter dimensions.

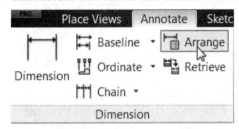

Figure 5-85

Moving and Centering Dimension Text

To move a dimension by either lengthening or shortening the extension lines or moving the text, position the cursor over the dimension until it becomes highlighted, as shown in the following image on the left. An icon consisting of four diagonal arrows will appear attached to your cursor. Notice the appearance of a centerline. This represents the center of the dimension text. You can drag the dimension text up, down, right, or left in order to better position it, re-center the dimension text, drag the text toward the centerline. The dimension will snap to the centerline. In the image on the right, the centerline changes to a dotted line to signify that the dimension text is centered. This centerline action will work on linear dimensions including horizontal, vertical, and aligned but will not be displayed when repositioning the text of radius, diameter, or hole note dimensions.

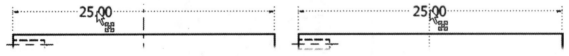

Figure 5-86

Editing a Model Dimension's Value in a Drawing

While working in a drawing view, you may find it necessary to change the model (parametric) dimensions of a part. You can open the part file, change a dimension's value, and save the part, and the change will then be reflected in the drawing views. You can also change a model dimension's value in the drawing view by right-clicking on the dimension and selecting Edit Model Dimension from the menu, as shown in the following image on the left.

The Edit Dimension text box will appear. Enter a new value and click the checkmark, as shown in the image on the right, or press ENTER. The associated part will be updated and saved, and the associated drawing view(s) will be updated automatically to reflect the new value.

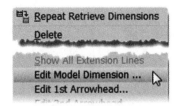

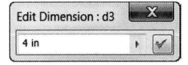

Figure 5-87

 TIP: The function to edit model dimensions in a drawing is an option that can be turned on or off when you install Autodesk Inventor. It is recommended that you make all dimension changes through the part model.

Creating General Dimensions

After laying out the drawing views, you may find that a dimension other than the retrieved model dimension is required to define the part. You can add a general dimension to the drawing view. A general dimension is not a parametric dimension; it is associative to the geometry to which it is referenced. A general dimension reflects the size of the geometry being dimensioned. After you create a general dimension, and the value of the geometry that you dimensioned changes, the general dimension will be updated to reflect the change. You add a general dimension by using the General Dimension command on the Annotate tab > Dimension panel as shown in the following image on the left, right-click in a blank area in the graphics screen and click the General Dimension command from the marking as shown in the image on the right, or press the D key.

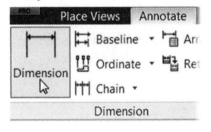 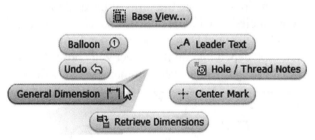

Figure 5-88

The general dimensions you create in a drawing follow a similar process that you did when creating a dimension in a part's sketch, except when a drawing dimension is placed, the Edit Dimension dialog box will appear as shown in the following image. In the Edit Dimension dialog box the <<>> symbols represents that value of the geometry being dimensioned. You can add text or symbols before or after the <<>>. You can also add a tolerance or add an inspection symbol to the dimension from the two other tabs. By default, when a drawing dimension is placed, the Edit Dimension dialog box will appear. You can turn off this behavior by unchecking the Edit dimension when created option at the bottom of the dialog box or from the Application Options > Drawing tab. You can edit an existing drawing dimension by double-clicking on a dimension or right-clicking on a dimension and click Edit from the menu. The Edit Dimension dialog box will appear. Edit the dimension as needed.

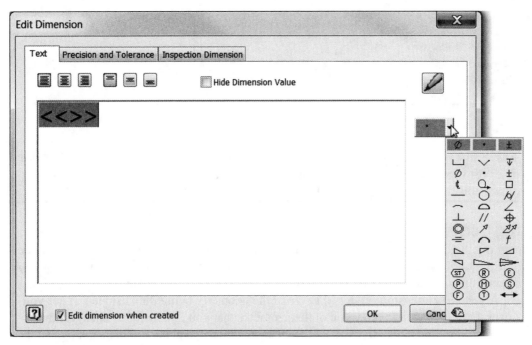

Figure 5-89

Adding General Dimensions to a Drawing View

The following image on the right illustrates a simple object with various dimension types. General dimensions can take the form of linear dimensions labeled (A) and (B), diameter dimensions labeled (C), radius dimensions labeled (D), and angular dimensions labeled (E). When using the General Dimension command, Autodesk Inventor automatically chooses the dimension type depending on the object you chose. In this example, the counterbore hole is dimensioned using the hole note command which will be cover later in this chapter.

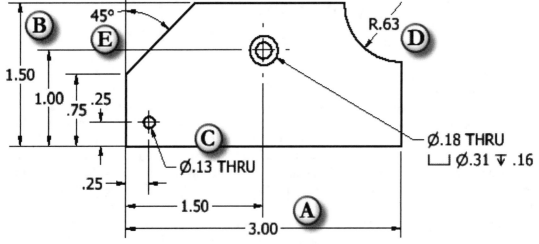

Figure 5-90

Adding Dimensions to Isometric Views

You can retrieve model dimensions or use the General Dimension command to add dimensions to isometric drawing views as well as to standard orthographic views. When placing a dimension on an isometric view, the dimension text, dimension lines, extension lines, and arrows are oblique and aligned to the geometry being dimensioned. The following image shows an isometric view complete with oblique dimensions.

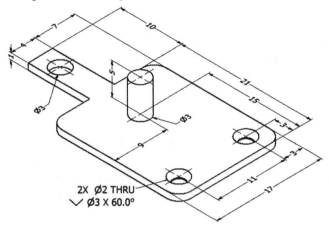

Figure 5-91

Depending on the object being dimensioned, additional controls are available to manipulate the isometric dimension being created. Once edges or points in a drawing are selected, the dimension previews on an annotation plane, as shown in the following image on the left. If more than one annotation plane is possible, you can toggle between these planes by pressing the spacebar before locating the dimension. The image on the right shows the results after pressing the spacebar. Once the dimension is previewed correctly, locate the dimension by clicking.

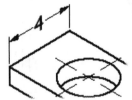

Figure 5-92

EXERCISE 5-6: ADDING DIMENSIONS

In this exercise, you add dimensions to a drawing of a clamp and edit and create a dimensions style.

1. Open the drawing *ESS_E05_06.dwg* in the Chapter 05 folder. The drawing file contains four drawing views with centerlines.

2. In this step, you retrieve model dimensions for use in the drawing view. Begin by zooming in on the front view.

3. Move the cursor outside of a drawing view, right-click and click Retrieve Dimensions from the marking menu. The Retrieve Dimensions dialog box will open.

4. Click in the front view, and in the Retrieve Dimensions dialog box, click the Select Dimensions button. The model dimensions will appear on the view.

5. Drag a selection window around all dimensions. This will select the dimensions to retrieve. When finished, click the OK button. The model dimensions that are planar to the view are displayed, as shown in the following image.

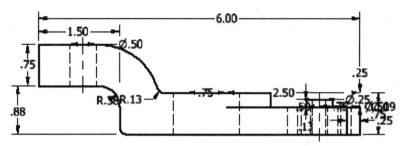

Figure 5-93

6. Instead of manually dragging dimensions to new locations, click the Arrange Dimensions command on the Annotate tab > Dimension panel.

7. Drag a selection window around all dimensions. This will select the dimensions to arrange. When finished, right-click and click OK from the menu. The dimensions are arranged according to the settings in the current dimension style.

8. There are nine dimensions that were retrieved that are not needed. Hold down the Ctrl key and select the nine dimensions that are highlighted in the following image and press the Delete key on the keyboard or right-click and click Delete from the menu. The dimensions that were deleted can be retrieved again if needed.

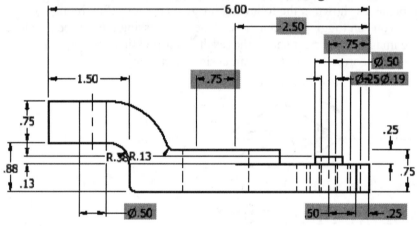

Figure 5-94

9. Use the Arrange Dimensions command again to arrange the dimensions. When done your view should resemble the following image.

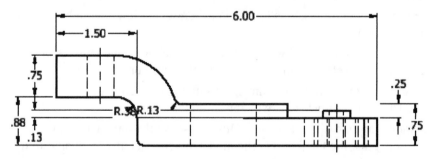

Figure 5-95

10. A few of the dimensions need to be repositioned. Click and drag the highlighted dimensions to locations similar to what is shown in the following image. Note that

additional dimensions could be added to the view as will be described in the next few steps.

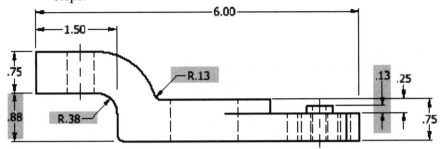

Figure 5-96

TIP: Before you reposition the dimension text, exit the active command.

11. In the top view you could retrieve dimensions but instead you will manually add dimensions to the top view. Pan to display the top view.

12. Click the General Dimension command on the Annotate tab > Dimension panel.

13. Place the nine dimensions as shown in the following image. If needed, you can double-click on a dimension to edit a dimension's text. To change a radius dimension to a diameter dimension or vice versa you must right-click and select the dimension type before the dimension is placed.

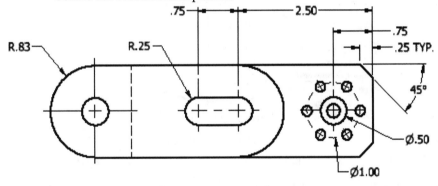

Figure 5-97

14. Next you add text to a dimension. Double-click on the .25 horizontal dimension and then type in **TYP.** after the <<>> as shown in the following image.

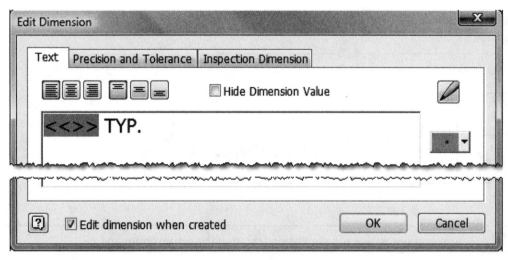

Figure 5-98

15. Next you change a model dimension's value via the drawing. In the front view, right-click on the **6.00** dimension and click Edit Model Dimension from the menu. Enter a value of **7** and then click on the green check mark in the Edit Dimension dialog box.

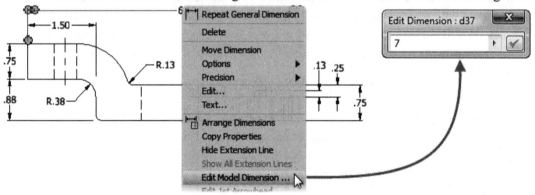

Figure 5-99

16. Notice how the drawing views and dimensions update to reflect the new value.

17. Next you will open the part file and change the horizontal dimension back to its original value. Move the cursor into a blank area in one of the drawing views and click Open from the menu as shown in the following image on the left.

18. Edit Sketch1 under Extrusion1 as shown in the image on the right.

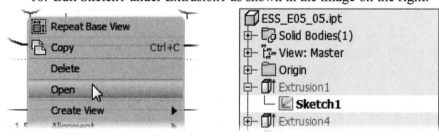

Figure 5-100

19. Double-click on the **7.000** horizontal dimension and enter a value **6** and then press ENTER on the keyboard.

20. Finish the sketch and then save and close the part file.

21. The drawing should be the current file; if not, make it the active file by clicking on the *ESS_E05_06.dwg* tab.

22. The drawing views should update to reflect the updated model.

23. Next you change the dimension style. Move the cursor over any dimension and right-click and click Edit Dimension Style from the menu.

24. In the Style and Standard Editor dialog box the Default (ANSI) style should be current. From the Units tab, change the Precision to 1.1 (represents one decimal place) and in the Display area, check the Leading Zeros option, as shown in the following image, and then click Save on the top of the dialog box.

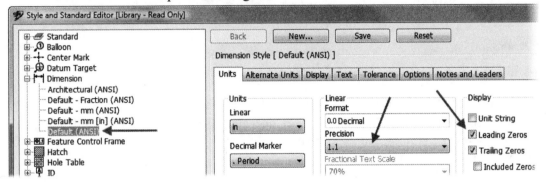

Figure 5-101

25. To close the dialog box, click Done on the bottom-right corner of the dialog box. All the dimensions should update to a single decimal place and a leading zero will be displayed on the dimensions smaller than one inch in length or radius.

26. Next you create a new dimension style. Right-click on the 6.0 horizontal dimension and click New Dimension Style from the menu. The new dimension style will take on the properties of the dimension style of the selected dimension.

27. In the New Dimension Style dialog box in the upper left corner, enter a name for the new style as **3 Decimal (ANSI)**; from the Units tab change the Precision to 3.123. Click OK in the dialog box to create the dimension style.

28. The 6.0 dimension should now be 6.000 but the other dimensions still display a single decimal place. Only the 6.000 dimension is using the new 3 Decimal place dimension style.

29. Next you change a few dimensions to the new style. In the drawing, hold down the CTRL key and select a few dimensions. From the Annotate tab Format panel select the 3 Decimal (ANSI) dimension style from the list as shown in the following image on the left.

TIP: Another option to change dimension properties is to take on the properties of another dimension. To copy properties, right-click on the dimension whose properties you want to copy and click Copy Properties from the menu as shown in the following image on the right. Then select the dimension(s) who you want the properties copied to. You can also right-click and click Settings from the menu and from the Copy Dimension Properties dialog box you can uncheck the properties you do not want copied.

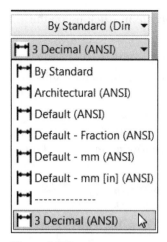

Figure 5-102

30. Practice editing and creating new dimension styles.

31. In Exercise 5-8, you will continue to work on a similar drawing where you will add hole notes, a texture symbol, and a text note.

32. Close all open files. Do not save changes. End of exercise.

Creating Baseline Dimensions

To add multiple general dimensions to a drawing view in a single operation, use the Baseline Dimension command, which will place a baseline dimension about the selected geometry. The dimensions can be either horizontal or vertical. Two commands are available to assist with the creation of these dimensions: Baseline Dimension and Baseline Dimension Set.

Baseline Dimensions

The Baseline Dimension command allows you to create a group of horizontal or vertical dimensions from a common origin. However, the group of dimensions are not considered one group of objects; rather, each dimension that makes up a Baseline Dimension is considered a single dimension.

To create and edit baseline dimensions, follow these steps:

1. Select the Baseline Dimension command from the Annotate tab > Dimension panel as shown in the following image.

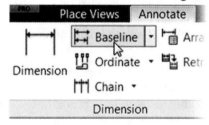

Figure 5-103

2. Individually select or drag a selection window around the geometry that you want to dimension. To window select, move the cursor into position where the first point of the box will be. Press and hold down the left mouse button, and move the cursor so the preview box encompasses the geometry that you want to dimension, as shown in the following image on the left, and then release the mouse button.

3. When you are finished selecting geometry, right-click, and click Continue from the marking menu.

4. Move the cursor to a position where the dimensions will be placed, as shown in the image on the right. When the dimensions are in the correct place, click the point with the left mouse button to anchor the dimensions.

5. To change the origin of the dimensions, move the cursor over the extension line that will be the origin, right-click, and click Make origin from the marking menu.

6. To complete the operation, right-click and click Create from the marking menu.

7. After creating dimensions using the Baseline Dimension command, the same editing operations can be performed on these dimensions as general dimensions. To perform these edits, move the cursor over the baseline dimension, and small green circles will appear on the dimension. Right-clicking will display the menu, as shown in the image on the right.

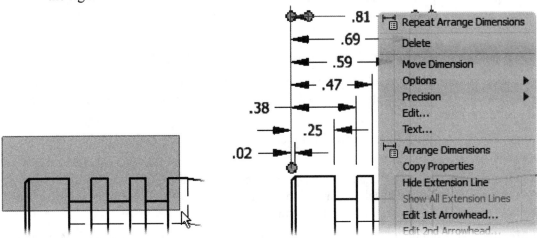

Figure 5-104

Creating a Baseline Set Dimensions

Creating Baseline Set dimensions is similar to the Baseline Dimensions as explained in the previous section, except with the Baseline Set dimension command, the dimensions are grouped together into a set. Select the Baseline Set command from the Annotate tab > Dimension panel by clicking the down arrow next to the Baseline Dimension command, as shown in the following image.

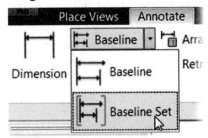

Figure 5-105

Members can be added and deleted from the set, a new origin can be placed, and the dimensions can be automatically rearranged to reflect the change. Right-clicking on any dimension in the set will highlight all dimensions and display the menu, as shown in the following image.

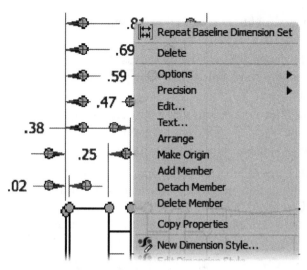

Figure 5-106

The main options for editing a baseline dimension set are described as follows:.

Delete. This option will delete all baseline dimensions in the set. Move your cursor over any dimension in the set. When the green circles appear on each dimension, right-click, and select Delete from the menu.

Arrange. This command will rearrange the dimensions to the spacing defined in the active Dimension Style.

Make Origin. This option will change the origin of the baseline dimensions. Move the cursor over an extension line of the baseline dimension set that you want to define as the new baseline, right-click, and click Make Origin from the menu.

Add Member. This option will add a drawing dimension to the baseline dimensions. Move the cursor over the baseline dimension set, when the green circles appear on the dimensions, right-click and click Add Member from the menu and then click a point that you want to add a dimension to. The dimension will be added to the set of baseline dimensions and rearranged in the proper order.

Detach Member. This option will remove a dimension from the set of baseline dimensions. Move your cursor over any dimension in the set. When the green circles appear on each dimension, right-click on the green circle on the dimension that you want to detach, right-click, and select Detach Member from the menu. The detached dimension can be moved and edited like a normal drawing dimension.

Delete Member. This option will erase a dimension from the set of baseline dimensions. Move your cursor over the dimension in the set that you want to erase, and then select Delete Member from the menu. The dimension will be deleted.

Creating Chain Dimensions
Another option for placing dimensions is to create chain dimensions, dimensions whose extension lines are shared between two dimensions. Chain dimensions can be arranged horizontal or vertical. Like the baseline dimension commands, there are two Chain dimension commands, Chain and Chain Set.

Chain Dimensions

The Chain Dimension command allows you to create a group of horizontal or vertical dimensions. However, the dimensions are not considered one group of objects; rather, each dimension that makes up the chain dimension are considered single dimensions.

To create and chain dimensions, follow these steps:

1. Select the Chain dimension command from the Annotate tab > Dimension panel as shown in the following image.

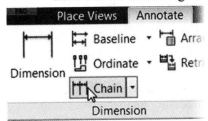

Figure 5-107

2. Individually select or drag a selection window around the geometry that you want to dimension. To window select, move the cursor into position where the first point of the box will be. Press and hold down the left mouse button, and move the cursor so the preview box encompasses the geometry that you want to dimension. The following image on the left shows four objects that were selected.

3. When you are finished selecting geometry, right-click, and click Continue from the marking menu.

4. Move the cursor to a position where the dimensions will be placed and click to anchor the dimensions. The image on the right shows the placed dimensions.

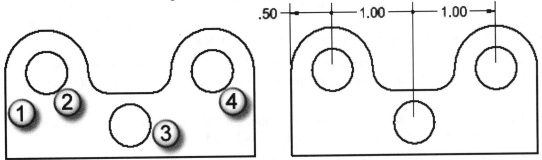

Figure 5-108

5. To complete the operation, right-click and click Create from the marking menu.

6. After creating dimensions using the Chain dimension command, the same editing operations can be performed on these dimensions as general dimensions.

Chain Set Dimensions

Creating a Chain Set dimensions is similar to Chain dimensions as explained in the previous section except with the Chain Set command, however, dimensions are grouped together into a set. Select the Chain Set command from the Annotate tab > Dimension panel by clicking the down arrow next to the Chain dimension command, as shown in the following image.

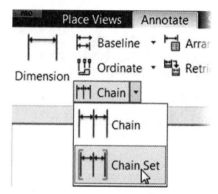

Figure 5-109

Members can be added and deleted from the set. Right-clicking on any dimension in the set will highlight all dimensions and display the menu, as shown in the following image.

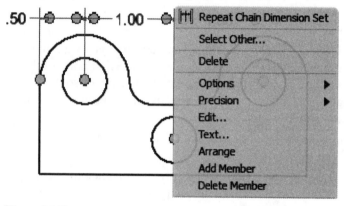

Figure 5-110

The main options for editing a chain dimension set are described as follows:

Delete. This option will delete all chain dimensions in the set. Move your cursor over any dimension in the set. When the green circles appear on each dimension, right-click, and select Delete from the menu.

Options. From the Options area you can lock the chain, control the arrowheads and add a leader to a dimension that the cursor was over when you right-clicked.

Add Member. This option will add a drawing dimension to the chain dimensions. Move the cursor over the chain dimension set, when the green circles appear on the dimensions, right-click and click Add Member from the menu and then click a point that you want to add a dimension to. The dimension will be added to the set of chain dimensions and rearranged in the proper order.

Delete Member. This option will erase a dimension from the set of chain dimensions. Move your cursor over the dimension in the set that you want to delete. When the green circles appear on each dimension, right-click, and then select Delete Member from the menu. The dimension will be deleted.

EXERCISE 5-7: CREATING BASELINE DIMENSIONS AND CHAIN DIMENSIONS

In this exercise, you will add annotations using baseline and chain dimensions.

1. Open *ESS_E05_07.dwg* in the Chapter 05 folder.

2. In this step you add baseline set dimensions. Click the Baseline Set command from the Annotate tab > Dimension panel by clicking the down arrow next to the Baseline Dimension command.

3. Select the three edges as shown in the following image on the left.

4. Right-click, and click Continue from the marking menu.

5. Click a point above the geometry to position the dimension set as shown in the middle image.

6. Right-click, and click Create from the marking menu. The baseline dimension set is created.

7. Next you change the origin for the dimensions to reference the opposite edge of the part. To perform this task, move the cursor over the extension line on the right, right-click, and click Make Origin from the menu. Notice how the dimensions are regenerated from the new origin, as shown in the following image on the right.

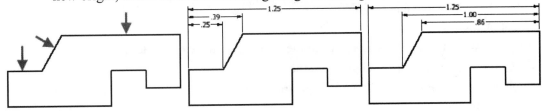

Figure 5-111

8. To add a dimension to the set, move the cursor over the baseline dimension set, when the green circles appear on the dimensions, right-click and click Add Member from the menu and then click the point as shown in the following image on the left. Right-click and click Done from the menu and the dimension will be added to the set and the dimensions will be rearranged as shown in the image on the right.

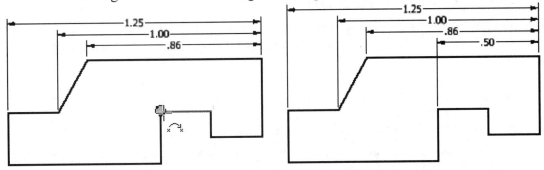

Figure 5-112

9. To delete a dimension from the set, move the cursor over the .86 dimension, right-click and click Delete Member from the menu. The dimension will be deleted as shown in the following image on the left. Notice the dimensions were not automatically arranged.

10. Next you arrange the dimensions, move the cursor over the dimension set, when the green circles appear on the dimension right-click and click Arrange from the menu. The dimensions will be rearranged as shown in the image on the right.

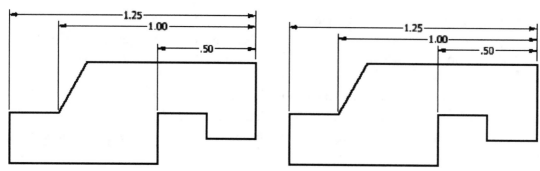

Figure 5-113

11. Next delete the baseline dimension set. Move the cursor over the dimension set, when the green circles appear on the dimensions, right-click and click Delete from the menu. The dimension set will be deleted.

12. Next you create chain set dimensions. Select the Chain Set command from the Annotate tab > Dimension panel by clicking the down arrow next to the Chain dimension command.

13. Window select the edges as shown in the following image on the left.

14. Right-click, and click Continue from the marking menu.

15. Click a point below the geometry to position the chain set as shown in the following image on the right.

16. Right-click, and click Create from the marking menu and the chain set dimensions will be created.

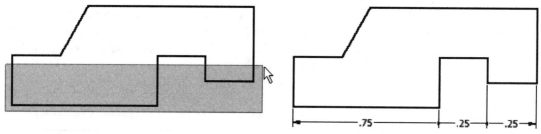

Figure 5-114

17. To add a dimension to the set, move the cursor over the chain set dimensions, when the green circles appear on the dimensions, right-click and click Add Member from the menu and then click the point as shown in the following image on the left.

18. Right-click and click Done from the menu. The dimension will be added to the set and the dimensions will be rearranged as shown in the image on the right.

TIP: If a dimension does not fit within its extension lines, you can right-click on the dimension and from the menu click Options > Leader and then drag the dimension and leader as needed.

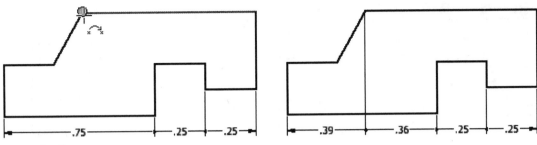

Figure 5-115

19. Delete a dimension, move the cursor over the .39 dimension, right-click, and click Delete Member from the menu.

20. To center the text, right-click on the dimension set and click Arrange from the menu. Notice the dimensions were automatically arranged as shown in the following image.

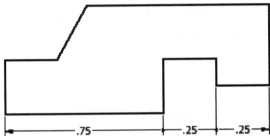

Figure 5-116

21. Practice adding and editing baseline and chain dimensions.

22. Close all open files. Do not save changes. End of exercise.

Creating Ordinate Dimensions

Ordinate dimensions are used to indicate the location of a particular point along the X or Y axis from a common origin point. This type of dimensioning is especially suited for describing part geometry for numerical control tooling operations. Two commands are available for creating ordinate dimensions: Ordinate Dimension and Ordinate Dimension Set. Both commands will create drawing dimensions that reference the geometry and will be updated to reflect any changes in the geometry to which they are dimensioned. Ordinate dimensions can be placed on circular or straight edges.

Ordinate Dimensions

Ordinate dimensions created with the Ordinate Dimension command are recognized as individual objects, and an origin indicator will be created as part of the operation. If the origin indicator location is moved, the other ordinate dimensions will be updated to reflect the change.

To create an ordinate dimension using the Ordinate Dimension command, follow these steps:

1. Create a drawing view.

2. Click the Ordinate Dimension command on the Annotate tab > Dimension panel, as shown in the following image on the left.

3. In the graphics window, select in the view to dimension.

4. Select a point to set the origin indicator for the dimensions (the zero) as shown in the image on the right.

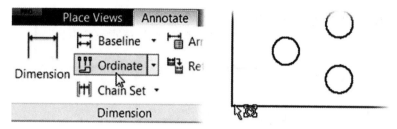

Figure 5-117

5. Select geometry that the ordinate dimensions will be applied to. When done selecting geometry, right-click and click Continue from the marking menu.

6. Locate the dimensions horizontally or vertically by moving the cursor and then click a point when the dimensions are previewed in the correct orientation, as shown in the following image on the left.

7. To create the dimensions and end the operation, right-click, and click OK from the menu.

8. To edit a dimension, right-click on a dimension and click the desired option from the menu, as shown in the following image on the right.

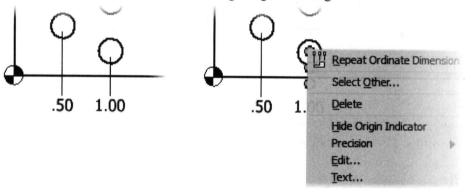

Figure 5-118

9. To move an ordinate dimension, click on the dimension, and then click and drag on an anchor point (a green circle), and drag it to the desired location.

10. To edit the origin indicator, do one of the following:

- Move the cursor over the origin indicator, and drag it to the desired location.
- Double-click the origin indicator, and enter the precise location in the Origin Indicator dialog box.

Ordinate Dimension Set

In an ordinate dimension set, all the ordinate dimensions that are created in a single operation will be grouped together and can be edited individually or as a set. When creating an ordinate dimension set, the first dimension created will be used as the origin. The origin dimension needs to be a member of the set and can later be changed to a different dimension. If the location of the origin or the origin member changes, the other members will be updated to reflect the new location.

When you place ordinate dimensions, they will automatically be aligned to avoid interfering with other ordinate dimensions.

To create an ordinate dimension set, follow these steps:

1. Create a drawing view.

2. Click the Ordinate Dimension Set command on the Annotate tab > Dimension panel by clicking the down arrow next to the Ordinate Dimension command, as shown in the following image on the left.

3. Select a point on the geometry to set the origin for the dimensions, as shown in the following image on the right.

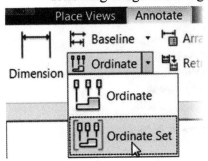
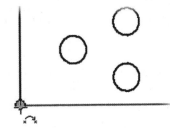

Figure 5-119

4. Select geometry that the ordinate dimensions will be applied to. When done selecting geometry, right-click and click Continue from the marking menu.

5. Locate the dimensions horizontally or vertically by moving the cursor and then click a point when the dimensions are previewed in the correct orientation, as shown in the following image on the left. The image on the right shows the placed dimensions.

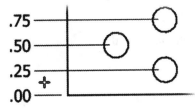
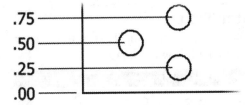

Figure 5-120

6. To change options for the dimension set, right-click, and then click Options, as shown in the following image on the left. This can also be done after creating the dimensions by moving the cursor over the dimension set, right-click and click Options from the marking menu.

7. To create the dimensions set and end the command, right-click, and click Create from the menu.

8. To edit the origin, right-click on the dimension that will be the origin and click Make Origin from the menu as shown in the image on the right. The other dimension values will be updated to reflect the new origin.

9. To edit a dimension set, right-click on a dimension in the set and click the desired option from the menu as shown in the image on the right.

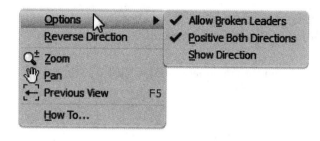

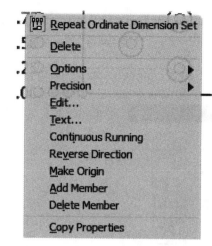

Figure 5-121

ADDING TEXT AND ADDITIONAL SYMBOLS

When documenting a drawing you will need to add additional annotations to describe the design. In this section you learn how to add text and annotation symbols.

Text and Leader Text

To add text to a drawing, click either the Text or the Leader Text command on the Annotate tab > Text panel, as shown in the following image.

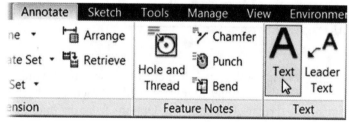

Figure 5-122

The Text command will only add text while the Leader Text command will add a leader with the text. Select the desired text command, and define the leader points and/or text location. Once you have chosen the location in the graphics window, the Format Text dialog box will appear. When placing text through the Format Text dialog box, select the orientation and text style as needed and type in the text, as shown in the following image. Click the OK button to place the text in the drawing. To edit the text or text leader position, move your cursor over it, click one of the green circles that appear, and drag to the desired location. To edit the text or text leader content, right-click on the text, and select Edit Leader Text or Edit Text from the menu.

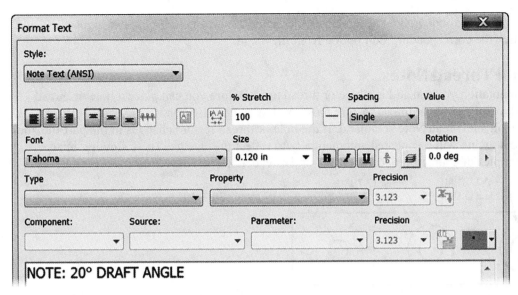

Figure 5-123

Annotation Symbols

To add more detail to your drawing, you can add symbols; surface texture symbols (GD& T), welding symbols, feature control frames, feature identifier symbols, datum identifier symbols, and datum targets by clicking the corresponding command on the Annotate tab > Symbols panel, as shown in the following image. Note that the Import AutoCAD Block command is only available when you are in an Inventor DWG file.

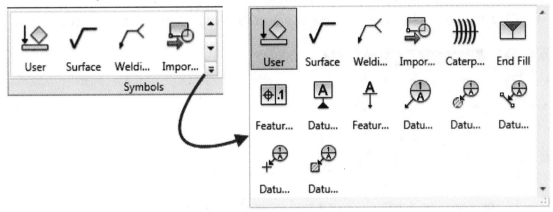

Figure 5-124

Follow these steps for placing symbols:

1. Click the appropriate symbol command on the Annotate tab > Symbols panel.
2. Select a point at which the leader will start. If you don't want a leader, click a point that the symbol will be placed and proceed to step 4.
3. Continue selecting points to position the leader lines.
4. Right-click and click Continue from the marking menu.
5. Fill in the information as needed in the dialog box.
6. When done, click the OK button in the dialog box.
7. To complete the operation, right-click, and click Cancel [ESC] from the marking menu.

---

8. To edit a symbol, move the cursor over it. When the green circles appear, right-click, and click the corresponding Edit option from the menu.

Hole and Thread Notes

Another annotation you can add is a hole or thread note. Before you can place a hole or thread note in a drawing, a hole or thread feature must exist. You can also annotate extruded circles using the Hole or Thread Note command. If the hole or thread feature changes in the part file, the note in the drawing will be updated automatically to reflect the change. The following image shows examples of counterbore, countersink, and threaded/ tapped hole notes.

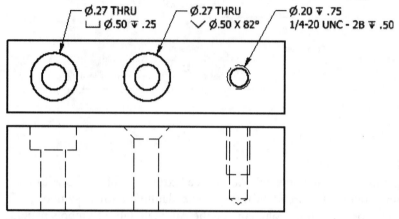

Figure 5-125

To create a hole or thread note, follow these steps:

1. Click the Hole and Thread Notes command on the Annotate tab > Feature Notes panel, as shown in the following image.

Figure 5-126

2. In a drawing view select a hole or thread feature to annotate.
3. Click a second point to locate the leader and the note.
4. To complete the operation, right-click, and select OK from the marking menu.

Editing Hole Notes

To edit a hole note either double-click on an existing hole or right-click on a hole note and click Edit Hole Note from the menu as shown in the following image.

Figure 5-127

The Edit Hole Note dialog box appears; in the dialog box you can add options to the hole note from the Values and Symbols area. For tapped holes you can add information about the tap drill by checking the Tap Drill option on the right side of the dialog box. To add a quantity of the number of holes to the hole note, move the cursor to the beginning or the end of the hole note and then click the # (Quantity Note) in the Values and Symbols area. You can modify how the quantity note is calculated by clicking on Edit Quantity Note in the Options area of the Edit Hole Note dialog box. The following image on the left shows the Tap Drill and Quantity information added in the dialog box and the updated hole note in the image on the right.

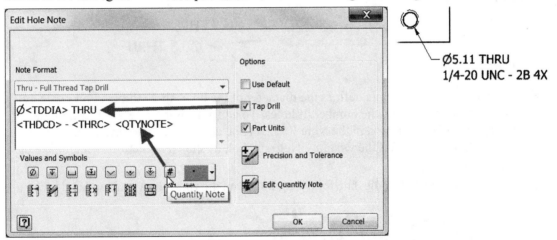

Figure 5-128

EXERCISE 5-8: ADDING ANNOTATIONS

In this exercise, you add hole notes, a surface texture symbol, and a text note.

1. Open the drawing *ESS_E05_08.dwg* in the Chapter 05 folder. The drawing file contains four drawing views with centerlines and dimensions.

2. First you add three hole notes. Begin by zooming in on the top view.

3. Click the Hole and Thread Notes command on the Annotate tab > Feature Notes panel.

4. Select the tapped hole on the left side of the drawing view and click a point to place the hole note, as shown in the following image on the left, and complete the command by right-clicking and click OK in the marking menu.

5. Notice in the hole note that there is no information about the tap drill. To add tap drill information, double-click on the hole note and in the Options area, in the Edit Hole Note dialog box, check the Tap Drill option as shown in the following image on the right.

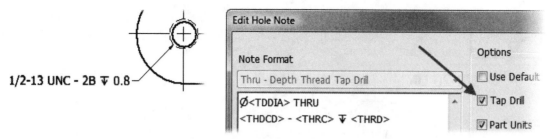

Figure 5-129

6. Click OK to finish the edit. The following image on the left shows the updated hole note.

7. On the right side of the top view, add two hole notes as shown in the following image on the right.

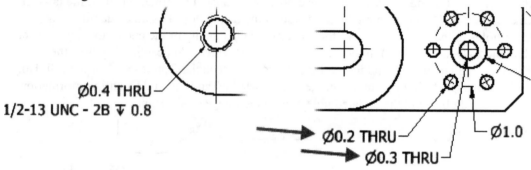

Figure 5-130

8. The Ø0.2 THRU hole note defines the diameter of the holes that fall on a bolt circle but the note does not define the number of holes. To add a quantity note, double-click on the Ø0.2 THRU hole note and in the Note Format area, add a space after the word THRU and then click on #, which is the Quantity Note symbol, as shown in the following image on the left.

9. Click OK to finish the edit. The following image on the right shows the updated hole note.

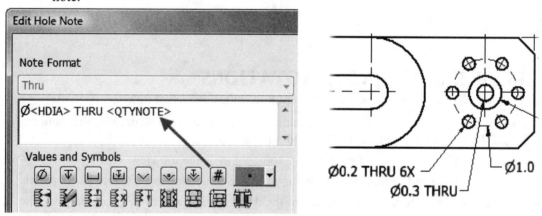

Figure 5-131

10. Next you add a surface finish note. Pan the screen so you can see the front view.

11. Click the Surface Texture Symbol command on the Annotate tab > Symbols panel.

12. Click on the middle horizontal edge of the part as shown in the following image and then right-click and click Continue from the marking menu. Since the symbol will sit on the edge you don't need to click again to create an arrow.

13. In the Surface Texture dialog box enter **32** in the B Production method area as shown in the following image.

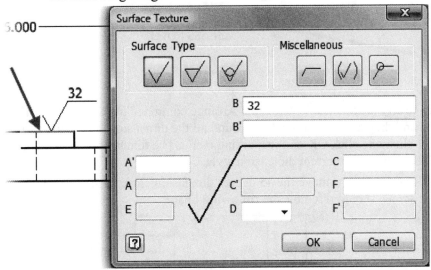

Figure 5-132

14. Click OK to create the surface texture symbol.

15. Next you add a text note. Click the Text command on the Annotate tab > Text panel.

16. To locate the position where the text will start, click on a point below the front view and in the Format Text dialog box enter the text as shown in the following image. To add the ± symbol, select the ± symbol from the Insert symbol area in the dialog box.

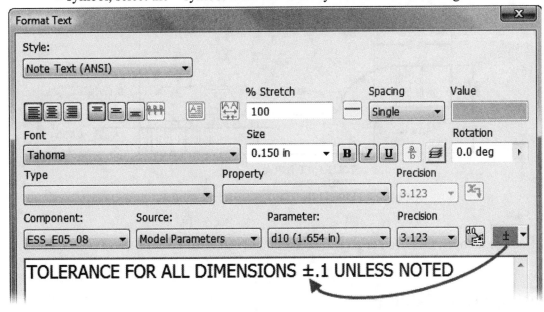

Figure 5-133

17. To place the text, click OK in the dialog box, then right-click and OK on the marking menu.

18. The text is displayed on a single line. To change the text so it appears on multiple lines, click on the text in the graphics window and then click and drag the lower-right green circle of the text's bounding area and drag it to the left as shown in the following image on the left. Release the mouse button and the text will be fitted with the new defined area as shown in the following image on the right.

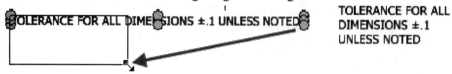

Figure 5-134

19. Lastly, you arrange all the dimensions. Click the Arrange command in the Annotate tab > Dimension panel and drag a selection window around all the dimensions in the top and front views, right-click and click OK on the marking menu. The dimensions are arranged according to the settings in the current dimension style.

20. On the right side of the top view move the 45 degree dimension closer to its geometry. When done, your screen should resemble the following image.

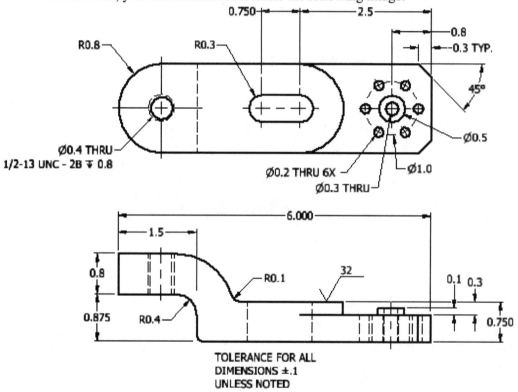

Figure 5-135

21. Close all open files. Do not save changes. End of exercise.

Creating a Hole Table

If the drawing view that you are dimensioning contains holes, you can locate them by placing individual dimensions or by creating a hole table that will list the location and size of all the holes, or just the selected holes, in a view. The hole locations will be listed in both X and Y axis coordinates with respect to a hole datum that will be placed before creating the hole table.

After placing a hole table, if you add, delete, or move a hole, the hole table will automatically be updated to reflect the change after the part is saved and the drawing is the active document. Each hole in the table is automatically given an alphanumeric tag as its name. It can be edited by double-clicking on the tag in the drawing view or hole table. Alternately, you can right-click on the tag in the drawing view or hole table, and select Edit Tag from the menu. Type in a new tag name, and the change will appear in the drawing view and hole table. There are three commands for creating a hole table; Selection, View and Features and are located on the Annotate tab > Table panel, as shown in the following image.

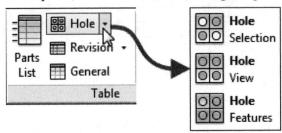

Figure 5-136

Following are descriptions of the hole table commands.

Hole Table - Selection

When using the Hole Table - Selection command, a hole table is created only from selected holes, as shown in the following image.

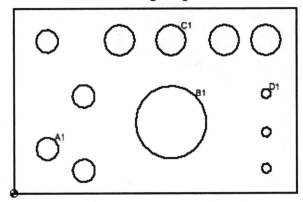

Hole Table			
HOLE	XDIM	YDIM	DESCRIPTION
A1	14.28	18.40	Ø0.38 THRU
B1	66.53	29.23	Ø1.18 THRU
C1	66.53	63.09	Ø0.50 THRU
D1	106.89	40.89	Ø0.16 THRU

Figure 5-137

Hole Table - View

When using the Hole Table - View command, a hole table is created based on all the holes in a selected view, as shown in the following image. Notice that all holes are given an alphanumeric identifier, which locates each hole by X and Y axis coordinates.

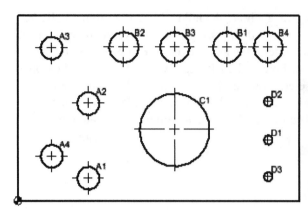

Hole Table			
LOC	XDIM	YDIM	SIZE
A1	29.77	9.39	Ø0.38 THRU
A2	29.77	40.02	Ø0.38 THRU
A3	14.28	62.73	Ø0.38 THRU
A4	14.28	18.40	Ø0.38 THRU
B1	89.23	63.09	Ø0.50 THRU
B2	44.91	63.09	Ø0.50 THRU
B3	66.53	63.09	Ø0.50 THRU
B4	106.89	63.09	Ø0.50 THRU
C1	66.53	29.23	Ø1.18 THRU
D1	106.89	25.12	Ø0.16 THRU
D2	106.89	40.89	Ø0.16 THRU
D3	106.89	10.11	Ø0.16 THRU

Figure 5-138

Hole Table – Selected Features

When using the Hole Table – Selected Features command, a hole table is created based on holes that are identical to the selected hole. The following image shows one of the larger holes, located in the upper part of the object (A4), selected using the Hole Features command.

When the hole table is created, all holes that share the same type and size are added to the hole table, as shown in the following image.

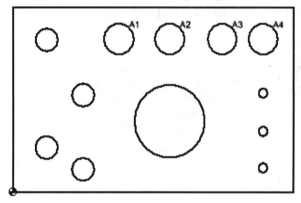

Hole Table			
HOLE	XDIM	YDIM	DESCRIPTION
A1	44.91	63.09	Ø0.50 THRU
A2	66.53	63.09	Ø0.50 THRU
A3	89.23	63.09	Ø0.50 THRU
A4	106.89	63.09	Ø0.50 THRU

Figure 5-139

To create a hole table based on an existing drawing view that contains holes in a plan view, follow these steps:

1. Select the desired Hole Table command from the Hole drop list on the Annotate tab > Table panel.

2. Select the view on which the hole table will be based.

3. Select a point to locate the origin (0,0). Typical origins include the corners of rectangular objects and the centers of drill holes used for data.

4. For the Hole Selection and the Hole Features commands select the hole(s) on which to base the hole table on and then right-click and click Create from the marking menu.

5. Click a point in the drawing to locate the table.

6. The contents of the hole table can be edited by either double-clicking or right-clicking on the hole table and click Edit Hole Table from the menu.

EXERCISE 5-9: CREATING HOLE TABLES

In this exercise, you create a hole table for a shim plate. After creating the hole table, you will modify the plate model to add new holes and update the hole table accordingly.

1. Open the drawing file *ESS_E05_09.idw* in the Chapter 05 folder.

2. To create the hole table, Click the Hole Table – View command from the Annotate tab > Table panel by clicking the down arrow next to Hole and click the Hole Table - View command.

3. Click the front view of the plate as the view to which the hole table will be associated.

4. To place the hole table datum (0,0), acquire the theoretical intersection of the lower left corner of the front view by moving the cursor over the bottom horizontal and left vertical line until the intersection is displayed and then click, as shown in the following image on the left.

5. Then place the hole table on the right side of the sheet as shown in the following image on the right.

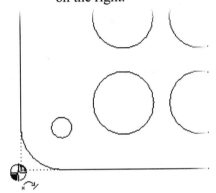

HOLE TABLE			
HOLE	XDIM	YDIM	DESCRIPTION
A1	.25	.25	Ø0.13 THRU
B1	.63	.39	Ø0.38 THRU
B2	1.10	.39	Ø0.38 THRU
B3	1.57	.39	Ø0.38 THRU
B4	2.05	.39	Ø0.38 THRU
B5	2.52	.39	Ø0.38 THRU
B6	.63	.91	Ø0.38 THRU
B7	1.10	.91	Ø0.38 THRU
B8	1.57	.91	Ø0.38 THRU
B9	2.05	.91	Ø0.38 THRU
B10	2.52	.91	Ø0.38 THRU
C1	.38	2.00	Ø0.25 THRU
C2	2.75	2.00	Ø0.25 THRU

Figure 5-140

6. The top two holes in the plate need to be changed to Spotface holes. Open the part file by right-clicking in the front view and click Open from the menu as shown in the following image.

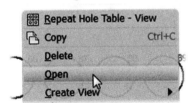

Figure 5-141

7. In the browser double-click the Hole1 feature.

8. In the Hole dialog box, change the hole type to Spotface and change the hole specifications, as shown in the following image on the left. To update the hole features click OK in the dialog box.

9. Save the part file.

10. Make the drawing file current by clicking the tab labeled *ESS_E05_09.idw* near the bottom of the screen. Note the updated hole table; the holes labeled with the letter C reflect the change to the holes, as shown in the following image on the right.

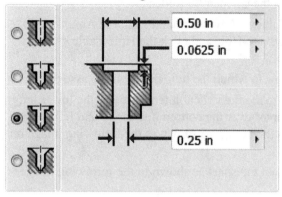

HOLE TABLE			
HOLE	XDIM	YDIM	DESCRIPTION
A1	.25	.25	⌀0.13 THRU
B1	.63	.39	⌀0.38 THRU
B2	1.10	.39	⌀0.38 THRU
B3	1.57	.39	⌀0.38 THRU
B4	2.05	.39	⌀0.38 THRU
B5	2.52	.39	⌀0.38 THRU
B6	.63	.91	⌀0.38 THRU
B7	1.10	.91	⌀0.38 THRU
B8	1.57	.91	⌀0.38 THRU
B9	2.05	.91	⌀0.38 THRU
B10	2.52	.91	⌀0.38 THRU
C1	.38	2.00	⌀0.25 THRU ⌴ ⌀0.50
C2	2.75	2.00	⌀0.25 THRU ⌴ ⌀0.50

Figure 5-142

11. Two countersink mounting holes needs to be created in the part file. Make the part file *ESS_E05_09.ipt* current by clicking on its tab.

12. Add two countersink through all holes using the specifications shown in the following image by creating a sketch, adding and constraining two center points and placing the holes on the points.

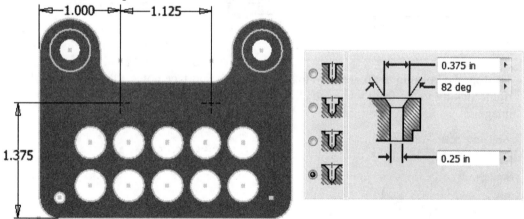

Figure 5-143

13. Save the part file.

14. Make the file *ESS_E05_09.idw* current. Notice that the new holes have automatically been added to the hole table as shown in the following image.

C2	2.75	2.00	⌀0.25 THRU ⌴ ⌀0.50
D1	1.00	1.38	⌀0.25 THRU ∨ ⌀0.38 X 82°
D2	2.13	1.38	⌀0.25 THRU ∨ ⌀0.38 X 82°

Figure 5-144

15. A hole tag will now be modified. Move the cursor over the tag A1 on the drawing view, then click on the green circle (location where the tag is attached to the geometry) and drag and position the A1 hole tag, as shown in the following image on the left.

16. Next double-click on the A1 tag to open the Format Text dialog box, add the text " - **TOOLING HOLE**" after A1 to the hole tag, and click OK. The tag updates as shown in the image on the right.

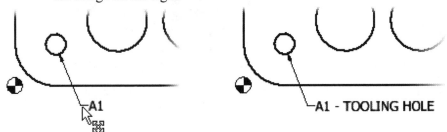

Figure 5-145

17. The hole table updates to include – TOOLING HOLE after A1. You can also resize the hole table columns by clicking and dragging on a table border, as shown in the following image.

HOLE TABLE			
HOLE	XDIM	YDIM	DESCRIPTION
A1 - TOOLING HOLE	.25	.25	⌀0.13 THRU
B1	.63	.39	⌀0.38 THRU

Figure 5-146

18. If desired, you can combine the descriptions that are identical in the hole table. Combine the descriptions by right-clicking on the hole table and click Edit Hole Table from the menu. In the Edit Hole Table dialog box, on the Options tab, select the Combine Notes option and click OK in the dialog box.

19. Close all open files. Do not save changes. End of exercise.

SHORTCUT FOR OPENING REFERENCED FILES

To prevent laborious searches to open referenced part, assembly, presentation or drawing files, you can open the file directly from within the file they are referenced.

Opening a Model File from a Drawing

While working inside of a complex drawing view, you may need to make changes to a part, assembly, or presentation file. Rather than starting the open command and searching for the part, assembly, or presentation file, you can open them directly from the drawing that they are referenced. The part, assembly or presentation file must have the same name as the drawing file. There are multiple techniques to do this.

- One technique is to right-click in a drawing view to display the menu as shown in the following image on the left, and then click Open to open the part file. In this example, an assembly file was opened from the drawing view.
- Another technique involves expanding the drawing view in the browser to expand the assembly and continue expanding the browser until the file you want to open is visible in

the list. Right-click the desired file in the browser and select Open from the menu to display the part model as shown in the following image on the right.

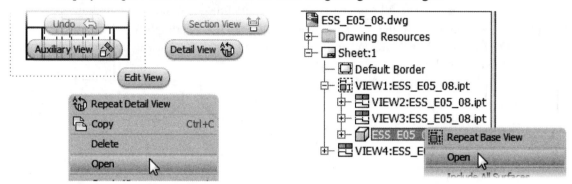

Figure 5-147

Opening a Drawing from a Model File

You can open a drawing from a part, assembly, or presentation file by right-clicking on the part, assembly presentation file name and clicking Open Drawing from the menu as shown in the following image. This will open the drawing file associated with the file. The drawing file must have the same name as the part, assembly or presentation file.

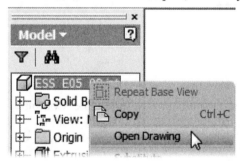

Figure 5-148

APPLYING YOUR SKILLS

Skills Exercise 5-1

In this exercise, you create a drawing of a part.

1. Create a new drawing based on the English ANSI (in).idw template.
2. Change the sheet size to A.
3. Create drawing views from the file *ESS_Skills_5-1.ipt* from the Chapter 05 folder. Use a scale of 1:1 for all views.
4. Add centerlines, dimensions, and hole notes.
5. When done your drawing should resemble the following image.

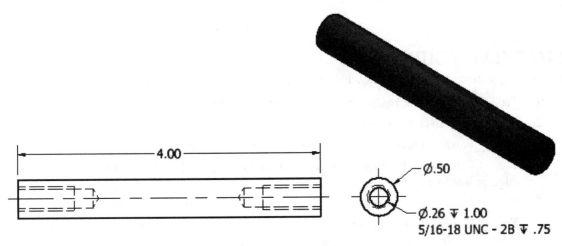

Figure 5-149

Skills Exercise 5-2

In this exercise, you create a drawing for a drain plate cover.

1. Create a new drawing using an English ANSI (in).dwg template.

2. Change the sheet size to A.

3. Create three views of the part *ESS_Skills_5-2*.ipt located in the Chapter 05 folder. Use a scale of 1:1 for all views.

4. Add center marks to the views.

5. Change the Default (ANSI) dimension style as follows:

    a. Set the length that the extension line extends beyond the dimension leader line to **.0625 inches**.

    b. Set the precision to **3.123** (three decimal places).

    c. Set text height to **.100 inches**.

6. Add dimensions and annotations.

7. When done your drawing views should resemble the following image.

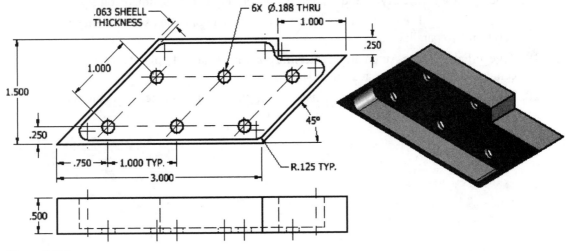

Figure 5-150

CHECKING YOUR SKILLS

Use these questions to test your knowledge of the material covered in this chapter.

1. True__ False__ A drawing can have an unlimited number of sheets.
2. Explain how to change a sheet's size.
3. True__ False__ There can only be one base view per sheet.
4. True__ False__ An inclined view is a view that is projected perpendicular to a selected edge or line in a view.
5. True__ False__ An isometric view can only be projected from a base view.
6. True__ False__ A section view is a view created by sketching a line or multiple lines that will define the plane(s) that will cut through a part or assembly.
7. True__ False__ Drawing dimensions can drive dimensional changes parametrically back to the part.
8. Explain how to shade an isometric drawing view.
9. True__ False__ When creating a hole note using the Hole and Thread Notes command, circles that are extruded to create a hole can be annotated.
10. While in a drawing file, explain how to open the part file that is referenced in the drawing.
11. True__ False__ When you create a title block in a drawing, the new title block will automatically be written back to the template file.
12. True__ False__ When creating a section view that goes through a slot at an angle, you use the projected option to prevent the slot from being distorted.
13. True__ False__ A hatch pattern in a section view is changed via the Document Settings.
14. True__ False__ Before creating a section view, you must first create a work plane in the part file that the section will be based on.
15. True__ False__ When creating a Detail View you can use a circular or rectangular fence.
16. True__ False__ Use the Break Out command to remove a middle section from a drawing view of long part.
17. True__ False__ The Styles and Standards Editor only controls dimension styles.
18. True__ False__ The Centerline Bisector command can only be used to create a centerline between two parallel edges.
19. True__ False__ The Automatic Centerline command can only place centerlines and center marks in one view at a time.
20. True__ False__ After placing dimensions with the Baseline Dimension command you cannot change the origin.

Chapter 6 – Creating and Documenting Assemblies

INTRODUCTION

In the first four chapters, you learned how to create a component in its own file. In this chapter, you will learn how to place individual component files into an assembly file. You will also learn to create components in the context of the assembly file. After creating components, you will learn how to constrain the components to one another using assembly constraints, edit the assembly constraints, check for interference, and create presentation files that show how the components are assembled or disassembled. Manipulating and editing a Bill of Materials (BOM) is also discussed, including the placement of a Parts List and identifying balloons.

OBJECTIVES

After completing this chapter, you will be able to:

- ☐ Understand the assembly options
- ☐ Place components into an assembly
- ☐ Create components and assemblies
- ☐ Constrain components together using assembly constraints
- ☐ Edit assembly constraints
- ☐ Use assembly joints to control the location and motion of components
- ☐ Pattern components in an assembly
- ☐ Check parts in an assembly for interference
- ☐ Drive constraints
- ☐ Create a presentation file
- ☐ Create drawing views from an assembly or presentation file
- ☐ Manipulate and edit the Bill of Materials (BOM)
- ☐ Create individual and automatic balloons
- ☐ Create and perform edits on a parts list in a drawing

ASSEMBLY OPTIONS

Before creating an assembly, review the assembly option settings. On the Tools tab > Options panel click Application Options, and the Application Options dialog box will appear. Click on the Assembly tab, as shown in the following image. Consult the help system for information about the Assembly Application Options. These settings are global and will affect how new components are created, referenced, analyzed, or placed in the assembly.

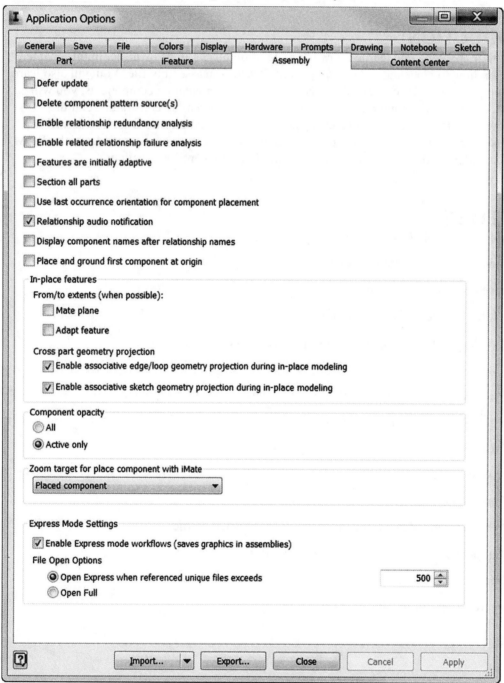

Figure 6-1

CREATING ASSEMBLIES

As you have already learned, part files have the .ipt extension, and only consist of a single component. In this chapter, you will learn how to create an assembly file (.iam file extension) where multiple part files are assembled together. All of the components in an assembly are referenced in, meaning that each component exists in its own component .ipt file, and its definition is linked into the assembly. You can edit the components while in the assembly, or you can open the component file and edit it. When you have made changes to a component and saved the component, the changes will be reflected in the assembly after you open or update it. There are three methods for creating assemblies: bottom-up, in-place, and a combination of both. Bottom-up refers to an assembly in which all of the components were created in individual component files and are referenced into the assembly. The in-place approach refers to an assembly in which the components are created from within the context of the assembly. In other words, the user creates each component from within the top-level assembly. Each component in the assembly is saved to its own .ipt file. The following sections describe the bottom-up and in-place assembly techniques.

Note that assemblies are not made up only of individual parts. Complex assemblies are typically made up of subassemblies, and therefore you can better manage the large amount of data that is created when building assemblies.

To create a new assembly file use one of the following methods:

- From the Quick Access toolbar click the down arrow on the right side of the New icon and click Assembly from the drop list as shown in the following image on the left.
- Click Assembly on the Home page as shown in the middle image.
- From the Inventor Application menu click New > Assembly as shown in the image on the right.

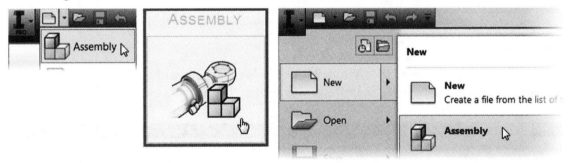

Figure 6-2

You can also create an assembly file from a template that is not the default by clicking the New file command from one of these areas:

- Quick Access toolbar as shown in the following image on the left.
- Inventor Application menu, as shown in the following image, second on the left.
- Get Started tab > Launch Panel as shown in the following image, third from the left.
- On the Home page, as shown in the following image, on the right.
- Or press CTRL + N.

Figure 6-3

The Create New File dialog box appears, click the desired template folder on the left side of the dialog box, and in the Assembly – Assemble 2D and 3D components area, click the desired template file as shown in the following image.

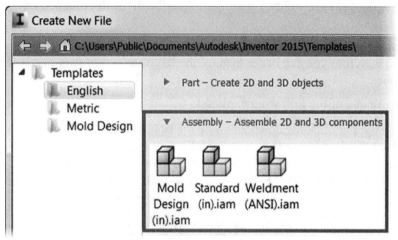

Figure 6-4

After creating a new assembly file, Autodesk Inventor's commands will change to reflect the Assembly environment as shown in the following image. The assembly commands are covered throughout this chapter.

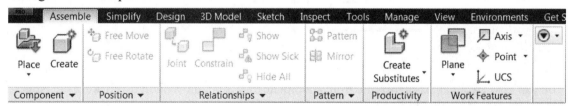

Figure 6-5

In the next sections you will learn approaches to creating an assembly. You can place existing components into an assembly, create a component in the context of the assembly, or use a combination of both techniques. With experience, you will determine which method works best for the assembly that you are creating. Whether you place components into an assembly or create components in the assembly, all of the components will be saved to their own individual .ipt files, and the assembly will be saved as an .iam file.

Placing Components

To place a component(s) you first create the components in their individual files and then place them into an assembly. If you place an assembly file into another assembly, it will be brought in as a subassembly. Be sure to include the path(s) for the file location(s) of the placed components in the project file; otherwise, Autodesk Inventor may not be able to locate the referenced component when you reopen the assembly.

To insert a component into the current assembly follow one of these techniques to start the Place Component command:

- Click the Place Component command on the Assemble tab > Component panel as shown in the following image on the left.
- Right-click in the graphics window and click Place Component from the marking menu as shown in the following image on the right.
- Press the shortcut key P.

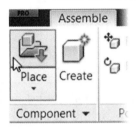
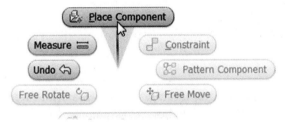

Figure 6-6

After starting the Place Component command, the Place Component dialog box appears as shown in the following image. Select the component to place and then either double-click or click the Open button in the dialog box. You can also select multiple components by holding down the CTRL or SHIFT key and select the components from the list and then click the Open button.

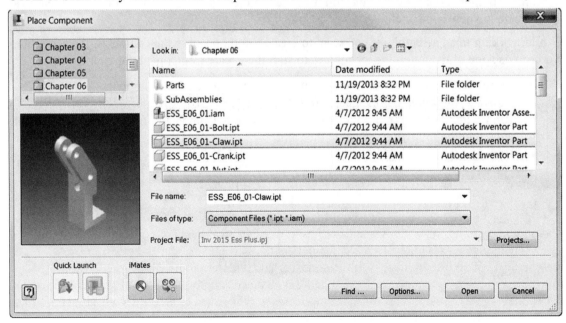

Figure 6-7

After selecting a component(s) and either double-clicking or pressing Open in the Place Components dialog box, the component(s) will be previewed in the graphics window. Before placing the component(s) you can rotate the component about the X, Y or Z axis (based on the coordinates of the component and not the assembly's coordinates) or ground the component at the origin (lock it from moving) by right-clicking and click an option from the marking menu as shown in the following image. If the Place Grounded at Origin option is selected the components you are inserting will be placed in the assembly and grounded. If you need multiple occurrences of the component in the assembly, continue selecting placement points. If the Place Grounded at Origin option is not selected, select placement points. When done, press the ESC key or right-click and click OK from the menu. To ground a component after it is placed, right-click on the component and click Grounded from the menu.

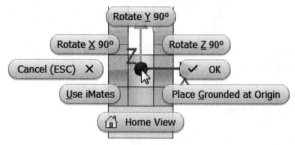

Figure 6-8

 TIP: When placing or creating components in an assembly, it is recommended to list them in the order in which they are assembled. To reorder a component, in the browser click and drag on a component to move it up or down.

Creating a Component in an Assembly

Most components in the assembly environment are created in relation to existing components in the assembly. When creating an in-place component, you can sketch on the face of an existing assembly component or a work plane and if desired, project geometry from another component to help create the new component.

While working in an assembly, if you want to create a component in the context of the assembly, you can use one of the following techniques to start the Create Component command:

- Click the Create Component command on the Assemble tab > Component panel as shown in the following image on the left.
- Right-click in the graphics window and click Create Component from the marking menu shown in the following image on the right.
- Press the shortcut key N.

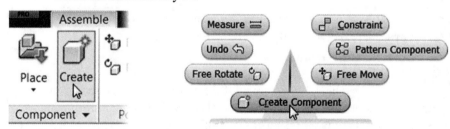

Figure 6-9

After starting the Create Component command the Create In-Place Component dialog box appears as shown in the following image. Enter the following information in the dialog box.

- Enter a name for the file.
- Select the desired template.

- Select the location where the file will be saved.
- Select the BOM (bill of material) structure.
- To sketch on an existing plane of a part in the assembly keep the Constrain sketch plane to selected face or plane option checked.

Then click OK; if the Constrain sketch plane to selected face or plane option is checked select on a planar face or work plane to constrain the part to and the new part is created. The browser and ribbon switch to the part environment even though you are in an assembly.

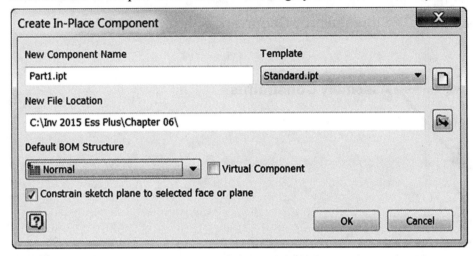

Figure 6-10

Notice that the 3D Model tab is current, as shown in the following image and the component is nested in the browser. You can create the part using the processes previously described in the book including the ability to project edges from other components.

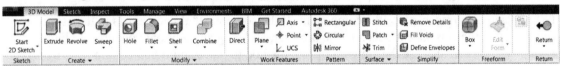

Figure 6-11

When finished modeling the part, you can return to the top level assembly by double-clicking the assembly name in the browser or clicking the Return command on the 3D Model tab > Return panel. The Return command will be described in the upcoming Editing a Component in Place section.

The assembly environment will become active, here you can assemble the components and analyze the assembly which will be covered through the remainder of this chapter.

The Assembly Browser

While in an assembly, the browser displays the hierarchy of the part occurrences, subassembly occurrences, and assembly constraints that make up the assembly, as shown in the following image. Each occurrence of a component is represented by a unique name. In the browser, you can select a component for editing, move components between assembly levels, reorder assembly components, control component status, rename components, edit assembly constraints, and manage design views and representations.

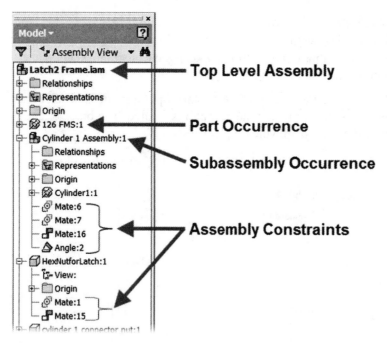

Figure 6-12

Occurrences

An occurrence is a copy of an existing component that has the same name as the original component with a colon and a sequenced number. For example, after placing a component named Bracket it will be the first occurrence and in the browser it will be labeled Bracket:1 and a subsequent occurrence will be Bracket:2, as shown in the following image. If the original component changes, all of the component occurrences will update to reflect the change.

To create an occurrence, place the component. If the component already exists in the assembly, you can click the component's icon in the browser, and drag an additional occurrence into the assembly. You can also use the copy-and-paste method to place additional components by right-clicking on the component name in the browser, or on the component in the graphics window, and then click Copy from the menu. Then right-click and click Paste from the menu. You can also use the Windows shortcuts CTRL-C and CTRL-V to copy and paste the selected component.

If you want an occurrence of the original component to have no relationship with its source component, make the original component active, use the Save Copy As command by clicking the Inventor Application menu > Save As > Save Copy As and enter a new name. The new component will have no relationship to the original, and then place it in the assembly using the Place Component command.

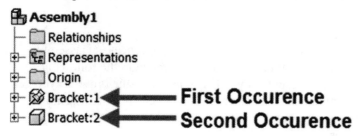

Figure 6-13

The Assembly Capacity Meter

To provide feedback on the resources used by an assembly model, use the Assembly Capacity Meter. This meter is located in the lower-right corner of the screen and is present only in the assembly environment. Two types of information are displayed in the status bar of this meter. The first set of numbers reflects the number of occurrences in the active assembly and the second set of numbers displays the total number of files (also referred to as Documents) open in Inventor.

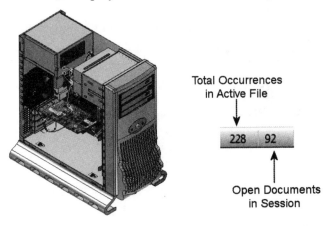

Figure 6-14

Editing a Component in Place

To edit a component while in an assembly, activate the component. Only one component in the assembly can be active at a time. To make a component active, double-click on the component in the graphics window, or double-click on the file name or icon in the browser. Alternately, right-click on the component name in the browser or graphics window and click Edit from the menu. Once the component is active, the other components in the browser will appear shaded, as shown in the following image. In the graphics window the non-active components will appear faded if the Component Opacity option in Application Options > Assembly tab is set to Active Only.

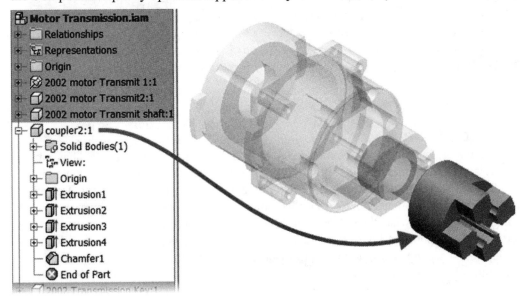

Figure 6-15

When the component is active you can edit the component as normal. If you save the file while in the editing mode, only the active component will be saved. To return to the assembly environment, click the Return button on the 3D Model panel > Return panel as shown in the following image on the left. You can also double-click on the assembly name in the browser or right-click in the graphics window and select Finish Edit from the marking menu as shown in the following image on the right. Under the Return button there are two other commands, as shown in the middle image; Return to Parent will return you up one level (from the part level to the part subassembly) and Return to Top will return you to the top level in the browser no matter how deep you are in the browser tree.

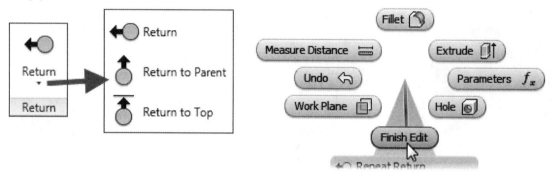

Figure 6-16

Opening a Component in an Assembly

Another way to edit a component in the assembly is to open the component file in another window by right-clicking on the component in the graphics window and click Open from the marking menu, as shown in the following image on the left, or right-click on the component's name in the browser and click Open from the menu as shown in the image on the right. The component will open in a new window. Edit the component as needed, save the changes, activate the assembly file, and the changes will appear to the component(s) in the assembly.

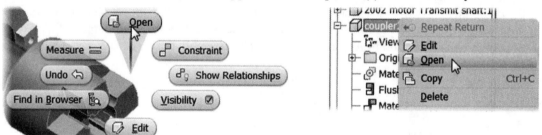

Figure 6-17

Grounded Component

When assembling components it is recommended to have at least one component or subassembly grounded so it is stationary, meaning that it will not move. When applying assembly constraints, the ungrounded and unconstrained components will move to the grounded component. There is no limit to how many components can be grounded but usually only one component in the assembly is grounded; otherwise, the entire assembly can move. A grounded component is represented with a pushpin superimposed on its icon in the browser, as shown in the following image on the left. To ground or unground a component, right-click on the component's name in the browser, and select or deselect Grounded from the menu, as shown in the following image on the right.

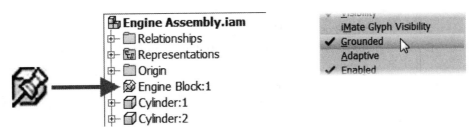

Figure 6-18

Degrees of Freedom (DOF)

You have learned how to create an assembly but the components have no relationship to one another except for the relationship that was defined when you created a component from the context of an assembly and in reference to a face on another component. For example, if you placed a bolt in a hole and the hole moved, the bolt would not move to the new hole position. You apply assembly constraints to create relationships between components. With the correct constraint(s) applied, components will move as the parts changes. From the previous example, if an insert constraint is applied between the hole and the bolt and the hole is edited to a new location, the bolt will move to the new location of the hole.

In Chapter 2, you learned about constraints that apply geometric constraints to sketches and reduce the number of dimensions or constraints required to fully constrain a profile. When you apply assembly constraints, they reduce the degrees of freedom (DOF) that allow the components to move freely in space.

There are six degrees of freedom: three are translational and three are rotational. Translational means a component can move along an X, Y, or Z axis. Rotational means that a component can rotate about an X, Y, or Z axis. As you apply assembly constraints, the number of degrees of freedom decreases.

To see a graphical display of the degrees of freedom remaining on all of the components in an assembly, select the Degrees of Freedom command on the View tab > Visibility panel as shown in the following image on the left. The image on the right shows the resulting symbols visible on the components in the assembly.

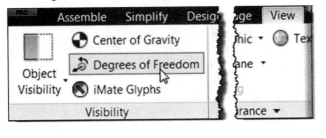
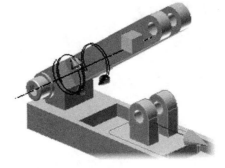

Figure 6-19

An icon will appear in the center of the component that shows the remaining degrees of freedom. The line and arrows represent translational freedom, and the arc and arrows represent rotational freedom. To turn off the DOF icons, again click Degrees of Freedom on the View menu.

ADDING ASSEMBLY CONSTRAINTS

When constraining components to one another, you will need to understand the terminology. The following terminology is used with assembly constraints:

Line. This can be the centerline of an arc, a circular edge, a cylindrical surface, a selected edge, a work axis, or a sketched line.

Normal. This is a vector that is perpendicular to a planar face.

Plane. This can be defined by the selection of a plane or face to include the following: two non-collinear but coplanar lines or axes, three points, or one line or axis and a point that does not lie on the line or axis. When you use edges and points to select a plane, this creates a work plane, and it is referred to as a construction plane.

Point. This can be an endpoint or midpoint of a line, the center or end of an arc or circular edge, or a vertex created by the intersection of an axis and a plane or face.

Offset. This is the distance between two selected lines, planes, or points, or any combination of the three.

Autodesk Inventor does not require components to be fully constrained. As discussed earlier, it is recommended to ground a component then other components will move in relation to the grounded component.

Assembly Constraint Command

Autodesk Inventor uses five types of assembly constraints (mate, angle, tangent, insert, and symmetry), two types of motion constraints (rotation and rotation-translation), a transitional constraint, and a constraint set. You can access the constraints through the Constrain command found on the Assemble tab > Relationships panel as shown in the following image on the left, by right-clicking and clicking Constraint from the marking menu as shown in the middle image, or by using the C key.

The Place Constraint dialog box appears, as shown in the following image on the right. The dialog box is divided into four areas, which are described in the following sections. Depending upon the constraint type, the option titles may change.

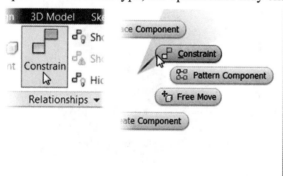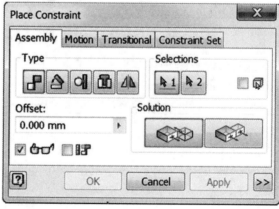

Figure 6-20

Assembly Tab Options

Type. Select the type of assembly constraint to apply: mate, angle, tangent, insert or symmetry.

Selections. Click the button with the number 1, and select a component's edge, face, point, and so on, on which to base the constraint type. Then click the button with the number 2, and select a component's edge, face, point, and so on, on which to base the constraint type. By default, the second arrow will become active after you have selected the first input.

Color-coding is also available to assist with the assembly process. For example, when picking a face with the number 1 button, the color blue is associated with this selection. In the same way, the color green is associated with the number 2 button selection. This schema allows you to better recognize the selections, especially if they need to be edited.

You can edit an edge, face, point, and so on, of an assembly constraint that has already been applied by clicking the number button that corresponds to the constraint and then selecting a new edge, face, point, and so on. While working on complex assemblies, you can click the box on the right side of the Selections section called Pick part first. If the box has a check, select the component before selecting a component's edge, face, point, and so on.

Offset/Angle. Enter or select a value for the offset or angle. The Offset option changes to Angle when the Angle constraint is being applied.

Solution. Select how the constraint will be applied; when two planar faces are selected, the surface normals will be pointing in the same or opposing direction.

Show Preview. Click, and when constraints are applied to two components, you will see the under-constrained components previewed in their constrained positions. If you leave the box clear, you will not see the components assembled until you click the Apply button.

Predict Offset and Orientation. Click to display the existing offset distance between two components. This allows you to accept this offset distance or enter a new offset distance in the edit box.

Motion Tab
From the motion tab you can apply a rotation or rotation translation constraint, which allows two components to rotate in relation to one another.

Transitional Tab
A transitional constraint will maintain contact between the two selected faces. You can use a transitional constraint between a cylindrical face and a set of tangent faces on another part.

Constraint Set Tab
This option will constrain two UCSs together.

Constraint Limits
While adding assembly constraints you may want to allow the component to move or rotate a specific value, or when constraining geometry that may not perfectly fit with the value of the constraint but may fit within a tolerance, you can apply a limit. By setting constraint limits you specify the distance or rotation that the geometry can deviate from an exact location without having the constraint fail. To set a limit for a constraint, click the More button >> on the lower-right corner of the Place Constraint dialog box and the Limits section will appear as shown in the following image on the left. An assembly constraint that has limits will appear in the browser with a +/- symbol appended to its name as shown in the following image on the right.

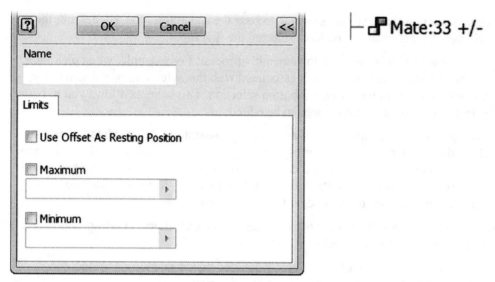

Mate:33 +/-

Figure 6-21

Assembly Constraint Examples
This section shows examples of common assembly constraints being applied.

Mate Constraint
When the Mate constraint, with the mate solution, is selected you can apply a constraint between: planes, edges/lines, and points or a combination of the three. Following are a few examples of the mate constraint with different geometry selected.

Mate: Plane/Plane
When two planar faces are selected, the planes can be aligned so the surface normals are pointing towards each other (mate solution), as shown in the following image on the right, or the normals can be pointing in the same direction (flush). The flush solution is explained in a following section.

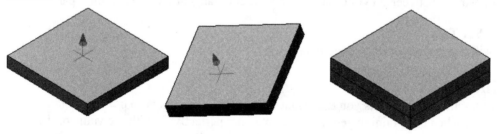

Figure 6-22

Mate: Edge/Edge
When two edges are selected, the edges will be collinear as shown in the following image.

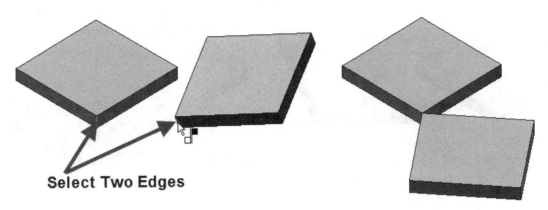

Select Two Edges

Figure 6-23

You can also align circular faces by selecting two circular faces or centerlines as shown in the following image.

Figure 6-24

Mate: Point/Point

When two points, such as centers of arcs and circular edges, endpoints or the midpoint of an edge are selected, they will be coincident as shown in the following image.

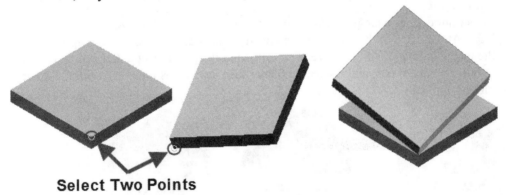

Select Two Points

Figure 6-25

Mate with Flush Solution

When applying a mate constraint you have an option to use the flush solution that aligns two components so that the surface normal on the selected planar faces or work planes are pointing in the same direction, as shown in the following image.

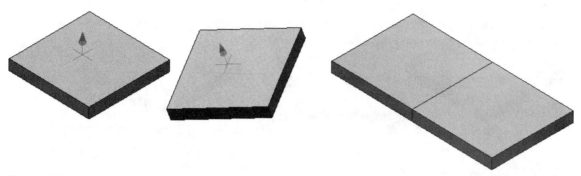

Figure 6-26

Angle Constraint

The angle constraint specifies the degrees between selected planes or faces or axes. The following image shows the angle constraint applied between two planes selected and a 30° angle applied.

Three solutions are available when placing an angle constraint: directed angle, undirected angle, and Explicit Reference Vector. The Explicit Reference Vector option requires a third selection that defines the Z axis.

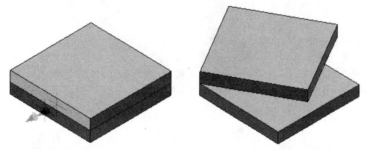

Figure 6-27

Tangent Constraint

The tangent constraint defines a tangent relationship between planes, cylinders, spheres, cones, and ruled splines. At least one of the faces selected needs to be a curve, and you can apply the tangency to the inside or outside of the curve. The following image shows the tangent constraint applied to one outside curved face and a selected planar face, as well as the piece with the outer and inner solutions applied.

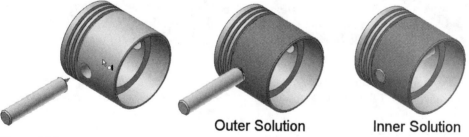

Outer Solution   Inner Solution

Figure 6-28

Insert Constraint

The insert constraint is used to align circular edges removing five degrees of freedom (DOF) with one operation. The insert constraint can only be applied between two circular edges. Select circular edges on two components and the centerlines of the selected circles or arcs will be aligned and the selected edges will be mated together. This single constraint aligns and mates the selected geometry in one operation because a circular edge has a defined centerline/axis and a plane. The following image shows the insert constraint applied between with two circular edges and the opposed solution applied.

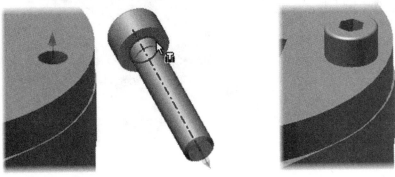

Figure 6-29

Symmetry Constraint

The Symmetry constraint allows you to make two parts or two subassemblies symmetric about a plane. If needed add a work plane that the parts will be symmetric about. Select two planar faces that will be symmetric labeled (1) and (2) in the following image on the left. Select a work plane or a planar face that the components will be symmetric about, labeled (3) in the following image on the left. The following image on the right shows the symmetry constraint applied.

Motion Constraints

There are two types of motion constraints: rotation and rotation-translation, as shown in the Type section of the following image. Motion constraints allow you to simulate the motion relationships of gears, pulleys, rack and pinions, and other devices. By applying motion constraints between two or more components, you can drive one component and cause the others to move accordingly.

Both types of motion constraints are secondary constraints, which means that they define motion, but do not maintain positional relationships between components. Constrain your components fully before you apply motion constraints. You can then suppress constraints that restrict the motion of the components you want to animate.

Rotation Constraint Type

The rotation constraint defines a component that will rotate in relation to another component by specifying a ratio for the rotation between them. Use this constraint for showing the relationship between gears and pulleys. Selecting the tops of the gear faces displays the rotation glyph, as shown in the following image. You may also have to change the solution type from Forward to Backward, depending on the desired results.

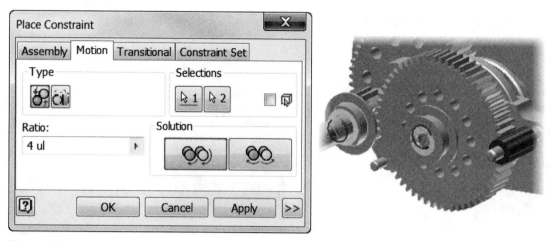

Figure 6-30

Rotation-Translation Constraint Type

The rotation-translation constraint defines the rotation relative to translation between components. This type of constraint is well suited for showing the relationship between rack and pinion gear assemblies. In a rack and pinion assembly, as shown in the following image, the top face of the pinion and one of the front faces of the rack are selected. You supply a distance the rack will travel based on the pitch diameter of the pinion gear, and then you can drive the constraints and test the travel distance of the mechanism.

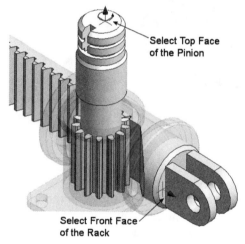

Select Top Face
of the Pinion

Select Front Face
of the Rack

Figure 6-31

Transitional Constraint

The transitional constraint specifies the intended relationship between, typically, a cylindrical part face and a contiguous set of faces on another part, such as a cam follower in a cam slot. The transitional constraint maintains contact between the faces as you slide the component along open degrees of freedom. Access this constraint type through the Transitional tab of the Place Constraint dialog box, as shown in the following image.

Figure 6-32

Select the moving face first on the cam, as shown in the following image on the left. Next, select the transition face, as shown in the middle of the following image. The transitional face will now contact and follow the cam rotation, as shown in the following image on the right.

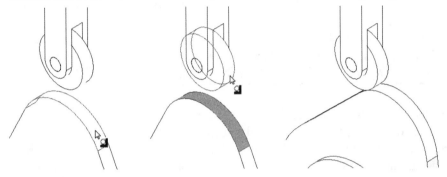

Figure 6-33

Constraint Set Constraint

If User Coordinate Systems were defined in individual part or assembly files, these UCSs can be constrained together. The buttons found under the Type and Selections areas of the dialog box allow for the selecting of individual UCSs and having the constraints be applied to the selections.

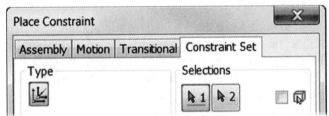

Figure 6-34

Selecting Geometry and the Select Other Command

After selecting the type of assembly constraint that you want to apply, the Selections button with the number 1 will become active; if it does not automatically become active, click the button. Position the cursor over the face, edge, point, and so on, to apply the first assembly constraint. But while selecting geometry you may need to select geometry that is behind the visible geometry, you can do this by using the Select Other command. This is the same technique that you learned in Chapter 3 to select faces in a part file except now you can cycle though geometry on different parts. Move the cursor over the face, edge or point that is in front of one that you want to select and hold the cursor still for two seconds. The Select Other tool appears, as shown in the following image on the left. Select the drop down arrow and move the cursor over the available objects in the list until the correct object is highlighted and then click to select it. The number of objects that appear in the list will depend upon the geometry and the location of the cursor. You can also access the Select Other command by right-clicking while on the desired location in the graphics window and click Select Other from the menu as shown in the image on the right.

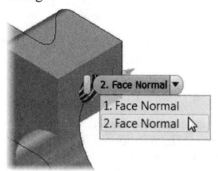 

Figure 6-35

 TIP: A work plane can also be used as a plane with assembly constraints, a work axis can be used to define a line, and a work point can be used to define a point.

Applying the Assembly Constraint

After picking the first selection of the geometry, select the second set of geometry. Again, you may need to cycle through the selection set until the correct location is highlighted. If the Show Preview option is selected in the Place Constraint dialog box, the components will move to show how the assembly constraint will affect the components, and you will hear a snapping sound when you preview the constraint. To change either selection, click on the button with the number 1 or 2, and select the new input. Enter a value as needed for the offset or angle, and select the correct Solution option until the desired outcome appears. Click the Apply button to complete the operation and leave the dialog box open to define subsequent constraint relationships.

ALT + Drag Constraining Technique

Another way to apply an assembly constraint is to hold down the ALT key while dragging a part's edge or face to another part's edge or face; no dialog box will appear. The key to dragging and applying a constraint is to select the correct area on the part. Selecting an edge will create a different type of constraint than if a face is selected. If you select a circular edge, for example, an insert constraint will be applied. To apply a constraint while dragging a part, you cannot have another command active.

To apply an assembly constraint using the ALT + drag technique, follow these steps:

1. While holding down the ALT key, select the face, edge, or other location/entity on the part that will be constrained.

2. Select a planar face, linear edge, or axis to place a mate or flush constraint. Select a cylindrical face to place a tangent constraint. Select a circular edge to place an insert constraint.

3. Drag the part into position. As you drag the part over features on other parts, you will preview the constraint type. If the face you need to constrain to is behind another face, pause until the Select Other command appears. Cycle through the possible selection options, and then click to accept the selection.

MOVING AND ROTATING COMPONENTS

While working in an assembly, you may need to temporarily move or rotate a component to see geometry that is hidden behind it or to rotate a component so it is easier to visualize the assembly or apply an assembly constraint. To accomplish either task use the Free Move and Free Rotate commands on the Assemble tab > Position panel, as shown in the following image.

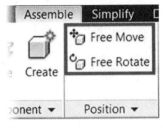

Figure 6-36

Free Move

To perform a Free Move operation on a component in an assembly follow these steps:

1. Start the Free Move command.

2. Drag the component to a new location. If the component is constrained to other components, an elastic band will display these relationships as shown in the following image on the right.

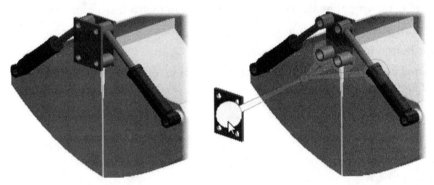

Figure 6-37

3. When the component is at its correct location, release the mouse button.

4. To return constrained components to their constrained position, click the Update command on the Quick Access toolbar.

5. An unconstrained component remains in the new location until you constrain it to another component or move it.

When a constrained component is moved the following will appear:

- A glyph will appear for each assembly constraint or joint that was applied to the moved component. To see more information about the constraint or joint, move the cursor over the glyph as shown in the following image on the left.

- To alter a constraint or a joint, right-click on its glyph and click an option from the menu as shown in the image on the right. Editing constraints and creating joints will be covered in the next sections.

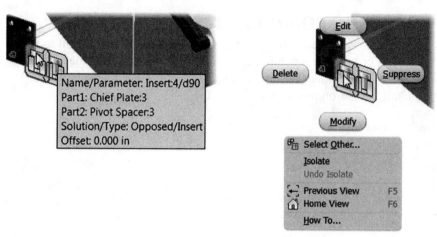

Figure 6-38

Free Rotate

Use the Free Rotate command to rotate a component in an assembly. This command is very useful when constraining faces that are hidden from your view. You can rotate the component and not have to change the viewpoint of the entire assembly.

Follow these steps to rotate a component in an assembly:

1. Activate the Free Rotate command, and select the component to rotate. Notice the appearance of the Rotate symbol on the selected component in the following image.
2. Drag your cursor until you see the desired view of the component.
3. Release the mouse button to complete the rotation.
4. To return constrained components to their constrained position, click the Update command on the Quick Access toolbar.

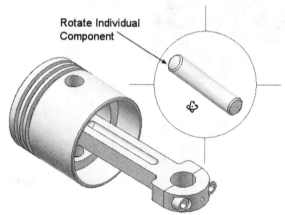

Figure 6-39

EDITING ASSEMBLY CONSTRAINTS

After you have added an assembly constraint, you may want to edit, suppress, or delete it to reposition the component. There are multiple ways to edit assembly constraints.

The first method is to display the assembly constraints on selected components using the Show Relationships command on the Assemble tab > Relationships panel as shown in the following image on the left. After selecting a component, glyphs will appear for all assembly constraints and joints that have been applied to the component. To edit the constraint or joint, right-click and click Edit from the menu, as shown in the following image on the right. The Edit Constraint dialog box appears, modify the constraint option as needed and click OK when done. After right-clicking on the glyph you can also use the other options in the menu to modify the constraint.

To remove the glyphs from the screen, click the Hide All Relationships command on the Assemble tab > Relationships panel.

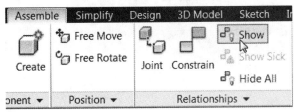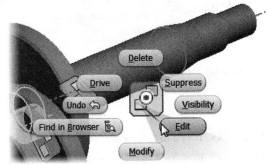

Figure 6-40

Two other methods to edit an assembly constraint are executed through the browser. In the browser, activate the assembly or subassembly that contains the constraints you want to edit and to display the constraints expand the component name.

To edit the offset value, double-click on the constraint you want to change or right-click on the constraint and click Modify from the menu as shown in the following image on the left. The Edit Dimension dialog box appears, enter a new value for the offset distance.

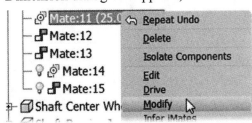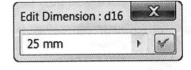

Figure 6-41

You can edit the constraint's options by right-clicking on the assembly constraint's name in the browser and click Edit from the menu, as shown in the following image on the left. The Edit Constraint dialog box will appear. Modify the constraint as needed.

Recover Assembly Constraint

After adding or editing an assembly constraint, if it conflicts with another constraint a yellow triangular icon with an exclamation point will appear in the browser to the left of the constraint icon that is in conflict, as shown in the middle of the following image. To edit a conflicting constraint in the browser, double-click on its name or right-click on its name and select Recover from the menu, as shown in the following image on the right or click the Red Cross in the Quick Access toolbar as shown in the following image on the right. The Design Doctor will appear and guide you through the steps to fix the problem.

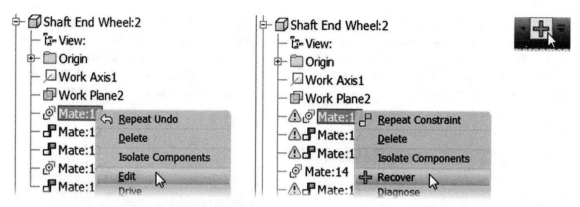

Figure 6-42

EXERCISE 6-1: ASSEMBLING PARTS

In this exercise you open an existing assembly of a lifting mechanism, place additional components, and constrain them.

1. Open *ESS_E06_01.iam* in the Chapter 06 folder.
2. Begin assembling the connector and sleeve:
   a. Zoom in on the small connector and sleeve.
   b. Drag the connector so that the small end (blue component) is near the sleeve, as shown in the following image.

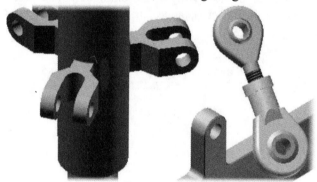

Figure 6-43

3. Next you add a mate constraint between the centerlines of both components.
   a. Click the Constrain command from the Assemble tab > Relationships panel. Mate is the default constraint.
   b. Move the cursor over the hole in the arm on the sleeve. Click when the centerline displays, as shown in the following image on the left.
   c. Move the cursor over the hole in the link. Click when the centerline displays, as shown in the following image on the left.
   d. If the green dot displays, move the cursor until the centerline displays, or use the Select Other tool to cycle through the available choices to select the centerline.
   e. Click Apply to accept this constraint.
4. Now add a mate constraint between planar faces of both parts.

a. With the Constrain command still active, select the small planar face on the ball in the link end, as shown in the following image on the right.

b. Click the inner planar face of the slot on the sleeve, as shown in the following image on the right.

c. Click OK to create this constraint and close the dialog box.

Figure 6-44

5. Drag the small link arm and the crank to see the effect of the constraints.

6. Next you place a crank into the assembly.

a. Click the Place Component command on the Assemble tab > Component panel and double-click on the file *ESS_E06_01-Crank.ipt* from the Chapter 06 folder.

b. Before placing the component, right-click and click Rotate Z 90° as shown in the following image on the left.

c. Move the crank near the end of the middle of the right arm of the spyder component (yellow part) and click to place the crank as shown in the image on the right.

d. End the command by right-clicking and click OK on the marking menu.

Figure 6-45

7. To assemble the crank to the spyder arm you will again use the Constrain Command, but simplify the process by applying an Insert constraint that will align the centerlines and edges of two holes in a single operation.

a. Click the Constrain command from the Assemble tab > Relationships panel.

b. In the Place Constraint dialog box, change the constraint type to Insert.

c. Select the inside edge of the hole on the crank and right edge of the hole in the middle of the spyder arm as shown in the following image on the left.

d. Click OK to complete the command.

e. Drag the crank so you can see the effect of the constraint and position it approximately as shown in the following image on the right.

Figure 6-46

8. Next you constrain the crank and the small link. Use the Constrain command to place a mate constraint between the centerlines of the two holes, as shown in the following image on the left.

9. Next you place a claw in the assembly.

   a. Click the Place Component command from the Assemble tab > Component panel and double-click on the file *ESS_E06_01-Claw.ipt*.

   b. Position the claw near the end of the right side of the spyder arm and click to place the component, as shown in the following image on the right.

   c. Complete the command by right-clicking and click OK on the marking menu.

Figure 6-47

10. Next you rotate the claw so it will be easier to apply an assembly constraint to.

    a. Start the Free Rotate command from the Assembly tab > Position panel.

    b. In the graphics window, select the claw.

    c. Then move the cursor in the rotate symbol (circle with lines at the quadrants) and click and drag, rotating the claw until you can see the inside face, similar to what is shown in the following image on the left.

    d. Right-click and click OK from the marking menu to exit the command.

11. Constrain the claw to the spyder.

    a. Apply an Insert constraint to the outside edge of the hole on the end of the spyder arm and the inside edge of the hole on the claw as shown in the following image on the right.

    b. Click OK to place the constraint and close the Place Constraint dialog box.

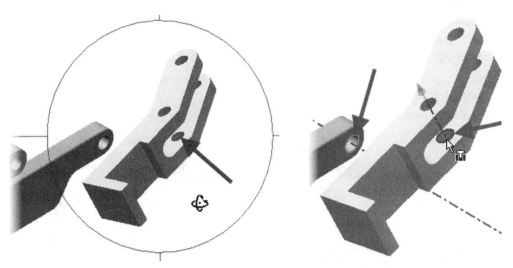

Figure 6-48

12. Next you assemble the link rod to the crank and claw.

    a. Drag the long link rod down so it is closer to the crank.

    b. Apply an Insert constraint to the left inside edge of the hole on the crank and the small planar face on the left ball in the link rod as shown in the following image on the left.

    c. Click Apply to create the constraint and keep the Place Constraint dialog box open.

    d. In the Place Constraint dialog box change the constraint type to Mate.

    e. Move the cursor over a top hole on the claw and click when the centerline displays, as shown in the following image on the right.

    f. Move the cursor over the right hole in the link rod and click when the centerline displays, as shown in the following image on the right.

    g. Click OK to create the constraint.

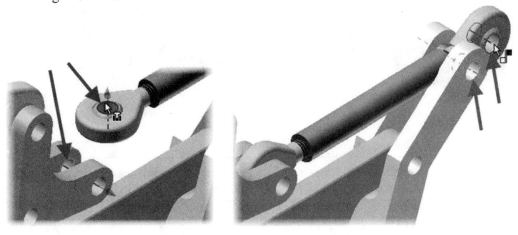

Figure 6-49

13. Drag the claw to see the effect of the assembly constraints, as shown in the following image on the left.

14. Next you add bolts and nuts to the spyder assembly.

a. Begin by clicking the Place Component command on the Assemble tab > Component panel. Hold down the CTRL key and select *ESS_E06_01-Bolt.ipt* and *ESS_E06_01-Nut.ipt* and click Open.

b. Place six nuts and bolts near their final position in the assembly, as shown in the following image on the right.

c. Complete the operation by right-clicking and click OK on the menu.

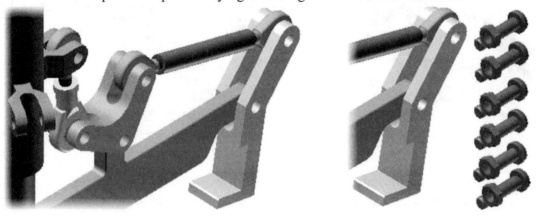

Figure 6-50

15. Place an Insert constraint with the ALT drag technique.

a. Press the ESC key twice to exit the active command.

b. Hold down the ALT key and then Click and drag on the outside circular edge of the bolt and an Insert glyph will appear as shown in the following image on the left.

c. Release the ALT key but keep the left mouse button pressed.

d. Drag the cursor over the circular edge of the hole on the claw until it is previewed in the correct location as shown in the image on the right.

e. Then release the mouse button to create the constraint.

Figure 6-51

 TIP: When applying an Insert constraint via the Place Constraint dialog box or with the ALT drag technique, ensure you select the edges that will be planar to one another.

16. Practice constraining the bolts and nuts into the holes in the spyder assembly. When done your assembly should resemble the following image.

Figure 6-52

17. Try editing a few assembly constraints by using the Show Relationships command on the Assemble tab > Relationships panel.

18. Also edit an assembly constraint by right-clicking on the constraint in the browser and click Edit from the menu.

19. Close all open files. Do not save changes. End of exercise.

ASSEMBLY JOINTS

Another option to position components in an assembly is to apply joints. Assembly joints are similar to the assembly constraints, but a joint can fully define how a component will move and rotate in a single operation. Depending upon the geometry that is selected, a joint type will be automatically selected, but you can override the default. The joints use endpoints, midpoints and center points to locate the components. The Joint command can be used in conjunction with assembly constraints or alone. Following are explanations of the types of joints that you can apply.

Joint	Degrees of Freedom	Example
Rigid	Removes all degrees of freedom (DOF).	Two plates that are welded together is an example of a rigid joint.
Rotational	Leaves one rotational degrees of freedom.	A door hinge is an example of a rotational joint.

Slider	Leaves one translational degrees of freedom.	A block sliding along a track is an example of a slider joint.
Cylindrical	Leaves one translational and one rotational degree of freedom.	The shaft in a cylinder that can rotate and move in and out is an example of a cylindrical joint.
Planar	Leaves two translational and one rotational degree of freedom.	An example would be placing two plates on top of each other. One of the plates can move and rotate on top of the other plate.
Ball	Leaves three rotational degrees of freedom.	A ball joint is an example where the ball can rotate freely.

Creating an Assembly Joint

Follow these steps to create a Joint.

1. Start the Joint command from the Assemble tab > Relationships panel as shown in the following image.

Figure 6-53

2. The Place Joint dialog box and mini-toolbar appear as shown in the following image.

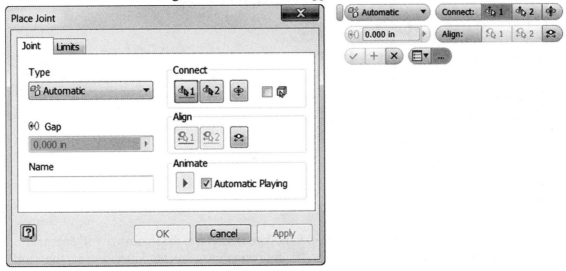

Figure 6-54

3. Select an endpoint, centerpoint, or midpoint on a face of the component that will move.

   a. If you select a component that is grounded or has no degrees of freedom, a dialog box will appear alerting you that the component is grounded, if you continue the component will be ungrounded.

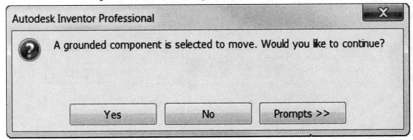

Figure 6-55

   b. If you select a component that is constrained, a dialog box will appear as shown in the following image stating that adding this joint will conflict with an existing constraint or joint and a Create/Edit Joint dialog box will appear giving you an opportunity edit the relationship.

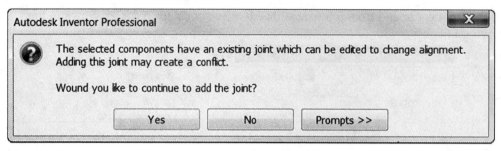

Figure 6-56

4. From the mini-toolbar or the Place Joint dialog box select the desired Joint type as shown in the following image. Note that the Automatic option will change depending upon the geometry that is selected.

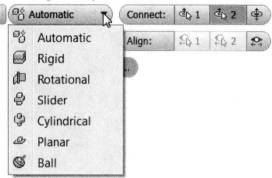

Figure 6-57

5. If a Rotational, Slider, or Cylindrical joint type is selected, green arrows will appear showing the direction of movement. The following image on the left shows a cylindrical joint with two degrees of movement; one translational and one rotational.

6. To change the direction of the movement or to rotate the component, click the First alignment button in the dialog box or in the mini-toolbar, as shown in the following image on the right, and select a face or an edge that you want aligned.

7. The Second Alignment option will be active, select an edge or face that the first selection will be aligned to.

Figure 6-58

8. If needed, click the Invert alignment button to flip the direction.

Figure 6-59

---

9. If desired, you can restrict the movement of the joint by clicking on the Limits tab and define a value in the start and end fields. This functionality is similar to limits for an assembly constraint.

10. Click the OK button to create the joint.

11. Edit the joint like you would an assembly constraint.

Tips for using the joint command

- Always select the component that will move first.
- You can view existing joints and assembly constraints from the Relationships folder located in the browser. The folder is available in both the Assembly View and the Modeling View as shown in the following image.

Figure 6-60

EXERCISE 6-2: ASSEMBLY JOINTS

In this exercise you apply and edit an assembly joint between a block and a beam.

1. Open *ESS_E06_02.iam* in the Chapter 06 folder.

2. Start the Joint command from the Assemble tab > Relationships panel.

3. First select the midpoint on the inside face of the slider block as shown in the following image on the left. This is the part that will move.

4. Select the midpoint on the top face of the track as shown in the following image on the right. The second selection is on the component that will remain stationary.

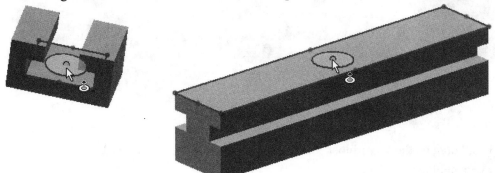

Figure 6-61

5. From the Place Joint dialog box or mini-toolbar select through the six different joint types, as shown in the following image on the left, and watch the animated movement of each joint.

6. Select Rigid from the list and click OK to create the joint.

7. Try to click and drag on the slider block and notice that it cannot move, because of the rigid joint.

8. Next you edit the Joint.

a. Start the Show Relationships command on the Assemble tab > Relationships panel.

b. In the graphics window, select the slider block.

c. Right-click on the glyph of the joint and click Edit from the marking menu, as shown in the following image on the right.

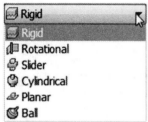
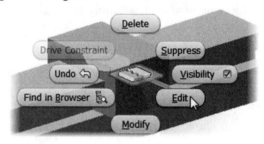

Figure 6-62

d. From the Edit Joint dialog box or from the mini-toolbar change the joint type to Slider.

e. Notice that the green arrow and animation shows the slider moving perpendicular to the length of the track.

f. Next you change the alignment. Click the First alignment button in the dialog box or mini-toolbar and then select bottom horizontal edge of the slider block, as shown in the following image on the left.

g. Then select the bottom horizontal edge of the track as shown in the middle of the following image.

h. Notice how the arrow is now parallel with the length of the track as shown in the following image on the right.

i. Click OK to complete the edit.

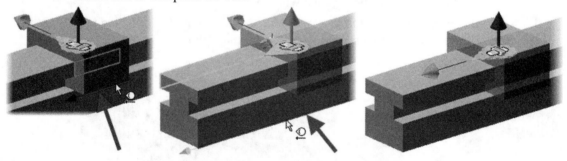

Figure 6-63

9. Click and drag on the slider block and notice that it can slide off the track.

10. Next you add limits to the joint.

a. Right-click on the glyph of the joint and click Edit from the marking menu.

b. In the Edit Joint dialog box click the Limits tab.

c. In the Linear area, check the Start option and change its value to **-2 inches.** Check the End option and change its value to **2 inches** as shown in the following image.

d. Click OK to complete the edit.

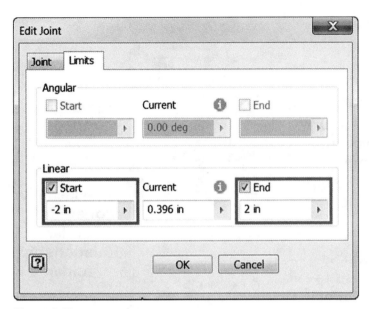

Figure 6-64

11. Click and drag on the slider block and notice that it is limited to 4 inches of travel along the length of the track.

12. Turn off the visibility of the glyph joint by clicking the Hide All Relationships command on the Assemble tab > Relationships panel.

13. Close all open files. Do not save changes. End of exercise.

ADDITIONAL ASSEMBLY COMMANDS

Additional commands are available to help you control and manage data in an assembly file, such as; controlling how constraints are viewed in the browser, finding the other half of an assembly constraint, using tooltips to learn about as assembly constraint, isolating assembly components, controlling visibility of components and editing a component in the context of the assembly. The following sections describe these operations.

Browser Views

Two modes for viewing assembly information are located in the top of the browser toolbar: Assembly View and Modeling View. Assembly View, the default mode, displays assembly constraint symbols nested below constrained components as well as under the Relationships folder, as shown in the following image on the left. In this mode, the features used to create the part are not displayed.

When Modeling View is active, all assembly constraints in the assembly are located in the Relationships folder at the top of the assembly tree, as shown in the following image on the right. In this mode, the features used to create the part are displayed just as they are in the part file and can be edited by right-clicking on the feature in the browser and selecting Edit Feature from the menu.

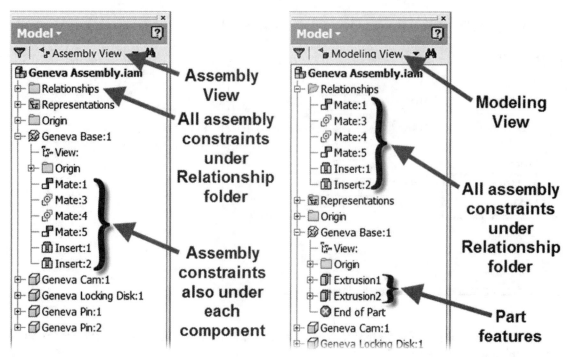

Figure 6-65

Other Half

You can use the Other Half command to find the matching part that participates in a constraint placed in an assembly. As you add parts, you may wish to highlight an assembly constraint and find the part to which it is constrained. To find the second part that the constraint is applied to, right-click on the constraint and click Other Half as shown in the following image on the left. The constraint will highlight in the graphics window, as shown in the middle of the following image, and the browser will expand the second part and highlight the second half of the constraint, as shown in the following image on the right.

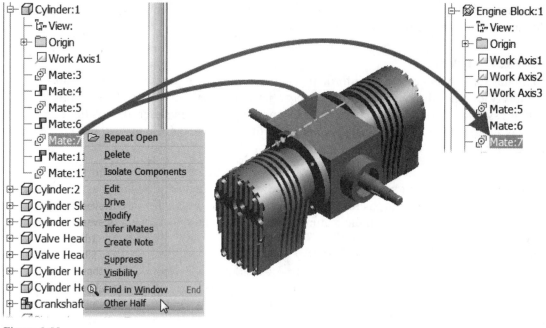

Figure 6-66

Constraint Tooltip

To display all property information for a specific constraint, move your cursor over the constraint icon, and a tooltip will appear, as shown in the following image. Although the constraint name is highlighted, you must hover your cursor over the constraint icon to view the tooltip.

The following information is displayed in the tooltip:

- Constraint and parameter names, applicable to offset and angle parameters
- Constrained components, that is, the two part names from the Assembly browser
- Constraint solution and type
- Constraint offset or angle value

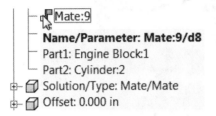

Name/Parameter: Mate:9/d8
Part1: Engine Block:1
Part2: Cylinder:2
Solution/Type: Mate/Mate
Offset: 0.000 in

Figure 6-67

User-Defined Assembly Folders

User-defined folders in an assembly allow you to organize your work by grouping assembly components under a single folder name. This method allows you to simplify the appearance of an assembly in the browser. To create a user-defined assembly folder, select those components that you want to group, right-click and pick Add to new folder, as shown in the following image on the left. You will be prompted in the browser to rename the default folder to something more meaningful, such as Fasteners, as shown in the following image on the right. Notice also a unique icon that identifies the user-defined assembly folder.

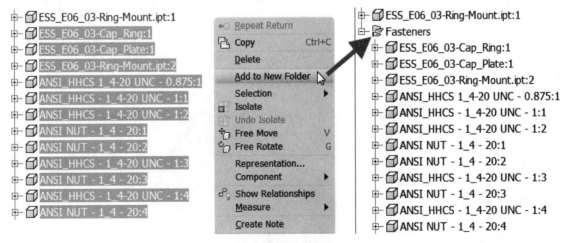

Figure 6-68

Isolating Assembly Components

Components can be isolated as a means of viewing smaller sets of components, especially in a large assembly. In the browser or in the graphics window select the component(s) to isolate, right-click and click Isolate from the menu as shown in the following image on the left. The visibility of all unselected components will be turned off.

To return the assembly to its previous assembled state, right-click inside the browser, or the graphics window, and click Undo Isolate from the menu, as shown in the following image on the right.

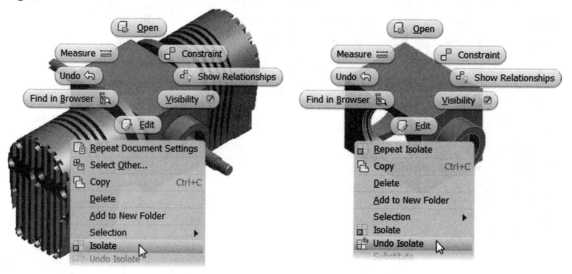

Figure 6-69

Visibility Control

Controlling the visibility of components is critical to managing assemblies. While working, there may be parts that are obscured by other components. You can turn off the visibility of components that are obstructing these components. You can control the visibility of any component in the active assembly even if the component is nested deep in the assembly hierarchy. To change the visibility of a component, expand the browser until the component occurrence is visible, right-click the occurrence and click Visibility from the menu. You can also right-click on a component in the graphics window and select Visibility from the marking menu, as shown in the following image on the left.

After turning the visibility of a component off it will also be grayed out in the browser. To change the visibility of a component back on, right-click on a component in the browser and click Visibility from the menu, as shown in the image on the right.

Figure 6-70

Editing a Component in an Assembly

The level of the assembly that is currently active determines whether or not you can edit components or features. You can take some actions only in the active assembly and its first-level children, while other operations are valid at all levels of the active assembly.

Double-click any subassembly or part occurrence in the browser or graphics window to activate it, or right-click the occurrence in the browser or graphics window, and click Edit from the menu. All components not associated with the active component appear shaded in the browser and appear translucent in the graphics window, as shown in the following image.

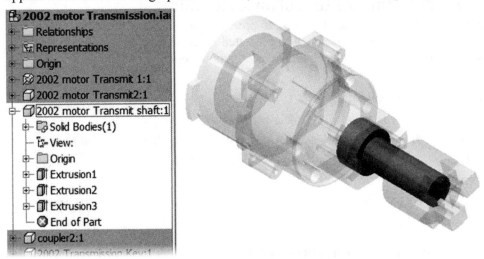

Figure 6-71

Then edit the component as you would if it were open in its own file. To return to the previous level in the assembly, either double-click on the top name of the assembly in the browser, as shown in the following image on the left, or click the Return command on the 3D Model tab > Return panel, as shown in the following image on the right.

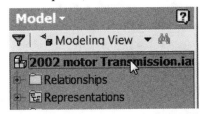
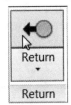

Figure 6-72

ADAPTIVITY

This section will introduce you to the concept of adaptivity. Adaptivity is the function in Autodesk Inventor that allows the size of a part to be determined by setting up a relationship to another part in an assembly. Adaptivity allows under-constrained sketches—features that have undefined dimensions, angles or extents, and hole features—to adapt to changes. An example of adaptivity would be determining the diameter of a pin from the size of a hole. You could determine the diameter of the hole from the size of the pin. Following are some key points to know about adaptivity:

- The adaptive relationship is defined by applying assembly constraints between an adaptive sketch or feature and another part.
- If a sketch is fully constrained, it cannot be made adaptive; however, the extruded length or revolved angle of the part can be.
- A part can only be adaptive in one assembly at a time.
- In an assembly that has multiple placements of the same part, only one occurrence can be adaptive. The other occurrences will reflect the size of the adaptive part.

Project Geometry in the Context of an Assembly

While working in the context of an assembly you can project geometry from one part onto another part creating an adaptive relationship. The projected geometry created is adaptive to the geometry it was projected from. To project geometry while in the context of an assembly follow these steps:

1. Open or create an assembly file.
2. Create or edit a part where you will project geometry.
3. Make a sketch active or create a sketch where the geometry will be projected onto.
4. Use the Project Geometry command on the Sketch tab > Create panel and project edges from another part.

To learn more about the Project Geometry command, refer to the Projecting Geometry section in Chapter 3.

Creating an Adaptive Sketch/Part Manually

Follow these steps to make a sketch and a part adaptive:

1. In a part file create a sketch and draw a sketch, but under constrain it in the direction it will adapt. The following image on the left shows a rectangle that is under constrained in the horizontal and vertical direction (it contains no dimensions).
2. Make the sketch adaptive by right-clicking on the sketch in the browser and click Adaptive in the menu, as shown in the middle of the following image. The Adaptive icon will appear to the left of the sketch, as shown in the following image on the right.

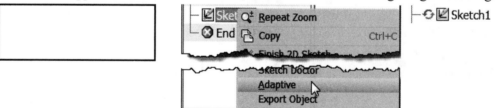

Figure 6-73

3. Extrude or revolve the sketch. The Adaptive icon is displayed to the left of the feature, similar to the following. ⊕–↺◌ Extrusion1.
4. Save the file.
5. Open an assembly file that contains the part to which the adaptive part will be sized to.
6. Place the adaptive part into an assembly.
7. Make the part adaptive in the assembly by right-clicking on the part's name in the browser and click Adaptive in the menu, as shown in the following image on the left.
8. Define the size of the adaptive part by applying assembly constraints. The following image on the right shows the Adaptive Plate constrained to the outside faces of the Base

component by applying two flush constraints. Notice how the plate matches the horizontal length of the base.

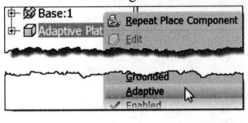

Figure 6-74

EXERCISE 6-3: DESIGNING A PART IN THE CONTEXT OF AN ASSEMBLY

In this exercise, you create a lid for a container, based on the geometry of the container, by projecting geometry in the context of the assembly. The projected geometry is adaptive and automatically updates to reflect design changes in the container.

1. Open *ESS_E06_03.iam* in the Chapter 06 folder. The following image on the left shows the container component in the assembly.

2. Begin the process of creating a new component in the context of an assembly.

   a. Click the Create Component command on the Assemble tab > Component panel.

   b. Enter ***ESS_E06_03-Lid*** for the New Component Name.

   c. Click the Browse Templates button, and in the English tab, double-click Standard (in).ipt.

   d. Change the location the file will be saved to by selecting *C:\Inv 2015 Ess Plus\Chapter 06*.

   e. Ensure there is a checkmark beside the Constrain sketch plane to selected face or plane option at the bottom of the Create In-Place Component dialog box.

   f. Click the OK button to exit the dialog box

   g. Select the top planar face of the container, as shown in the following image on the right.

 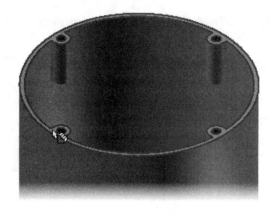

Figure 6-75

3. Create a new sketch by clicking the Start 2D Sketch command on the 3D Model tab > Sketch panel. The origin planes for the new part will be displayed in the graphics window. Select the XY origin plane, as shown in the following image. The selected plane becomes the active sketch plane for the new part.

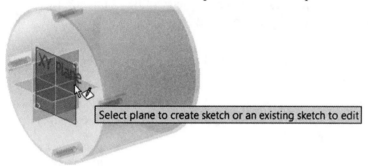

Figure 6-76

4. You will now project all geometry contained on this top face of the container.

   a. Click the Project Geometry command from the Sketch tab > Create panel.

   b. Move the cursor over the left face of the base part until the profile of the entire planar face is highlighted, as shown in the following image on the left.

   c. Click to project the edges. Your display should appear similar to the following image on the right.

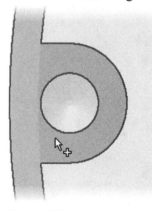 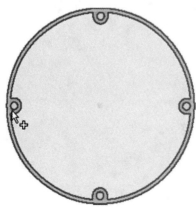

Figure 6-77

5. Next, you create a series of circles that will act as clearance holes. Zoom in to view a tapped hole.

6. Add four circles that are concentric to and larger than the four projected circles, as shown in the following image.

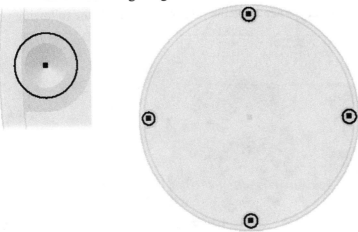

Figure 6-78

7. All four circles need to have the same diameter. You do this by adding an equal constraint between the circles as described in the following steps.

a. Click the Equal constraint command on the Sketch tab > Constrain panel.

b. Click the left circle, and then click the top circle.

c. Click the left circle, and then click the circle on the right.

d. Click the left circle, and then click the bottom circle.

e. Next, you fully constrain the circles by adding a **.15 inch** diameter dimension to the left most circle. When done your sketch should resemble the following image.

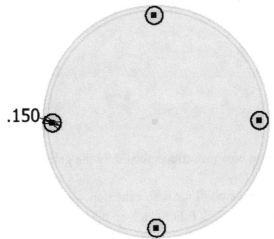

Figure 6-79

8. Next, exit the Sketch environment by right-clicking and click Finish 2D Sketch on the marking menu.

9. Next you extrude two profiles.

a. Select one of the edges on the sketch and click Extrude from the mini-toolbar.

b. To create the entire lid, select the two profiles as shown in the following image on the left. If only one profile is selected, the lid will be missing a section.

c. In either the Extrude dialog box or the mini-toolbar, enter an extrude value of **.25 inches**

d. Click OK to create the extrusion. When done the lid should resemble the following image on the right.

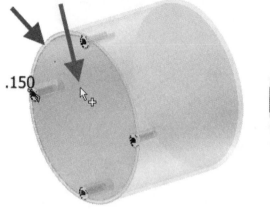

Figure 6-80

10. To make the top-level assembly active, click the Return command on the 3D Model tab > Return panel. When done, your display should appear similar to the following image.

Figure 6-81

11. You will now modify the container and observe how this affects the lid. In the graphics window double-click on *ESS_E06_03-Container:1*.

12. Next you change the diameter dimension of the sketch of the base extrusion.

a. Select the cylindrical face on the container and click Edit Sketch on the mini-toolbar, as shown in the following image on the left.

b. Double-click the 2.000 diameter dimension, and change the value to **1.5 inches**.

c. Finish the sketch. Notice that the lid is now larger than the container as shown in the following image on the right.

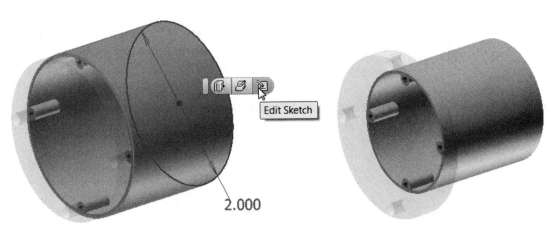

Figure 6-82

13. Click the Return command to return to the top-level assembly. Notice that the lid adapts to the modified dimensions of the container, as shown in the following image.

Figure 6-83

14. If desired, change the viewpoint to the Home View, as this will display the container from its original viewpoint.

15. Close all open files. Do not save changes. End of exercise.

PATTERNING COMPONENTS

To speed the process of placing and constraining the same component or components that follow a set direction and have a fixed distance between them, you can use the Pattern Component command. This command has three options; pattern a component(s) about an existing feature pattern, or the components can be patterned in a rectangular or a circular pattern. Each of these options are described in the next sections. Start the Pattern Component command from the Assemble tab > Pattern panel, as shown in the following image on the left. The Pattern Component dialog box will appear that has three tabs; Associative, Rectangular, and Circular, as shown in the following image on the right and are used to create the pattern in three different ways.

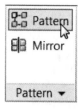

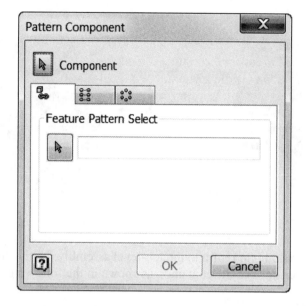

Figure 6-84

Associative Pattern

An associated component pattern will maintain a relationship to the feature pattern that you select. For example, a bolt is component-patterned to a part's bolt-hole circular pattern that consists of four holes. If the feature pattern, the bolt-hole, changes to six holes, the bolts will move to the new locations, and two new bolts will be added for the two new holes. To create an associative component pattern, there must be a feature-based rectangular or circular pattern, and the part that will be patterned should be constrained to the parent feature, that is, the original feature that was patterned in the component.

By default, the Component selection option is active. Select the component, such as the cap screw, or components to pattern. Next, click the Feature Pattern Select button in the dialog box and select a feature, such as a hole, that is part of the feature pattern. Do not select the parent feature. After selecting the pattern, it will highlight on the part and the pattern name will appear in the dialog box. When done, click OK to create the component pattern, as shown in the following image on the right.

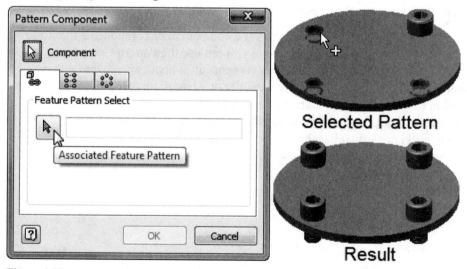

Figure 6-85

Rectangular Pattern

When performing a rectangular pattern operation, you select two edges to define the direction of the rows or columns. Note that a rectangular pattern can consist of a single row or column. When defining a pattern with a single row/column, you define a single direction. To define a direction, you can select an edge, work axis, origin axis or a face. After selecting the direction(s) enter the number of columns and rows and then the spacing or distance between these rows and columns. The resulting pattern acts like a feature pattern. After creation, you can edit the pattern to change its numbers, spacing, and so on.

The following image illustrates the rectangular pattern option used to pattern a bolt by using the bottom horizontal edge and the right-angled edge of the plate to define the directions.

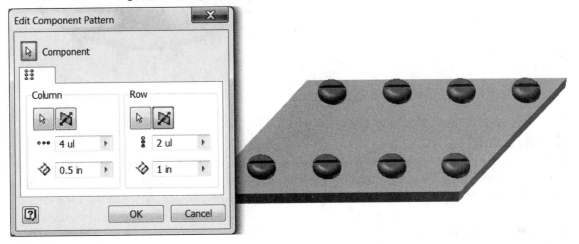

Figure 6-86

Circular Pattern

Circular patterns will copy selected components in a circular direction. After selecting the component or components to pattern, select an axis direction. In the following example, this element takes the form of the centerline of the circular plate and acts as a pivot point for the pattern. You then enter the number of occurrences or items that will make up the pattern and the circular angle. The following image shows an example of a bolt patterned with a count of 12 and 30 degrees between them.

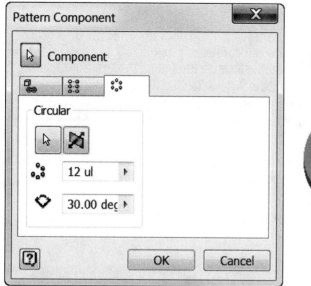

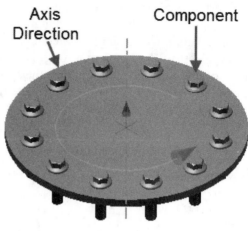

Figure 6-87

Editing a Pattern

When done patterning a component with any of the three methods, the patterned is consumed into a Pattern entry in the browser. Expand the Pattern entry to see the elements, which represent the count. Expand the browser entry to view the component occurrences as shown in the following image.

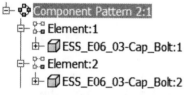

Figure 6-88

You can edit the original component pattern by right-clicking on the pattern in the graphics window and clicking Edit from the menu or right-click on the pattern's name in the browser and click Edit from the menu, as shown in the following image on the left.

You can also suppress an element (part occurrence) by right-clicking on the Element's name in the browser and clicking Suppress from the menu, as shown in the middle of the following image. The suppressed component will be grayed out in the browser and a line will be struck through it, as shown in the following image on the right.

You can remove an individual occurrence from the pattern by right-clicking on it and clicking Independent from the menu, as shown in the middle of the following image. Once a part is independent, an X will appear on the icon of the element in the browser. An independent component has no relationship with the pattern. However, you can rejoin an element to the pattern by right-clicking on the element's name in the browser and clicking Independent from the menu to remove the checkmark next to the item in the menu.

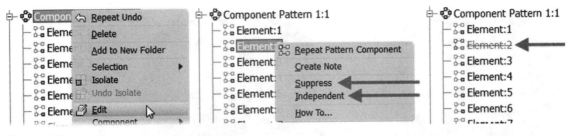

Figure 6-89

EXERCISE 6-4: PATTERNING COMPONENTS

In this exercise, you pattern a fastener to match an existing hole pattern and then change the count of the original hole pattern in a T-pipe assembly.

1. Open *ESS_E06_04.iam in* the Chapter 06 folder.

2. In the browser, select Assembly View if it is not already the active browser view.

3. In the browser, expand the parts *ESS_E06_04-Cap_Bolt.ipt:1* and *ESS_E06_04-Cap_Nut.ipt:1*. Notice that the parts already have an insert constraint applied to them, as shown in the following image.

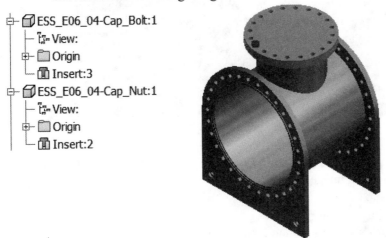

Figure 6-90

4. Next, you create a circular pattern consisting of a collection of nuts and bolts. Click the Pattern Component command from the Assemble tab > Pattern panel.

   a. Select the components to pattern, press and hold the CTRL key and select *ESS_E06_04-Cap_Bolt.ipt:1* and *ESS_E06_04-Cap_Nut.ipt:1* parts in the graphics window or in the browser.

   b. Click the Associated Feature Pattern button found under the Feature Pattern Select area of the Pattern Component dialog box. In the graphics window, move the cursor over a patterned hole in *ESS_E06_04-Cap_Plate:1*. When the circular pattern of holes in the cap plate is highlighted, select the edge of one of the holes, as shown in the following image on the left.

   c. You should see a preview of the component pattern, as shown in the following image on the right.

   d. Click the OK button to create the component pattern.

Figure 6-91

5. Next, you edit the original hole pattern on the Cap Plate.

    a.   In the graphics window, double click on *ESS_E06_04-Cap_Plate:1* (the top circular plate) as shown in the following image on the left.

    b.   Select a circular face of one of the patterned holes and select Edit Circular Pattern from the marking menu, as shown in the following image on the right.

    c.   Change the Placement count to **10**.

    d.   Click OK to complete the edit.

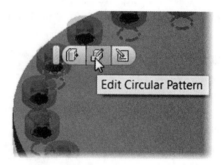

Figure 6-92

6. Click the Return command on the 3D Model tab > Return panel. When done your screen should resemble the following image.

Figure 6-93

7. Close all open files. Do not save changes. End of exercise.

ANALYSIS COMMANDS

Various commands are available to assist you in analyzing sketch, part, and assembly models. You can calculate the minimum distance between components, the center of gravity of parts and assemblies, and perform interference detection.

Minimum Distance

In chapter 2 you learned about the distance command, while in an assembly there is additional functionality to measure the minimum distance between components (subassemblies), parts, or faces and edges. While in the assembly, select the Measure Distance command from the Inspect tab > Measure panel, as shown in the following image on the left. Then change the selection priority, depending on what you want to measure. The three available selection modes are shown in the image on the right.

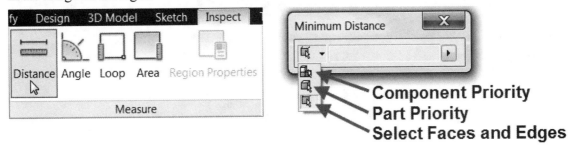

Figure 6-94

Identifying the Center of Gravity of an Assembly

Knowledge of where the center of gravity is in an assembly could be critical to the overall design of that assembly. In chapter 3 you learned how to change the material of a part and see the physical properties of the part through its iProperties. You can also use the iProperties command to see the center of gravity of an assembly. Start the iProperties command with one of the following techniques.

- Right-click on the assembly's name in the browser and click iProperties from the menu.
- Click the Inventor Application Menu > iProperties.

The image on the left shows the center of gravity as displayed in the iProperties for an assembly. You can also see where the center of gravity is in the graphics window by clicking on the View tab > Visibility panel > Center of Gravity as shown in the middle of the following image. The image on the right shows the center of gravity icon applied to an assembly model. This icon consists of a triad displaying the X, Y, and Z directions. Three selectable work planes and a selectable work point area are also available for the purpose of measuring distances and angles that reference the center of gravity.

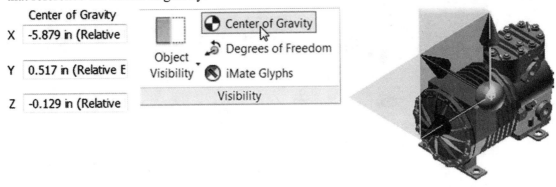

Figure 6-95

 TIP: Before finding the center of gravity of an assembly, ensure that each part has the correct material applied to it.

Interference Checking

You can check for interference in an assembly using one or two sets of objects. To check the interference among sets of stationary components, make the assembly or subassembly in question active. Then click the Analyze Interference command on the Inspect tab > Interference panel, as shown in the following image on the left. The Interference Analysis dialog box will appear, as shown in the following image on the right.

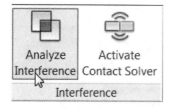
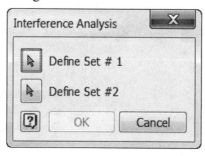

Figure 6-96

To run interference check, follow these steps.

1. Click on Define Set #1, and select the components that will define the first set.

2. Click on Define Set #2, and select the components that will define the second set. A component can exist in only one set.

TIP: Only use Define Set #1 if you want to check for interference against all selected components. Otherwise interference is only checked for set #1 vs. set #2.

3. To add or delete components from either set, select the button that defines the set that you want to edit. Click components to add to the set, or press the CTRL key while selecting components to remove from the set.

4. Once you have defined the sets, click the OK button. The order in which you selected the components has no significance.

5. If interference is found, the Interference Detected dialog box will appear, as shown in the following image.

Amount of Interference

Figure 6-97

The information in the dialog box defines the X, Y, and Z coordinates of the centroid of the interfering volume. It also lists the volume of the interference and the components that interfere with one another. A temporary solid will also be created in the graphics window that represents the interference. You can copy the interference report to the clipboard or print it from the commands in the Interference Detected dialog box. When the operation is complete, click the OK button, and the interfering solid will be removed from the screen.

TIP: Performing an interference check does not fix the interfering problem; it only presents a graphical representation of the problem. After analyzing and finding interference, edit the assembly or components to remove the interference. You can also detect interference when driving constraints.

EXERCISE 6-5: ANALYZING AN ASSEMBLY

In this exercise, you analyze a partially completed assembly for interference between parts in a linkage, as shown in the following image on the left, and check the physical properties to verify design intent.

1. Open *ESS_E06_05.iam* in the Chapter 06 folder.

2. Begin the process of checking for interferences in the assembly by zooming into the linkages, as shown in the following image on the right.

Figure 6-98

3. Click the Analyze Interference command on the Inspect tab > Interference panel.

4. In the Analyze Interference dialog box, define Set #1 by selecting two components; *ESS_E06_01-Crank:1* and *ESS_E06_05-Claw1:1,* labeled (1) in the following image on the left.

5. Click the Define Set #2 button, then select the *ESS_E06_05-Spyder1:1*, labeled (2) in the following image on the left.

6. Click the OK button. Notice that the Interference Detected dialog box is displayed, as shown in the following image on the right, and the amount of interference displays on the parts of the assembly.

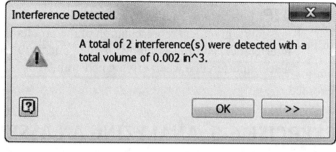

Figure 6-99

7. Click the More >> button to expand the dialog box and display additional information.

8. Click the OK button to close the Interference Detected dialog box.

9. The design intent of the lifting mechanism relies on the correct selection of materials. This impacts the strength and mass of the assembly. You will now display the physical properties of the entire assembly. Change the viewpoint to the Home View.

10. In the browser, right-click on the top level assembly *ESS_E06_05.iam*, and then click iProperties from the menu, as shown in the following image on the left.

11. When the iProperties dialog box displays, click the Physical tab and notice that the General Properties are displayed as N/A, noting that the properties are out of date.

12. Click the Update button, as shown in the following image on the right. Notice that the physical properties of the assembly are updated.

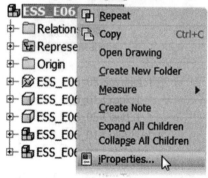

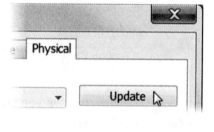

Figure 6-100

13. Click the Close button to dismiss this dialog box.

14. Close all open files. Do not save changes. End of exercise.

DRIVING A CONSTRAINT

You can animate mechanical motion by driving an angle, mate, tangent, or insert assembly constraint a set distance or angle. You can only drive one assembly constraint at a time, but you can use equations to create relationships to drive multiple assembly constraints simultaneously. To drive a constraint, right-click on the desired constraint in the browser and click Drive from the menu, as shown in the following image on the left.

The Drive dialog box will appear, as shown in the following image on the right. Enter a Start value; the default value is the angle or offset for the constraint. Enter a value for End and a value for Pause Delay if you want a dwell time between the steps. In the dialog box, click the Record button 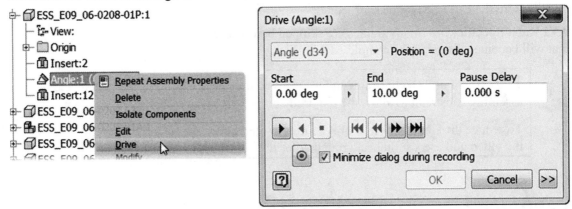 to save a video file (AVI or WMV) of the assembly motion. You can replay the recorded file without having Autodesk Inventor installed.

Figure 6-101

To set more conditions on how the motion will behave, click the More >> button. This action will display the expanded Drive Constraint dialog box, as shown in the following image. Following are descriptions of the options in this portion of the dialog box.

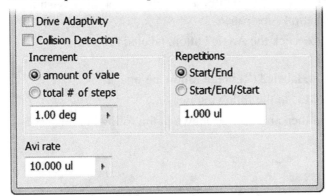

Figure 6-102

Drive Adaptivity. Click this option to adapt the component while the constraint is driven. It only applies to assembly components for which adaptivity has been defined and enabled.

Collision Detection. Click this option to drive the constraint until a collision is detected. When interference is detected, the drive constraint will stop and the components where the collision occurs will be highlighted. It also shows the constraint value at which the collision occurred.

Increment

The options and value in this area determine the method and value that the constraint will be incremented during the animation.

Amount of Value. Increments the offset or angle by this value for each step.

Total # of Steps. The constraint offset or angle is incremented by the same value per step based on the number of steps entered and the difference between the start and stop values.

Repetitions

Sets how the driven constraint will act when it completes a cycle and how many cycles will occur.

Start/End. Drives the constraint from the start value to the end value and resets at the start value.

Start/End/Start. Drives the constraint from the start value to the end value and then drives it in reverse from the end value to the start value.

AVI Rate. Specifies how many frames are skipped before a screen capture is taken of the motion that will become a frame in the completed AVI file.

> **TIP:** If you drive a constraint and it fails, you may need to suppress or delete another assembly constraint to allow the required component to have degrees of freedom.
>
> To reduce the size of a WMV or AVI movie file, reduce the screen size before creating the video and use a solid background color in the graphics window.

EXERCISE 6-6: DRIVING A CONSTRAINT

In this exercise, you drive an angle constraint to simulate motion in an assembly and then drive the constraint to determine if components interfere.

1. Open *ESS_E06_06.iam* in the Chapter 06 folder.

2. First you create an angle constraint between the pivot base and arm. Click the Constrain command on the Assemble tab > Relationships panel.

   a. In the Place Constraint dialog box, click the Angle button, labeled (1) in the following image.

   b. Click the Directed Angle solution, labeled (2) in the following image.

   c. Enter an angle of **45 deg**, labeled (3) in the following image.

   d. In order, select the Base face and then arm face as shown in the following image on the right.

   e. Click the OK button.

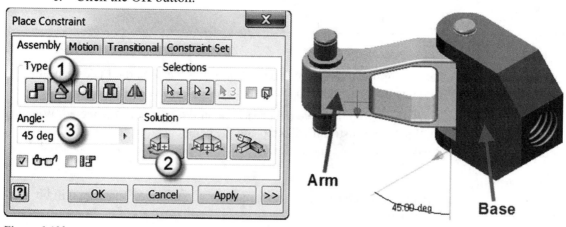

Figure 6-103

3. Now drive the angle constraint you just placed.

   a. In the browser, expand *ESS_E06_06-Pivot_Base:1*.

   b. Right-click on the Angle:1 constraint, and click Drive from the menu.

c. In the Drive Constraint dialog box click the More >> button.

d. Verify that **45.00 deg** is the Start value, labeled (1) in the following image.

e. Change the End value to **120.00 deg**, labeled (2) in the following image.

f. In the Increment section, enter **2 deg**, labeled (3) in the following image.

g. Click the Forward, button labeled (4) in the image. Notice that the arm subassembly interferes with the pivot base between 45.00° and 120.00° but Inventor continues to drive the constraint.

h. Click the Reverse button, labeled (5) in the image.

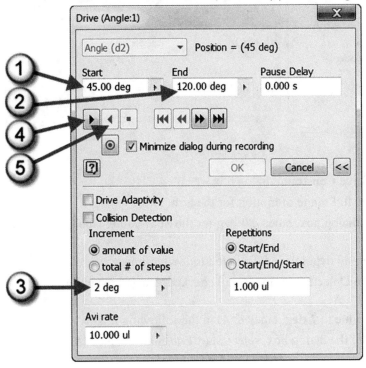

Figure 6-104

4. Next you run collision detection while driving the constraint.

a. In the Drive Constraint dialog box place a check in the Collision Detection section, labeled (1) in the following image.

b. Change the Increment value to **.1 deg**, labeled (2) in the following image.

c. Click the Forward button, labeled (3) in the following image.

d. Notice that a collision is detected at 80.7 degrees as displayed in the dialog box, labeled (4) in the following image.

e. In the graphics window, the parts that interfere are also highlighted, as shown in the following image.

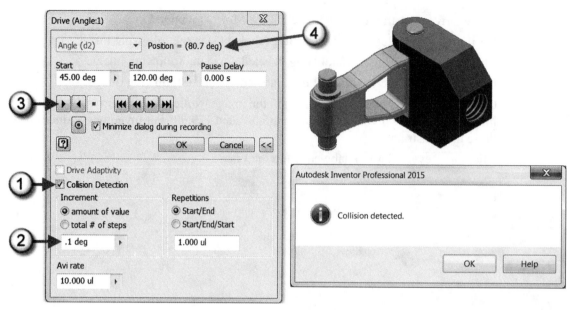

Figure 6-105

5. Click OK to return to the Drive Constraint dialog box.

6. Now perform a check on the full range of motion for the arm.

   a. In the Drive Constraint dialog box, enter **-80 deg** for the Start value, labeled (1) in the following image.

   b. Change the End value to **80 deg**, labeled (2) in the following image.

   c. Ensure that the Collision Detection option is still checked, labeled (3) in the following image.

   d. Change the Increment value to **2 deg**, labeled (4) in the following image.

   e. In the Repetitions area of the dialog box, select Start/End/Start, labeled (5) in the following image.

   f. Change the number of repetitions to **4**, labeled (6) in the following image.

   g. To test the full range of motion for interference, click the Reverse button labeled (7) in the following image.

   h. The arm rotates four times and no collision is detected in this range of motion,

7. In the Drive Constraint dialog box, click the OK button. The 80 degrees represents the maximum angle before collision, and is applied to the Angle constraint.

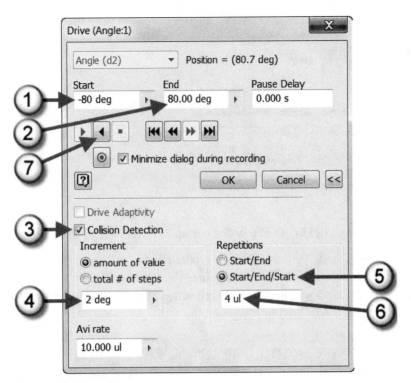

Figure 6-106

8. Close all open files. Do not save changes. End of exercise.

CREATING A PRESENTATION FILE

After creating an assembly, you can create a presentation file to show how the components will be assembled or disassembled, or show the components in different positions similar to an exploded view. In a presentation file you can move components to different positions, hide components, and create an animation that shows how to assemble and disassemble the components. A presentation file has a file extension of .ipn, and is associated with an assembly file. Changes made to the assembly file will be reflected in the presentation file but you cannot create components in a presentation file.

To create a new presentation file, follow one of these methods:

- In the Quick Access toolbar click the down arrow next to the New icon, and click Presentation, as shown in the following image on the left.
- From the Inventor Application menu click New > Presentation, as shown in the following image on the right.

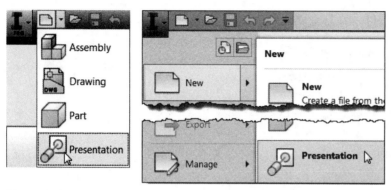

Figure 6-107

You can also create a presentation file by clicking the New file command from one of these areas:

- Quick Access toolbar as shown in the following image on the left
- Inventor Application menu, as shown in the following image second on the left
- Get Started tab > Launch Panel as shown in the following image, third from the left.
- On the Home page, as shown in the following image, on the right.
- Or press CTRL + N.

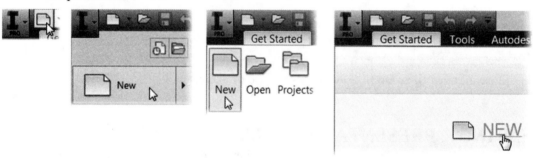

Figure 6-108

The Create New File dialog box appears. Then click the desired templates folder on the left side of the Create New File dialog box and then from the Presentation section on the right side of the dialog box click on the desired template file, as shown in the following image.

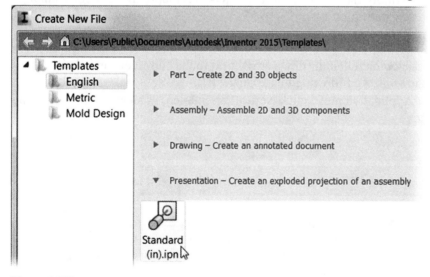

Figure 6-109

Creating Presentation Views

After creating a presentation file, the first step is to create a presentation view by starting the Create View command on the Presentation tab > Create panel as shown in the following image on the left, or right-click and select Create View from the marking menu. Note that you can create multiple presentation views of the same assembly in a presentation file. The Select Assembly dialog box appears, as shown in the following image on the right. The dialog box is divided into two sections: Assembly and Explosion Method.

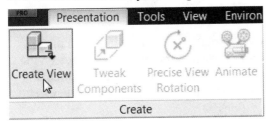

Figure 6-110

Assembly

In this section, you determine on which assembly and design view to base the presentation view.

File. If an assembly file is open it will appear in the drop-down list. Select an assembly file or navigate to and select an assembly file on which to base the presentation view.

Options. Click to display the File Open Options dialog box. Use this dialog box to select design view representations, positional representations, and level of detail representations.

Explosion Method

In this section, you can choose to manually or automatically explode the parts, meaning that you separate the parts a given distance.

Manual. The components will not be exploded automatically. After the presentation view is created, you can add tweaks that will move or rotate the parts.

Automatic. The parts will be exploded automatically with a given value.

Create Trails. If you clicked Automatic, check this option to create trails. Trails are lines that show how the parts are exploded.

Distance. If Automatic is selected, enter a value that the parts will be exploded.

After making your selection, click the OK button to create a presentation view. The components will appear in the graphics window and a presentation view will appear in the browser. If you clicked the Automatic option, the parts will be exploded automatically. To determine how the parts will be exploded, Autodesk Inventor analyzes the assembly constraints. If you constrained parts using the mate plane option and the arrows perpendicular to the plane (normals) for both parts were pointing outward, they will be exploded away from each other the defined distance.

Think of the mating parts as two magnets that want to push themselves in opposite directions. The grounded component in the browser will be the component that stays stationary, and the other components will move away from it. If you are creating trails automatically, they will generally come from the center of the part, not necessarily from the center of the holes. After expanding all of the children in the browser, you can see numerically how the parts exploded. Once the parts are exploded, the distance is referred to as a tweak. The number by each tweak reflects the distance that the component is moved from the base component.

Tweaking Components

After creating the presentation view, you manually move or rotate the components with the Tweak command on the Presentation tab > Create panel as shown in the following image on the left or right-click and click Tweak Component from the marking menu. The Tweak Component dialog box will appear, as shown in the following image on the right. The Tweak Component dialog box has two areas: Create Tweak and Transformations.

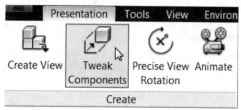 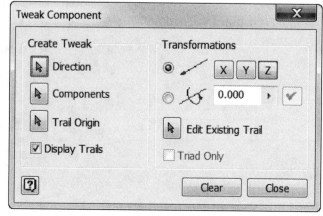

Figure 6-111

Create Tweak

In this section, you select the components to tweak, set the direction and origin of the tweak, and control trail visibility.

Direction. Determine the direction or axis of rotation for the tweak. After clicking the Direction button, select an edge, face, or feature of any component in the graphics window to set the direction triad (X, Y, and Z) for the tweak. The edge, face, or feature that you selected does not need to be on the components you are tweaking.

Components. Select the components to tweak. Click the Components button, and then click the components in the graphics window or browser to tweak. If you selected a component when you started the Create Tweak operation, it will be included in the components automatically. To remove a component from the group, press and hold the CTRL key and click the component.

Trail Origin. Set the origin for the trail. Click the Trail Origin button, and then click in the graphics window to set the origin point. If you do not specify the trail origin, it will be placed at the center of mass for the part.

Display Trails. Click if you want to see the tweak trails for the selected components. Clear the checkbox to hide the trails.

Transformations

In this section, you set the type and value of a tweak.

Linear. Click the button next to the arrow and line to move the selected components in a linear fashion.

Rotation. Click the button next to the arrow and arc to rotate the selected components.

X, Y, Z. Click the X, Y, or Z coordinate button to determine the direction for a linear tweak or the axis for a rotational tweak. Alternately, you can select the arrow on the triad that represents the X, Y, or Z direction.

Tweak Distance/Tweak Angle Field. Enter a positive or negative value for the tweak distance or rotation angle, or click a point in the graphics window and move the cursor with the mouse button depressed to set the distance.

Apply. After making all selections, click the Apply button to complete the tweak.

Edit Existing Trail. To edit an existing tweak, click the Edit Existing Trail button. Select the tweak in the graphics window, and change the desired settings.

Triad Only. Click the Triad Only option to rotate the direction triad without rotating selected components. Enter the angle of rotation, and then click the Apply button. After you rotate the triad direction, you can use it to define tweaks.

Clear. Click the Clear button to remove all of the settings and set up for another tweak.

To tweak a component, follow these steps:

1. Issue the Tweak Components command.
2. Determine the direction or axis of rotation for the tweak by clicking the Direction button and selecting an edge, face, or feature.
3. Select the components to tweak by clicking the Components button and clicking the components in the graphics window or browser that will be tweaked.
4. Select any additional trail origin points.
5. Determine whether or not you want trails to be visible.
6. Set the type of tweak to linear or rotation.
7. Click the X, Y, or Z coordinate button to determine the direction for a linear tweak or the axis for a rotational tweak.
8. Enter a value for the tweak in the text box, or select a point on the screen and drag the part into its new position.
9. Click the Apply button in the Tweak Component dialog box.

To edit a tweak, click the tweak in the browser and enter a new value in the cell that appears in the lower-left corner of the browser, as shown in the following image, and press ENTER to use the new value.

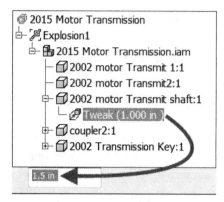

Figure 6-112

To extend all of the tweaks the same distance, right-click on the assembly's name in the browser, and select Auto Explode from the menu, as shown in the following image on the left. Enter a value, and click the OK button, as shown in the following image on the right, and all of the tweaks will be extended the same distance. You cannot use negative values with the Auto Explode method.

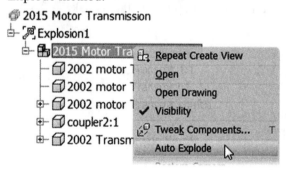 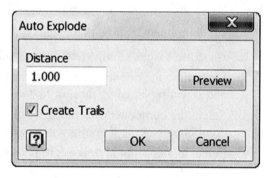

Figure 6-113

Animate Tweaks

After you have tweaked the components, you can animate the components to show how they assemble or disassemble. To animate the tweaks, click the Animate command on the Presentation tab > Create panel, as shown in the following image on the left. The Animation dialog box will appear as shown in the following image on the right. The Animation dialog box has three sections: Parameters, Motion, and Animation Sequence, which is located by selecting the More >> button.

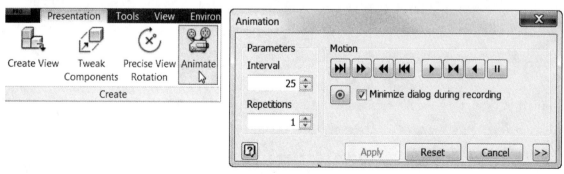

Figure 6-114

Parameters

In this section, you specify the playback speed and the number of repetitions for the animation.

Interval. Set this value for the playback speed of the animation in frames. The higher the number, the greater the number of steps in the tweak but slower the animation. A smaller number will speed up the animation.

Repetitions. Set the number of times to repeat the playback. Enter the desired number of repetitions, or use the up or down arrow to select the number. To change the number of repetitions after playing the motion, click the Reset button on the dialog box, and then enter a new value.

To animate tweaks, follow these steps:

1. Start the Animate command.
2. Set the number of repetitions.
3. Adjust the tweaks as needed.
4. Click the play button to view the animation in the graphics window.
5. To record the animation to a file, click the Record button, and then click one of the Play buttons to start recording.

Changing the Animation Sequence

Click the more button >> in the lower-right corner of the Animation dialog box to see and edit the sequence of the tweaks. In the Animation Sequence section, you can change the sequence in which the tweaks happen, select the tweak, and then select an operation at the bottom of the dialog box to move or group the selected tweak(s). The operations are explained next. For example, in the image on the left, each component will move until its complete cycle is over before another component starts to move. In the image on the right, notice all sequence numbers have changed to a value of 1. This means when the animation begins, all components will move at the same time at the same rate of speed. Experiment with the sequencing of an exploded assembly to gain more dramatic animation results.

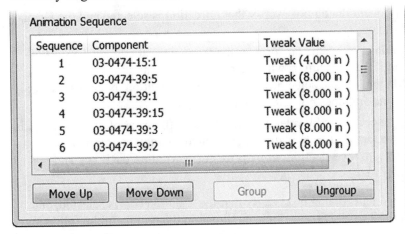
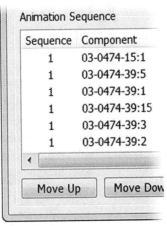

Figure 6-115

Move Up. Click to move the selected tweak up one place in the list.

Move Down. Click to move the selected tweak down one place in the list.

Group. Select a number of tweaks, and then click the Group button. When tweaks are grouped, all of the tweaks in the group will move together as you change the sequence. The group assumes the sequence order of the lowest tweak number.

Ungroup. After selecting a tweak that belongs to a group, you can click the Ungroup button, and the tweak can then be moved individually in the list. The first tweak in the group assumes a number that is one higher than the group. The remaining tweaks are numbered sequentially following the first.

EXERCISE 6-7: CREATING A PRESENTATION VIEW

In this exercise, you create a presentation view of an existing assembly, and you add tweaks to the components to create an exploded view.

1. Create a presentation file.

    a. Click the New command on the Quick Access toolbar.

    b. Select the English template folder, and in the Presentation area double-click Standard (in).ipn.

2. Next you create a presentation view.

    a. Click the Create View command on the Presentation tab > Create panel.

    b. Click the Open an Existing File button next to the File field. *Open ESS_E06_07.iam* in the Chapter 06 folder.

    c. In the Select Assembly dialog box, verify that the Explosion Method is set to Manual.

    d. Click OK to create the view. Your display should appear similar to the following image on the left.

3. In the browser, click the plus sign in front of Explosion1 and the plus sign in front of *ESS_E06_07.iam* to expand their components. The assembly components are displayed so you can select components in the graphics window or in the browser.

4. Next, you tweak the location of the nut.

    a. Click the Tweak Components command on the Presentation tab > Create panel.

    b. In the Tweak Component dialog box, verify that Direction is selected and the Display Trails option is checked.

    c. In the graphics window, move the cursor over the front circular edge of *ESS_E06-ValvePlate.ipt:1* until the triad aligns with the center of plate as shown in the following image on the left and select it to set the axis orientation. Note that this only sets the direction triad and does not select the component.

    d. Add the nut to the selection set by selecting on the nut at the front of the assembly. In the browser, observe that *ESS_E06-NutB* is highlighted. If another component is selected, remove it from the selection set by pressing down the CTRL key and selecting it.

    e. In the Tweak Components dialog box, verify that the Z button Z is selected, and then enter **1.75** in the Tweak Distance field as shown in the middle of the following image.

    f. Click the Apply button , to create the tweak. Your display should appear similar to the following image on the right.

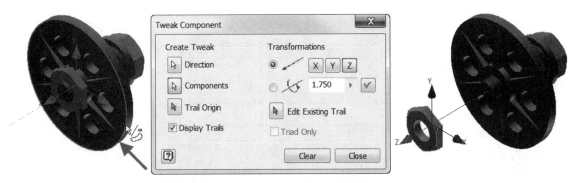

Figure 6-116

 TIP: After you define the tweak triad, you can select a component or group of components and then drag them to create a tweak. This way, you can quickly arrange your components visually. If needed, you can edit the values of the tweaks in the browser.

5. Next you tweak the valve plate.

   a. In the graphics window select *ESS_E06-ValvePlate.ipt:1*.

   b. Hold down the CTRL key, and click the nut to deselect it. Observe that the valve plate is the only entry highlighted in the browser.

   c. Enter **0.875** in the Tweak Distance field of the dialog box.

   d. Click Apply to create the tweak. Your display should appear similar to the following image on the left.

6. Next you tweak the nut on the back of the assembly.

   a. Deselect *ESS_E06-ValvePlate.ipt:1* from the selection set by holding down the CTRL key and selecting it in the graphics window.

   b. Release the CTRL key and select the back nut *ESS_E06-NutA.ipt:1*.

   c. Enter **-4.5** in the Tweak Distance field. The negative value will move the nut away from the other components.

   d. Click Apply to create the tweak. Your display should appear similar to the following image on the right.

Figure 6-117

7. Complete this phase of the exercise by adding the following tweaks:

Part Name	Tweak Value
ESS_E06-WasherB.ipt:1	-4
ESS_E06-Pin.ipt:1	-3.125
ESS_E06-Spring.ipt:1	-1.5
ESS_E06-WasherA.ipt:1	-1
ESS_E06-Diaphragm.ipt:1	-0.5

8. Close the Tweak Component dialog box when you are finished. Your display should appear similar to the following image on the left.

9. Next, you adjust an existing tweak. In the browser, expand *ESS_E06-Diaphragm.ipt:1*, *ESS_E06-Spring.ipt:1*, and *ESS_E06-WasherA.ipt:1*. The hierarchy displays tweaks below each component.

10. Turn off the trail display for the tweaks by right-clicking on each of the tweaks, and click Visibility from the menu.

11. Click Tweak (0.500 in) under *ESS_E06-Diaphragm.ipt:1* and below the browser, enter a new value of **-0.125** in the Offset field, and then press ENTER. Observe that the diaphragm moves to its new position as shown in the following image on the right.

Figure 6-118

12. Next, animate the tweaks.

    a. Click the Animate command from the Presentation tab > Create panel.

    b. Click the Play Forward button to view the animation.

    c. When finished, click Cancel in the Animation dialog box.

13. Close all open files. Do not save changes. End of exercise.

CREATING DRAWING VIEWS FROM ASSEMBLIES AND PRESENTATION FILES

After creating an assembly or presentation file, you may want to create drawing views that document them. You can create drawing views from a part file, which was described in Chapter 5, and you can also create drawing views based on an assembly or a presentation file. You can create a drawing view from any presentation view. You create drawing views in the same method you did for a part file, start a new drawing file or open an existing drawing file. Use the Base View command and select the .iam or .ipn file from which to create the drawing. If needed, specify the design view or presentation view in the dialog box. The following image shows a presentation view being selected after a presentation file was chosen.

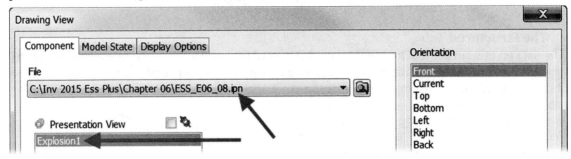

Figure 6-119

BILL OF MATERIAL (BOM)

A Bill of Materials, referred to as a BOM, is a table that contains information about the components that are used in an assembly. A BOM can include item number, quantity, part number, description, vendor, and other information needed to describe the assembly. The BOM is also associative to the assembly; when a component is added or removed from the assembly, the quantity field in the BOM will update to reflect this change in the assembly.

To facilitate managing item numbers, every item is automatically assigned a number, and the item number can be changed or reordered if necessary. Whenever these types of changes are made in the BOM, the same changes are updated automatically in the Parts List and balloons.

Values in the BOM can be changed in several ways. The first way is to add information while inside each individual part through the iProperties dialog box. Another way is to add the part information directly in the BOM with the BOM Editor; then, when the BOM is saved, the information supplied inside of the BOM is also saved back to each part whose information has changed. This is an efficient way to edit the iProperties of multiple parts in one operation.

In order to activate the BOM Editor, you must be inside an assembly file or editing a Parts List in a drawing. In an assembly click the Bill of Materials command on the Manage Tab > Manage panel, as shown in the following image on the left, and the Bill of Materials dialog box appears as shown in the following image on the right.

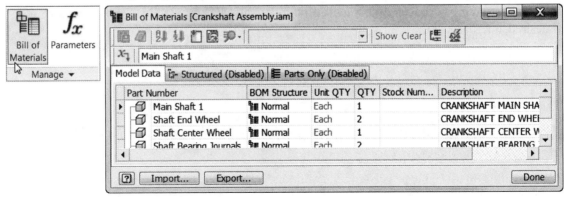

Figure 6-120

There are three tabs in the BOM Editor: Model Data, Structured, and Parts Only.

The Model Data Tab

On this tab the components that make up the assembly are arranged in a format that resembles the assembly browser, as shown in the following image on the left.

The Structured Tab

The data on this tab is the actual BOM data that is used to create a Parts List in a drawing. When arranging an assembly in Structured mode, all components are considered individual items, as shown in the middle of the following image.

Parts Only Tab

When this tab is current, all the parts that make up the assembly are listed, no subassemblies are listed, as shown in the following image on the right. This arrangement of parts is referred to as a flat list.

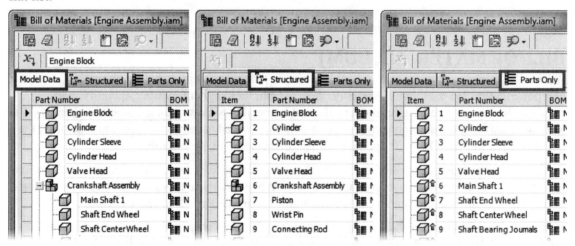

Figure 6-121

Following are common operations performed in the BOM:

Sorting Items in the BOM

Clicking on the Sort button, located in the BOM dialog box, will open the Sort dialog box, as shown in the following image. Sorting can be performed only when in the Structured and Parts Only tabs. In the Sort by area of the dialog box, select the first column to sort by, followed by selecting ascending or descending order. Columns can also be arranged by a secondary sort and, if desired, a tertiary sort.

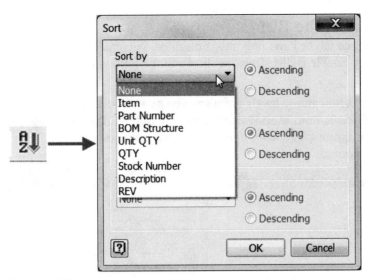

Figure 6-122

Renumbering Items in the BOM

Clicking on the Renumber Items button will display the Item Renumber dialog box, as shown in the following image. This operation is usually performed after sorting information in the BOM dialog box.

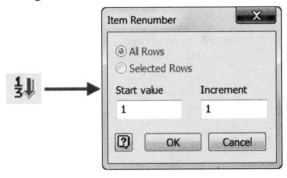

Figure 6-123

Adding Columns to the BOM

You can add columns to the BOM by clicking on the Choose Columns button and the Customization dialog box appears, as shown in the following image. Choose the desired property from the list, and then either double-click or drag and drop on the property so it is next to an existing column heading in the BOM dialog box. You can reorder the columns by dragging on its header and moving it to a new location. You can remove a column by dragging the column header and dropping it in the Customization dialog box.

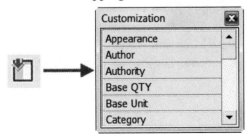

Figure 6-124

Changing the View Options of the BOM

When editing a BOM and the Structured tab or Parts only tab is disabled, you can enable them by right-clicking on the tab and selecting Enable BOM View, as shown in the following image on the left.

For a structured BOM, you can control how many levels are displayed by right-clicking on Structured tab or click the View Options button, as shown in the middle of the following image. The Structured Properties dialog box appears, as shown in the following image on the right, where you can adjust the settings as desired.

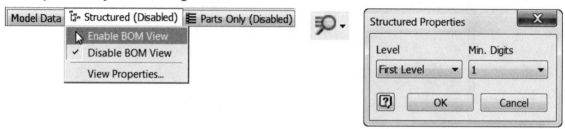

Figure 6-125

Opening a Part from the BOM Editor

The BOM editor can be used to open a part or assembly file. To perform this task, open the BOM editor, select the part from the list, right-click and select Open from the menu, as shown in the following image.

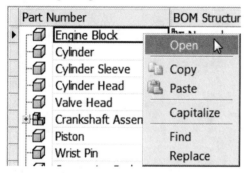

Figure 6-126

While editing a BOM, you can use the following tools, which are similar in functionality to Microsoft Excel:

- Use the SHIFT or CTRL keys to make selection sets of information while in the BOM editor.
- Use the grip point located in the lower-right corner of a cell to expand a cell or blocks of cells.
- BOM cells can be copied from the BOM Editor to another BOM view or to an external editor.
- Copy and paste information from the BOM editor into Microsoft Excel.
- Additional command options are available through a menu. These options include Open, Copy, Paste, Capitalize, Find, and Replace.

EXERCISE 6-8: EDITING A BILL OF MATERIAL (BOM)

In this exercise, you add descriptions, change the material and manipulate the number of items in the BOM.

1. Open *ESS_ E06_08*.iam in the Chapter 06 folder.

2. Start the Bill of Materials command from the Manage Tab > Manage panel.

3. Examine the BOM and if needed resize the columns to show all the data, as shown in the following image. Notice that the Description cells are blank.

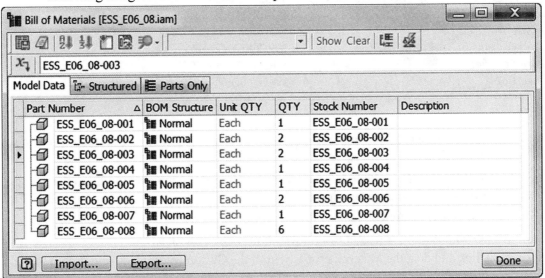

Figure 6-127

 TIP: The individual descriptions of each part can easily be added through the BOM Editor. Using this method, you will NOT have to open each part file and add a description via the iProperties.

4. In the Model Data tab, add a description to each part. Click in each Description cell and fill in the information, as shown in the following image. Only capitalize the first letter in each word.

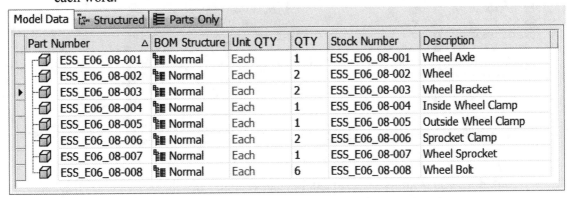

Figure 6-128

5. Most mechanical engineering / design drawing capitalize all words. You can easily capitalize all of the descriptions by doing the following.

   a. Click and drag to select all of the description cells.

b. Right-click and click Capitalize from the menu as shown in the following image on the left.

c. When done all of the descriptions should be capitalized, as shown in the following image on the right.

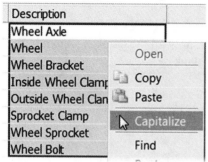

Figure 6-129

6. Next, add a Material column to the BOM. This will allow you to edit or add the material type for each part.

a. To add a column called Material, click the Choose Columns button ⬚ in the dialog box as shown in the following image.

b. The Customization box appears.

c. Scroll down in the Customization box and locate Material.

d. Click and drag the Material property from the Customization box, and drop it to the right of the Description Column heading, as shown in the following image.

e. When finished, dismiss the Customization box by clicking on the Close button (X) located in the upper right of the Customization box, not in the Bill of Materials dialog box.

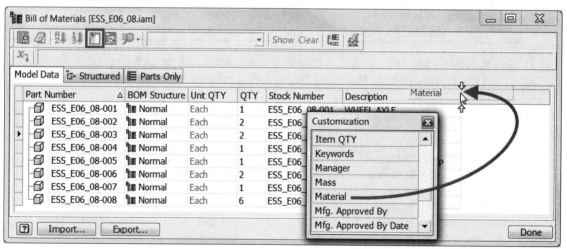

Figure 6-130

7. With the addition of the Material column added, notice that all Materials are listed as Generic. You will now add a material to each part.

a. Begin filling in the material type by double-clicking in the material cell to activate the material drop-down list, as shown in the following image on the left.

b. Select the material from the list for each component, as shown in the image on the right.

c. If you need to resort the parts to the original order click the up arrow in the Part Number column twice Part Number   ⊘.

 TIP: You can copy and paste data from one cell to another or click and drag on the square in the bottom-right corner of the cell ✛ and drag it up or down to copy the data to the highlighted cells.

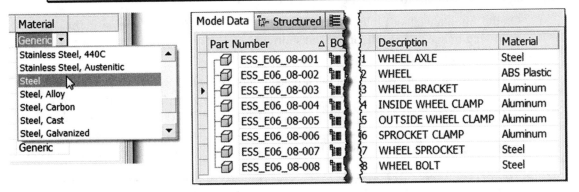

Figure 6-131

8. When finished, click the Done button.

9. If you were working on your own assembly, you would save the assembly and you will also be prompted to save the changes back to the part files whose properties have changed, as shown in the following image. If you save the files for this exercise and you want to run through the exercise again, you will need to copy the original exercise files over the modified files.

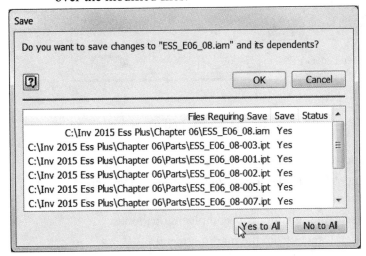

Figure 6-132

10. Close the file. Do not save changes. End of exercise.

CREATING BALLOONS

After you have created a drawing view of an assembly or a presentation file, you can add balloons to parts and/or subassemblies to document the component item numbers. The item numbers are received from the assembly's bill of material. Balloons and parts lists both reference the item numbers from the bill of material, so it does not matter if balloons or a parts list is placed first.

You can add balloons individually to components in a drawing, or you can use the Auto Balloon command to add balloons to selected components in one operation.

Placing Individual Balloons

To add individual balloons to a drawing, follow these steps:

1. On the Annotate tab > Table panel, click the Balloon command, as shown in the following image on the left, or use the shortcut key B.
2. Select a component to balloon.
3. If a balloon or a parts list has not been placed in the drawing, the BOM Properties dialog box will appear, as shown in the following image on the right. The options in this dialog box are explained in the next section. After selecting the BOM View setting click OK.

 TIP: The BOM Properties dialog box will not appear if a parts list or balloon exists in the drawing.

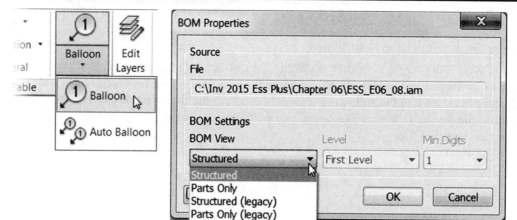

Figure 6-133

4. Position the cursor to place the second point for the leader, and press the left mouse button.
5. Continue to select points to add segments to the balloon's leader, if desired.
6. When finished adding segments to the leader, right-click, and select Continue from the marking menu to create the balloon.
7. Continue adding balloons by selecting components and placing balloons.
8. When done, right-click and click Cancel from the marking menu

 TIP: When placing balloons, the direction of the balloon leader line snaps to 15° increments, to freely move a balloon press the CTRL key while dragging.

A balloon can be aligned horizontally or vertically with another balloon by inferring a point.

BOM Properties Dialog Box Options

Source

Specify the source file on which the BOM will be based.

BOM Settings and BOM View

Structured. A Structured list refers to the top-level components of an assembly in the selected view. Subassemblies and parts that are NOT in a subassembly can be ballooned. Parts that are in a subassembly cannot be ballooned.

Parts Only View. This option allows you to select all the parts of the assembly regardless if they are in a subassembly. Subassemblies cannot be ballooned, but parts in the subassembly can be.

 TIP: In a Parts Only View, components that are in a subassembly are not presented in the list unless they are considered inseparable or purchased.

Level

First Level. Select this option to determine how many levels of subassemblies deep can be selected when placing balloons or displayed in a parts list. In the Min. Digit list you can select how many levels deep to display in a parts list or can be selected.

All Levels. Select this option to be able to select all levels of subassemblies and display all subassembly levels in a parts list.

Min.Digits

Use this command to set the minimum amount of digits displayed for item numbering. The range is fixed from 1 to 6 digits.

Auto Ballooning

In complex assembly drawings, it will become necessary to balloon a number of components. Rather than manually add a balloon to each component, you can use the Auto Balloon command to perform this operation on several components in a single operation automatically. Clicking on the Auto Balloon button under the Annotation tab will display the Auto Balloon dialog box, as shown in the following image. The areas in this dialog box allow you to control how you place balloons.

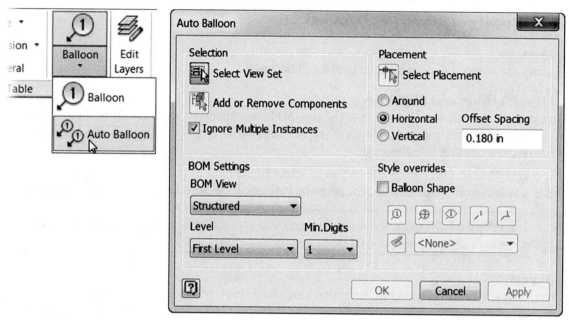

Figure 6-134

Selection

This area requires you to select where to apply the balloons. With the view selected, you then add or remove components to the balloon. The Ignore Multiple Instances option appears in this area, and when the box is checked, multiple instances of the same component will not be ballooned. This action greatly reduces the number of balloon callouts in the drawing. If your application requires multiple instances to each have a balloon, remove the check from this box.

Placement

Select the method to align the balloons: Around, Horizontal or Vertical.

Around

Places balloons for the selected components around the view's boundary. Move the cursor from the center of the view to readjust the balloons to different locations. The following image on the left shows an example where the balloons are located around the view boundary.

Horizontal

Align all balloons horizontally as shown in the middle of the following image; the Offset Spacing option determines the distance between the balloons.

Vertical

Aligns all balloons vertically, as shown in the following image on the right, the distance between the balloons is set with the Offset Spacing option

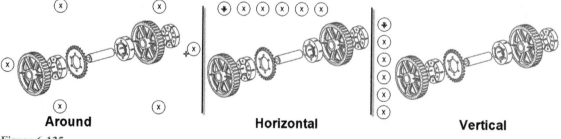

Figure 6-135

BOM Settings

This area allows you to control if balloons are applied to structured or parts only and determine how many levels deep can be ballooned.

Style Overrides

The Style overrides area allows you to change the shape of the balloon and assign a user-defined balloon shape. Click Balloon Shape to enable balloon shape style overrides.

To place balloons with the auto balloon command, follow these steps:

1. Select the view to which to add the balloons.

2. Select the components to which to add balloons. You will notice the color of all selected objects change. Balloons will be applied to these selected objects. To remove components, hold down the SHIFT or CTRL key, and click a highlighted component. This action will deselect the component. You can also select components using a window or crossing window selection technique.

3. Select one of the three placement modes for the balloons: Around, Horizontal or Vertical.

Moving and Aligning Balloons

After you have placed balloons, you can drag a balloon to new locations, as well as reposition the arrows to a different location or point it to a different component by moving the arrow to an edge on a part, as shown in the following image on the left. If a different component is selected the item number will change to reflect the item number of the new component.

To align two balloons vertically or horizontally, click and drag on the center of the balloon to move and drag it over the center of the balloon you want to align to, this infers the center point. Then drag the balloon vertically or horizontally, as long as dotted lines appear, the balloon is aligned. The following image on the rights shows the balloon on the right aligned horizontally to the other balloon.

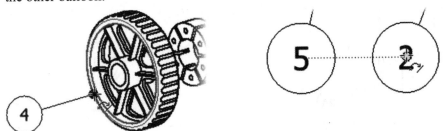

Figure 6-136

Editing a Balloon's Value

You can change the balloon's value/item number by either double-clicking on the balloon or right-clicking on the balloon and clicking Edit Balloon from the menu, as shown in the following image on the left. The Edit Balloon dialog box will appear, as shown in the following image on the right.

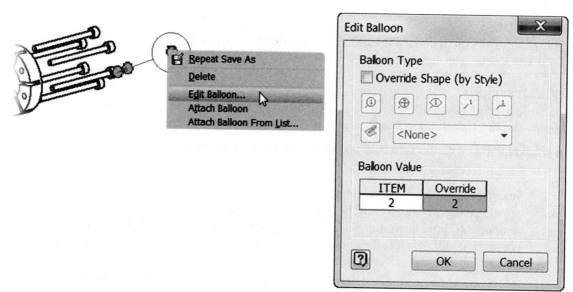

Figure 6-137

In the Balloon Value area you can change the balloon's value by changing the Item or Override. When you edit the Item value, changes will be made to the balloon and will be updated in the Parts List. In the following image on the left the Item was changed to 2A. Notice that both the balloon and the Parts List are updated to the new value.

When you change the value in the Override column, the balloon will update to reflect this change, but the Parts List remains unchanged. The following image on the right illustrates this; the balloon is overridden to a value of 2A, but the Parts List has the item Rod Cap still listed as 2.

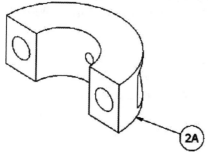

ITEM	QTY	PART NUMBER	Parts
1	1	Connecting Rod	
2A	1	Rod Cap	
3	2	Rod Cap Screw	
4	1	Piston	
5	1	Wrist Pin	

ITEM	QTY	PART NUMBER	Parts
1	1	Connecting Rod	
2	1	Rod Cap	
3	2	Rod Cap Screw	
4	1	Piston	
5	1	Wrist Pin	

Figure 6-138

PARTS LIST

After you have created the drawing views and placed balloons, you can also create a Parts List, as shown in the following image. As noted in the balloon section, components do not need to be ballooned before creating a Parts List.

ITEM	QTY	PART NUMBER	DESCRIPTION	ITEM	QTY	PART NUMBER	DESCRIPTION
		Parts List				Parts List	
8	2	HANDLE CAP	HANDLE CAP	1	1	Arbor Press	ARBOR PRESS
9	1	COLLAR	COLLAR	2	1	FACE PLATE	FACE PLATE
10	1	GIB PLATE	GIB PLATE	3	1	PINION SHAFT	PINION SHAFT
11	1	GROOVE PIN	GROOVE PIN	4	1	LEVER ARM	LEVER ARM
14	4	ANSI B18.3 - 1/4 - 20 UNC - 7/8	Hex Cap Screw	5	1	THUMB SCREW	THUMB SCREW
15	4	BS 4168 - M5 x 16	Hex Cap Screws	6	1	TABLE PLATE	TABLE PLATE
16	1	ISO 4766 - M5 x 5	Hex Cap Screws	7	1	RAM	RAM

Figure 6-139

To create a Parts List, select the Annotate tab >Table panel and click the Parts List command, as shown in the following image on the left. The Parts List dialog box will appear, as shown in the following image on the right. Select a view on which to base the Parts List. Specify the BOM Settings and Properties, see the Creating Balloons section for information about these setting as they are the same and are set upon placing a parts list or a balloon. After specifying your options, click the OK button, and a preview of Parts List will appear attached to your cursor. Click a point in the graphics window to place the Parts List. The information in the list is extracted from the iProperties of each component.

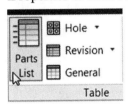

Figure 6-140

Wrapping a Parts List

When creating a parts list that is long, you can wrap it into multiple sections. In the Parts List dialog box place a check in the Enable Automatic Wrap box and then enter the number of sections to break the Parts List into or select the Maximum Rows option to specify the maximum number of rows for each section. You can also choose to have the sections added to the right or the left. The following image shows the results of wrapping the Parts List into two sections and having it added to the left.

Parts List				Parts List			
ITEM	QTY	PART NUMBER	DESCRIPTION	ITEM	QTY	PART NUMBER	DESCRIPTION
8	2	HANDLE CAP - 2028	HANDLE CAP	1	1	Arbor Press - 4571	Arbor Press
9	1	COLLAR - 5339	COLLAR	2	1	FACE PLATE - 5187	FACE PLATE
10	1	GIB PLATE - 8783	GIB PLATE	3	1	SHAFT - 5593	PINION SHAFT
11	1	GROOVE PIN - 3597	GROOVE PIN	4	1	LEVER ARM - 3016	LEVER ARM
14	4	HHCS - 8840	1/4 - 20 UNC - 7/8 HS HCS	5	1	THUMB SCREW - 1166	THUMB SCREW
16	1	ISO 4766 - M5 x 5 - 1411	Slotted Headless Set Screw	6	1	TABLE PLATE - 9591	TABLE PLATE
15	4	ISO 4026 - M5 x 16 - 1422	Hexagon socket set screws	7	1	RAM - 4017	RAM

Figure 6-141

While editing a Parts List you can also manually split the table. To do so, right-click on the row after the one that you want to split and click Wrap Table at Row, as shown in the following image. You can remove the wrap by right-clicking on the row and selecting the same option, to remove the checkmark next to the Wrap Table at Row option.

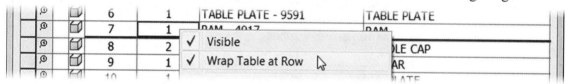

Figure 6-142

After wrapping a parts list, a thicker black line will appear in the Parts List dialog box representing where the wrap begins. You can remove the wrap by right-clicking on the row above where the wrap begins and clicking Wrap Text at Table, as shown in the following image.

Figure 6-143

Editing Parts List - BOM Data

Once a Parts List is created, and if there is missing or inaccurate data, you can open the BOM Editor directly from the drawing environment and edit the assembly BOM. You can save these changes back to the affected components by saving the drawing and accepting the prompt to also save the assembly and corresponding component files. To edit the BOM from a parts list, right-click on the Parts List in the drawing and then click Bill of Materials from the menu, as shown in the following image on the left. The Bill of Materials dialog box appears for the specific assembly file. The dialog box provides a convenient location to edit the iProperties and Bill of Material properties for all components in the assembly. Then edit the BOM as you learned in the previous Bill of Material (BOM) section. The following image on the right illustrates the Part Number and Description for the Arbor Press entry capitalized. Complete the edits by clicking the Done button and then save the drawing, assembly and the effected assembly and component files.

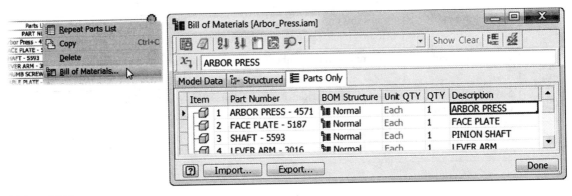

Figure 6-144

Editing a Parts List

After placing a parts list you can edit the appearance and override values in the parts list. To edit a parts list, right-click on the Parts List in a drawing and select Edit Parts List from the menu, or double-click on the Parts List in the drawing.

This action displays the Edit Parts List dialog box, as shown in the following image. The row of icons along the top of the dialog box consists of operations that allow you to change the Parts List.

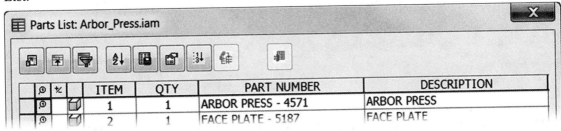

Figure 6-145

Following are descriptions of the icons in the Parts List dialog box:

Button	Function	Explanation
	Column Chooser	Opens the Parts List Column Chooser dialog box, where you can add, remove, or change the order of the columns for the selected Parts List. Data for these columns is populated from the properties of the component files.
	Group Settings	Opens the Group Settings dialog box, where you select Parts List columns to be used as a grouping key and group different components into one Parts List row. This button is active only when generating a Parts List using the Structured mode.
	Filter Settings	Opens the Filter Settings dialog box, where you can define such filter settings as Assembly View Representations, Ballooned Items Only, Item Number Range, Purchased Items, and Standard Content from which to filter the information. Once a filter is selected, you then filter out rows without changing the data in the Parts List. You can also add Parts List filters to a Parts List style.
	Sort	Opens the Sort Parts List dialog box, where you can change the sort order for items in the selected Parts List.
	Export	Opens the Export Parts List dialog box so that you can save the selected Parts List to an external file of the file type you choose.

	Table Layout	Opens the Parts List Table Layout dialog box where you can change the title text, spacing, or heading location for the selected Parts List.
	Renumber Items	Renumbers item numbers of parts in the Parts List consecutively.
	Save Item Overrides to BOM	Saves item overrides back to the assembly Bill of Materials.
	Member Selection	Used with iAssemblies. Clicking this button opens a dialog box where you can select which members of the iAssembly to include in the Parts List.

Creating Custom Parts

Custom parts are useful for displaying parts in the Parts List that are not components or graphical data, such as paint or a finishing process. To add a custom part, right-click on an existing part in the Edit Parts List dialog box, as shown in the following image, and click Insert Custom Part. When a custom part no longer needs to be documented in the Parts List, you can right-click in the row of the custom part, and click Remove Custom Part from the menu.

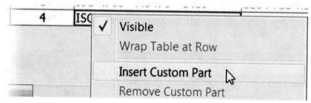

Figure 6-146

EXERCISE 6-9: CREATING A DRAWING FROM AN ASSEMBLY

In this exercise, you create drawing views of an assembly and then add a parts list and balloons.

1. Open the drawing *ESS_E06_09.idw* in the Chapter 06 folder. This drawing consists of one blank D size sheet with a border and title block.

2. First, you format the drawing sheet.

   a. In the browser, right-click Sheet:1 and click Edit Sheet from the menu.

   b. In the Edit Sheet dialog box, rename the sheet by typing **Assembly** in the Name field.

   c. In the Size list, select C as shown in the following image.

   d. When finished, click the OK button.

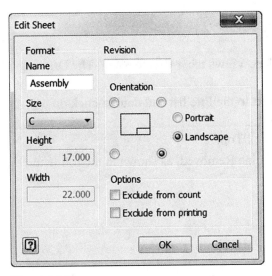

Figure 6-147

3. Next, you update the file properties in order to update the title block fields.

   a. Click the Inventor Application Menu > iProperties.

   b. Click on the Summary tab and make the following changes:

      i. In the Title area, enter **PUMP ASSEMBLY**.

      ii. In the Author area, enter your name or initials, as shown in the following image on the left.

   c. Click the Project tab and make the following changes:

      i. In Part number, enter **123-456-789** as shown in the following image on the right.

      ii. In Creation Date, click the down arrow, and then select Today's date.

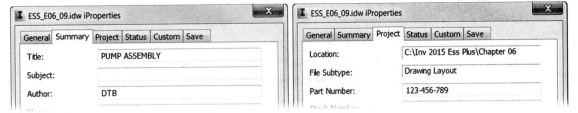

Figure 6-148

      iii. When finished, click the OK button.

   d. Zoom in to the title block and notice that the entries have updated, as shown in the following image.

DRAWN DTB	12/24/2013		
CHECKED		TITLE	
QA			
MFG		**PUMP ASSEMBLY**	
APPROVED			
		SIZE C	DWG NO 123-456-789	REV
		SCALE		SHEET 1 OF 1

Figure 6-149

4. Next you create drawing views.

    a. Zoom out to view the entire sheet.

    b. Click the Base View command on the Place Views tab > Create panel. The Drawing View dialog box appears.

    c. Click the Open an Existing File button next to the File list and double-click on *ESS_E06_09.iam* in the Chapter 06 folder.

    d. From the Orientation area in the dialog click Top.

    e. Set the Style to Hidden Line, not Hidden Line Removed, as shown in the following image.

Figure 6-150

    f. If needed set the Scale to 1:1

    g. Locate the view by clicking in the upper-left corner of the drawing sheet, similar to what is shown in the following image. Note that the preview of the view is shaded until you select a point to locate the view.

    h. Create the view by right-clicking and click Create from the marking menu.

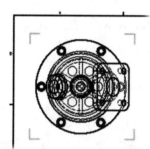

Figure 6-151

5. Before you create a section view, you turn off the Section property for some components so that they are not sectioned. Following these steps:

    a. In the browser, expand the Assembly sheet.

    b. In the browser, expand *View1: ESS_E06_09.iam*.

    c. Expand *ESS_E06_09.iam*.

    d. Hold down the CTRL key and select:

        i. *ESS_E06-Pin.ipt:1*

        ii. *ESS_E06-Spring.ipt:1*

        iii. *ESS_E06-NutA.ipt:1*

        iv. *ESS_E06-NutB.ipt:1*

    e. Right-click on one of the highlighted parts in the browser, and from the menu click Section Participation > None, as shown in the following image.

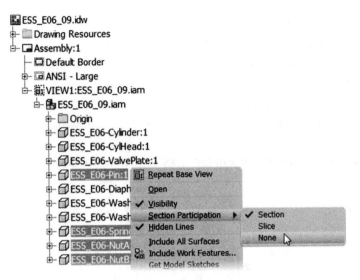

Figure 6-152

6. Next, you create a section view from the top view.

    a. Click the Section View command on the Place Views tab > Create panel.

    b. Select in the top view of the assembly, and draw a horizontal section line through the center of the top view, as shown in the following image on the left.

    c. Right-click and click Continue from the marking menu.

    d. Move the cursor down below the top view as shown in the middle of the following image.

    e. Click to place the view.

    f. Notice that the nuts, spring, and pin are visible in the sectioned view but are not sectioned, as shown in the following image on the right.

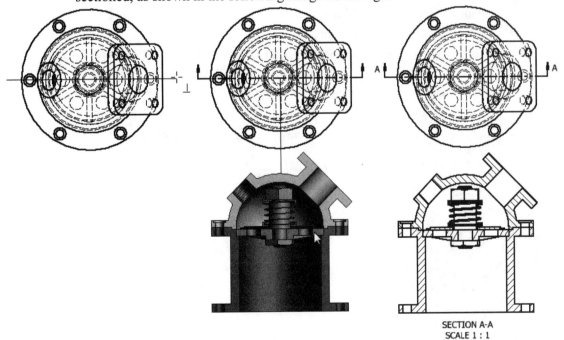

Figure 6-153

7. Now hide two components from displaying in the top view.

   a. In the browser, under the component listing VIEW1:ESS_E06_09.iam > *ESS_E06_09.iam*, hold down the CTRL key and select:

      i.   *ESS_E06-CylHead:1*

      ii. *ESS_E06-Spring:1*

   b. Right-click, and clear the checkmark from Visibility as shown in the following image on the left.

   c. The cylinder head and the spring do not display in the top view, as shown in the image on the right.

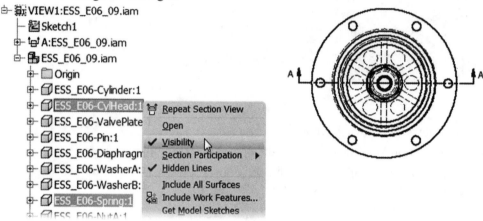

Figure 6-154

8. Next, add a text note stating that the cylinder head and spring are not visible.

   a. Click the Text command in the Annotate tab > Text panel.

   b. Select a point below the left of the top view.

   c. Change the text size to **.25 inches**.

   d. Change the text justification to center.

   e. In the text entry area, type **FOR CLARITY CYLINDER HEAD AND**, press ENTER to go to the next line, and type **SPRING REMOVED FROM VIEW**.

   f. Click OK and the text will be added to the top view.

   g. Right-click and click OK from the marking menu to exit the command.

   h. Reposition the text below the top view, similar to what is shown in the following image.

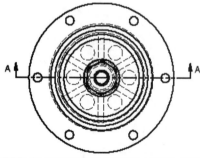

FOR CLARITY CYLINDER HEAD AND
SPRING REMOVED FROM VIEW

Figure 6-155

9. Next, you create a Parts List to identify the item number, quantity, part number, and description.

   a. Begin by clicking the Parts List command on the Annotate tab > Table panel.

   b. The Parts List dialog box will display, select the sectioned view.

   c. Verify that the BOM View is set to Structured, and click the OK button.

   d. Move the Parts List until it joins the title block and border (lower-right corner), and then click to place it. Zoom in to display the Parts List, as shown in the following image.

PARTS LIST			
ITEM	QTY	PART NUMBER	DESCRIPTION
1	1	Cylinder	CYLINDER
2	1	Cyl Head	CYLINDER HEAD
3	1	Valve plate	VALVE PLATE
4	1	Pin	THREADED PIN
5	1	Diaphragm	DIAPHRAGM
6	1	Washer A	RETAINING WASHER
7	1	ESS_E06_05-WasherB	RETAINING WASHER
8	1	Spring	SPRING - Ø1 X Ø22 X 25
9	1	Nut A	FLAT NUT, REG - M16 X 1.5
10	1	Nut B	FLAT NUT, THIN - M16 X 1.5

DRAWN			
DTB	12/24/2013		
CHECKED			
		TITLE	
QA			A
MFG		PUMP ASSEMBLY	

Figure 6-156

10. Next, you change the layout of the parts list.

    a. Double-click on the Parts List in the graphics window.

    b. In the Parts List dialog box, click the Table Layout button .

    c. Change the header so it is at the bottom of the parts list table by clicking the Bottom option (middle option in the list) in the Heading area, as shown in the following image.

    d. Click OK to close the Parts List Table Layout dialog box. Keep the Parts List dialog box open.

Figure 6-157

11. Next, you add a column to the parts list and reorder a column.

    a. Click the Column Chooser button to display the Parts List Column Chooser dialog box.

    b. In the Available Properties list, select MATERIAL.

c. Click the Add button in the middle of the dialog box, as shown in the following image on the left.

d. Move the Description Column up by selecting DESCRIPTION in the Selected Properties list and click the Move Up button twice, as shown in the image on the right.

e. Click OK to close the Parts List Colum Chooser dialog box, but again leave the Parts List dialog box open.

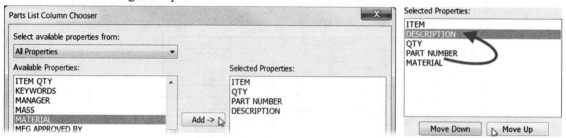

Figure 6-158

12. Next, you edit the column widths.

a. In the Parts List dialog box, right-click on the DESCRIPTION header and click Column Width from the menu, as shown in the following image on the left.

b. Enter **2.25** in the Column Width dialog box, as shown in the following image on the right.

c. Click OK to complete this edit.

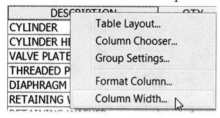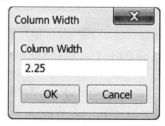

Figure 6-159

13. Change the width of the following columns
a. PART NUMBER = **2**
b. ITEM = **1**

14. Next, you change the order in which the items are sorted.

a. Click the Sort button ![sort] to display the Sort Parts List dialog box.

b. Change the Sort by option to ITEM.

c. Change the sort order to Descending, as shown in the following image.

Figure 6-160

15. Click the OK button to close the Sort Parts List dialog box.

16. Click OK to make the changes and close the Parts List dialog box.

17. Move the Parts List so that it is flush with the border and the title block. Your display should appear similar to the following image.

ITEM	DESCRIPTION	QTY	PART NUMBER	MATERIAL
10	FLAT NUT, THIN - M16 X 1.5	1	Nut B	Steel, Mild
9	FLAT NUT, REG - M16 X 1.5	1	Nut A	Steel, Mild
8	SPRING - Ø1 X Ø22 X 25	1	Spring	Stainless Steel
7	RETAINING WASHER	1	ESS_E06_05-WasherB	Steel, Mild
6	RETAINING WASHER	1	Washer A	Steel, Mild
5	DIAPHRAGM	1	Diaphragm	Stainless Steel
4	THREADED PIN	1	Pin	Steel, Mild
3	VALVE PLATE	1	Valve plate	Steel, Mild
2	CYLINDER HEAD	1	Cyl Head	Cast Iron
1	CYLINDER	1	Cylinder	Cast Iron

PARTS LIST

DRAWN DTB	12/24/2013		
CHECKED			
QA		TITLE	
MFG		PUMP ASSEMBLY	

Figure 6-161

TIP: You can resize the width of a column by clicking and dragging on a column's border , like you would with Microsoft Excel.

18. Zoom into the section view.

19. Next, you add a balloon.
    a. Click the Balloon command on the Annotate tab > Table panel.
    b. Select the right-outside edge of the cylinder as the start of the leader.
    c. Move the cursor up and to the right and click a point on the sheet to define the end of the first leader segment.
    d. Right-click and select Continue from the marking menu to place the balloon, as shown in the following image on the left.
    e. Note that the item number in the balloon corresponds to the item number in the Parts List.

20. Next, you add balloons with the Auto Balloon command.
    a. Start the Auto Balloon command from the Annotate tab > Table panel.
    b. Select the sectioned assembly view.
    c. Select all the components in the view by drawing a window around all of the components in the section view. The cylinder will not be selected because it has already been ballooned.
    d. Click the Select Placement button.
    e. Select Horizontal for the placement.
    f. Change the Offset Spacing to **0.5 inches**.
    g. Locate the balloons by clicking a point above the cylinder.

h.   Click OK in the Auto Balloon dialog box to create the balloons. When done, your view should resemble the following image on the right.

21.   If desired you can reposition the balloons.

22.   Close all open files. Do not save changes. End of exercise.

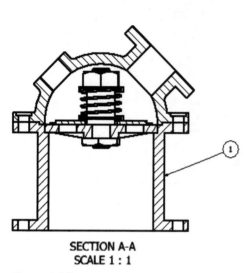

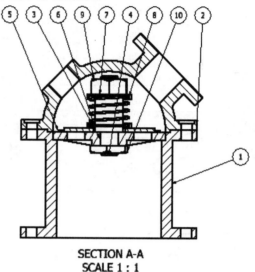

Figure 6-162

APPLYING YOUR SKILLS

Skills Exercise 6-1

In this exercise, you create a new component for a charge pump and then assemble the pump.

1.   Open *ESS_E06_10.iam* in the Chapter 06 folder.

2.   Place the following predefined components into the right side of the assembly as shown in the following image:

- 2 occurrences of *ESS_E06_10-M8x30.ipt*
- 1 occurrence of *ESS_E06_10-Seal.ipt*
- 1 occurrence of *ESS_E06_10-Union.ipt*

Figure 6-163

3. Next, create the Connector in the context of the assembly. Project edges from the *ESS_E06_10-Body.ipt:1* (pump body) to define the flange. Use the dimensions in the following image to complete the gland. The missing dimensions and constraints are acquired from the projected edges.

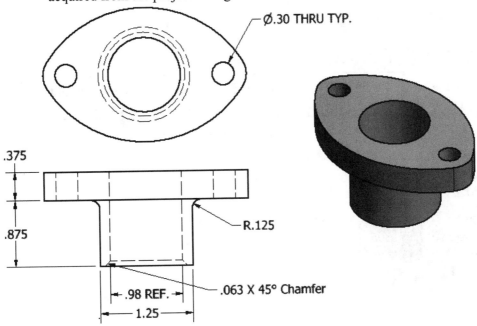

Ø.30 THRU TYP.

.375

.875

R.125

.98 REF.

.063 X 45° Chamfer

1.25

Figure 6-164

4. Use assembly constraints to build the assembly as shown in the following two images.

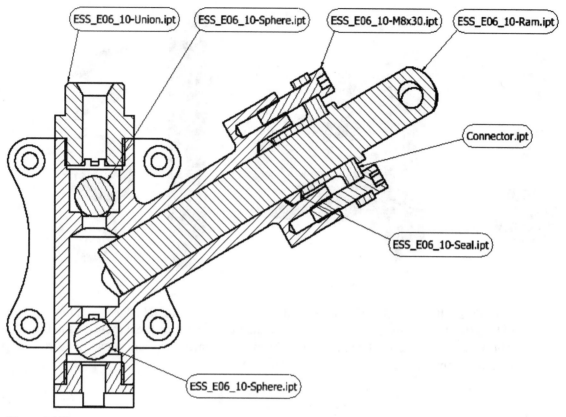

Figure 6-165

 TIP: Use the origin axis in the Valve Sphere part file to align it to the center of the body and use a tangent constraint to assemble the Valve Sphere to the inside chamfered face.

Figure 6-166

5. Close all open files. Do not save changes. End of exercise.

Skills Exercise 6-2

In this exercise, you create drawing views of an assembly, and add a parts list and balloons for a charge pump. The charge pump assembly is the completed version of the assembly that you created in skills exercise 6-1.

Create a new drawing using the ANSI (in) DWG or IDW template with a C size sheet named Assembly.

1. Use the Base View command to create a Top view of *ESS_E06_11.iam* with a scale of 1:1.

2. Use the top view to create a sectioned front view and exclude the following components from being sectioned:

   - *ESS_E06_10-Sphere:1*
   - *ESS_E06_10-Sphere:2*
   - *ESS_E06_10-Ram:1*
   - *ESS_E06_10-M8x30:1*
   - *ESS_E06_10-M8x30:2*

3. Use the Base View command to create an ISO Top Right view of *ESS_E06_11.iam* with a scale of 1:1. When done creating the views, your screen should resemble the following image.

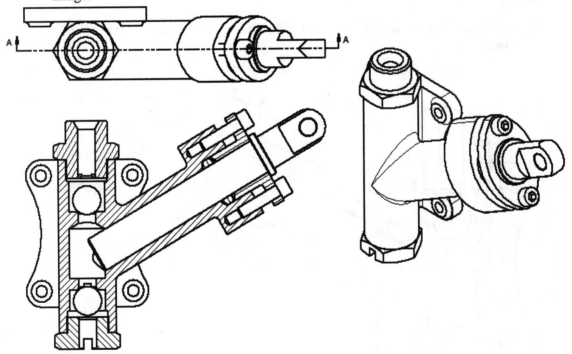

Figure 6-167

4. Insert a Parts List on top of the title block.

5. Add a Material column to the parts list and change the material of all components to steel.

6. Modify the parts list and title block to match what is shown in the following image. Note how the item numbers are sorted in descending order and the header row is at the bottom of the table.

ITEM	DESCRIPTION	QTY	PART NUMBER	MATERIAL
8	CONNECTOR	1	ESS_E06_11-CONNECTOR	STEEL
7	HHCS – PURCHASED	2	ESS_E06_10-M8x30	STEEL
6	SEAL	1	ESS_E06_10-Seal	STEEL
5	UNION	1	ESS_E06_10-Union	STEEL
4	SEAT	1	ESS_E06_10-Seat	STEEL
3	RAM	1	ESS_E06_10-Ram	STEEL
2	VALVE SPHERE	2	ESS_E06_10-Sphere	STEEL
1	BODY	1	ESS_E06_10-Body	STEEL
ITEM	DESCRIPTION	QTY	PART NUMBER	MATERIAL

PARTS LIST

DRAWN DTB	12/26/2013		
CHECKED			
QA		TITLE	
MFG		**CHARGE PUMP ASSEMBLY**	
APPROVED			
		SIZE **C**	DWG NO **ESS_E06_11**	REV
		SCALE	SHEET 1 OF 1	

Figure 6-168

7. Add balloons in the section view to identify the components, as shown in the following image.

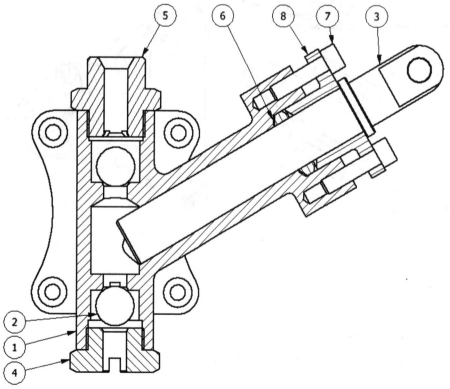

Figure 6-169

8. Close all open files. Do not save changes. End of exercise.

CHECKING YOUR SKILLS

Use these questions to test your knowledge of the material covered in this chapter.

1. True___ False___ The only way to create an assembly is by placing existing components into it.

2. Explain how to create a component in the context of an assembly.

3. True___ False___ An occurrence is a different version of an existing component.

4. True___ False___ Only one component can be grounded in an assembly.

5. True___ False___ Autodesk Inventor does not require components in an assembly to be fully constrained.

6. True___ False___ A sketch must be fully constrained before it can become adaptive.

7. What is the purpose of a presentation file?

8. True___ False___ Balloons can only be placed in a drawing after placing a Parts List.

9. True___ False___ When creating drawing views from a presentation file, you can create views from multiple presentation views.

10. True___ False___ A Bill of Materials only retrieves its data from a Parts List.

11. True___ False___ An animation of a presentation file can be exported to a video file.

12. True___ False___ A BOM Structured view shows all subassemblies and individual parts at the same assembly level.

13. True___ False___ An Associated Component Pattern will maintain a relationship to a feature pattern.

14. True___ False___ User-defined folders allow you to organize an assembly browser by grouping assembly constraints in a single folder.

15. True___ False___ In a Parts List, you can display custom parts that are not components or graphical data, e.g. paint.

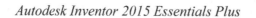

Chapter 7 – Advanced Modeling Techniques

INTRODUCTION

In this chapter, you will learn how to use advanced modeling techniques that will help you become more productive and efficient with Autodesk Inventor. You will learn how to display dimensions in alternate formats, set up relationships between dimensions, create parameters, section a part or assembly file, control the viewpoint, emboss text, and create features that sweep along a path or transition between profiles, suppress and reorder features, and validate your design by simulating stress on a part or assembly file.

OBJECTIVES

After completing this chapter, you will be able to:

- [ ] Change the display of dimensions
- [ ] Create relationships between dimensions
- [ ] Create an equation to define a dimension's value
- [ ] Create parameters
- [ ] Section a part or components in an assembly
- [ ] Create a design view representation
- [ ] Emboss text and close profiles
- [ ] Create sweep features
- [ ] Create 3D sketches
- [ ] Create coil features
- [ ] Create loft features
- [ ] Split a part
- [ ] Mirror model features
- [ ] Suppress features of a part
- [ ] Reorder part features
- [ ] Place components from the Content Center
- [ ] Simulate stress on a part and an assembly

DIMENSION DISPLAY, RELATIONSHIPS, AND EQUATIONS

When creating part features, you may want to set up relationships between features and/or sketch dimensions. For example, the length of a part may need to be twice that of its width, or a hole may always need to be in the middle of the part. In Autodesk Inventor, you can use several different methods to set up relationships between dimensions. The following sections will cover these methods.

Dimension Display

When you create a dimension, it is automatically tagged with a label, or parameter name, that starts with the letter "d" and a number: for example, "d0" or "d27." The first dimension created for each part is given the label "d0." Each dimension that you place for subsequent part sketches and features are sequenced incrementally, one number at a time. If you erase a dimension, the next dimension does not go back and reuse the erased value. Instead, it continues the sequencing from the last value on the last dimension created. When creating dimensional relationships, you may want to view a dimension's display style to see the underlying parameter label of the dimension. Five options for displaying a dimension's display style are available.

Value. Use to display the actual value of the dimensions on the screen.

Name. Use to display the dimensions on the screen as the parameter name: for example, d12 or Length.

Expression. Use to display the dimensions on the screen in the format of parameter# value, showing each actual value: for example, d7 = 20in or Length = 5in

Tolerance. Use to display the dimensions on the screen that have a tolerance style for example, 40±.3.

Precise Value. Use to display the dimensions on the screen and ignore any precision settings that are specified: for example, 40.3563123344.

To change the dimension display style, click the desired dimension display option from the status bar, as shown in the following image. After you select a dimension display style, all visible dimensions will change to that style. As you create dimensions, they will reflect the current dimension display style.

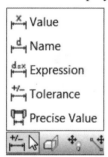

Figure 7-1

A Dimension's Relationship

When designing, you may want to define a dimension to be equal to another dimension. Instead of applying an equal constraint, you can set the value of one dimension to the value of another. Before creating a relationship between two dimensions that will be the same length, a dimension must exist that will be the value that the other dimension will be equal to. Then place or edit the dimension that will be equal to the first dimension and in the Edit Dimension dialog box, enter the dimensions parameter name (d#) of the other dimension, or click the dimension with which you want to set the relationship in the graphics window. The following image on the left shows the Edit Dimension dialog box for the vertical dimension after selecting the 1.25 inch horizontal dimension to which the new dimension will be related. Note that "d0" in the Edit Dimension dialog box replaced the original value. After establishing a relationship to another dimension, the dimension will have a prefix of fx:, as shown in the following image on the right.

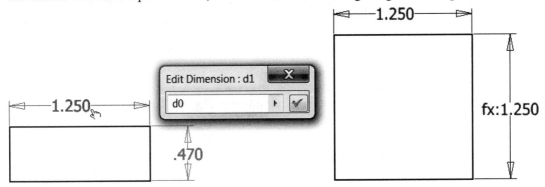

Figure 7-2

Equations

You can also use an equation to obtain the desired value. Two examples of equations would be: (d9/4)*2 or 50 – 11.625. When creating equations, Inventor allows prefixes, precedence, operators, functions, syntax, and units. To see a complete listing of valid options, use the Help system and search for "Functions, Prefixes, and Algebraic Operators".

You can enter numbers with or without units; when no unit is entered, the default unit will be assumed. As you enter an equation, Inventor evaluates it. An invalid expression will appear in red, and a valid expression will appear in black. For best results while using equations, include units for every term and factor in the equation.

To create an equation when a value is required, follow these steps:

1. Click in the cell where a value is required, for example; dimension, extrude length, number of feature to be patterned, etc.

2. Enter any valid combination of numbers, parameters, operators, or built-in functions. The following image shows an example of an equation that divides a number and then adds a number.

3. Press ENTER or click the green checkmark to accept the expression.

 TIP: Use ul (unitless) where a number does not have a unit. For example, use a unitless number when dividing, multiplying, or specifying values for a pattern count.

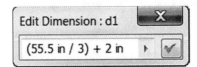

Figure 7-3

PARAMETERS

Another way to set up relationships between dimensions is to use parameters. A parameter is a user-defined name that is assigned a numeric value, either explicitly or through equations. You can use multiple parameters in an equation, and you can use parameters to define another parameter such as *depth = length - width*. You can use a parameter anytime a numeric value is required. There are four types of parameters: model, user, reference, and linked.

 TIP: Functions in Inventor such as sheet metal, stress analysis and design accelerator can automatically add parameter groups.

Creating Parameters

To create parameters via a dialog box, start the Parameters command on the Manage tab > Parameters panel, as shown in the following image on the left, or by clicking the Parameters icon from the Quick Access toolbar. The Parameters dialog box is displayed, as shown in the following image on the right. The following image shows an example of a part file with four types of parameters: model, user, reference and linked parameters.

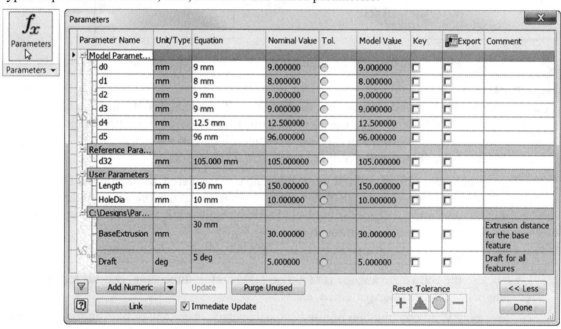

Figure 7-4

Parameter Dialog Box Sections

By default the Parameters dialog box has two sections: Model Parameters and User Parameters. A section called Reference Parameters is displayed if driven dimensions exist and a section will be created for every spreadsheet you link to. Following are descriptions of the parameter types.

Model Parameter. This parameter type is created automatically and assigned a name when you create a sketch dimension, feature parameter such as an extrusion distance, draft angle, or coil pitch, and the offset, depth, or angle value of an assembly constraint. Autodesk Inventor assigns a default name to each Model Parameter as you create it. The default name format is a "d" followed by an integer incremented for each new parameter. You can rename Model Parameters via the Parameters dialog box or specify a name upon initial creation in the Edit Dimension dialog box. This method is called "creating a parameter on the fly" and can be done in any field that you can specify a parametric dimensional value. The parameter that is being defined by the field will be renamed to the name specified at the beginning of the equation. For example, if you were defining a rectangular sketch and wanted to define a parameter named Length while dimensioning the sketch, you would enter "Length=10" (without the quotation marks) in the Edit Dimension dialog box. A parameter with the name of Length would be automatically created.

User Parameter. This type of parameter is created manually by clicking the Add Numeric button in the Parameters dialog box. You can change the names and equations of both types of parameters, and you can add comments by double-clicking in the cell and entering the new information. To learn more about user parameters, see the Creating User Parameter section later in this chapter.

Reference Parameter. This parameter type is created automatically when you create a driven dimension. Autodesk Inventor assigns a default name to each reference parameter as you create it. The default name format is a "d" followed by an integer incremented for each new parameter. You can rename reference parameters via the Parameters dialog box.

Linked Parameter. If you want to use the same parameter in multiple part and / or assembly files you can add the parameter data to a Microsoft Excel spreadsheet. You then embed or link the spreadsheet into a part or assembly file through the Parameters dialog box. When you embed a Microsoft Excel spreadsheet, there is no link between the spreadsheet and the parameters in the Inventor file, and any changes to the original spreadsheet will not be reflected in the Autodesk Inventor file. When you link a Microsoft Excel spreadsheet to an Autodesk Inventor part or assembly file, any changes in the original spreadsheet will update the parameters in the Autodesk Inventor file. You can link more than one spreadsheet to an Autodesk Inventor file, and you can link each spreadsheet to multiple part and assembly files. For more information see the Creating Linked Parameters section later in this chapter.

Parameter Dialog Box Columns
The columns available for the four types of parameters are the same, and the following sections define them.

Parameter Name. The name of the parameter will appear in this cell. To change the name of an existing parameter, click in the box, and enter a new name. When you update the model, all dependent parameters update to reflect the new name.

Unit/Type. Enter a new unit of measurement for the parameter in this cell. With Autodesk Inventor, you can build equations that include parameters of any unit type. All length parameters are stored internally in centimeters; angular parameters are stored internally in radians.

Equation. The equation will appear in this cell, and it will determine the value of the parameter. If the parameter is a discrete value, the value appears in rounded form to match the precision setting for the active document. To change the equation, click on the existing equation, and enter the new equation.

Nominal Value. The nominal tolerance result of the equation will appear in this cell. It can only be modified by editing the equation.

Tol. (Tolerance). From the drop-down list, select a tolerance condition: upper, median, nominal, or lower.

Model Value. The actual calculated model value of the equation, in full precision, will appear in this cell. This value reflects the current tolerance condition of the parameter.

Key. Click to specify which defined parameters will be identified as a key parameter. The display of parameters in the dialog box can be filtered based on this setting.

Export Parameters. Click to export the parameter to the Custom tab of the iProperties dialog box. The parameter will also be available when using the Derive command as well as in the Bill of Materials and Parts List Column Chooser dialog boxes.

Comment. You may choose to enter a comment for the parameter in this cell. Click in the cell, and enter the comment.

Creating User Parameters

User Parameters are ones that you define in a part or an assembly file. Parameters defined in one file type are not directly accessible in the other file type. If parameters are to be used in both file type use linked parameters via a Microsoft Excel spreadsheet. When creating a User Parameter, follow these guidelines:

- Assign meaningful names to parameters, as other designers may edit the file and will need to understand your thought process. You may want to use the comments field for further clarification.
- The parameter name cannot include spaces, mathematical symbols, or special characters.
- Autodesk Inventor detects capital letters and uses them as unique characters. Length, length, and LENGTH would be seen as three different parameter names.
- When defining a parameter equation, you cannot use the parameter name to define itself; for example, Length = Length/2 would be invalid.
- Duplicate parameter names are not allowed. Model, User, and Spreadsheet-driven parameters must have unique names.

To create and use a User Parameter, follow these steps:

1. Click the Parameters command on the Manage tab > Parameters panel.
2. Click the Add Numeric button at the bottom of the Parameters dialog box.
3. A new row in the User Parameters section will appear, enter data in the cells as required.
4. After creating the parameter(s), you can enter the parameter name(s) anywhere that a value is required. When editing a dimension, click the arrow on the right, and click List Parameters from the menu, as shown in the following image on the left. All the available User Parameters and any renamed Model Parameters will appear in a list similar to that in the following image on the right. Click the desired parameter from the list.

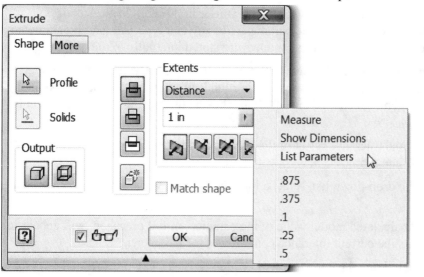
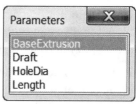

Figure 7-5

Creating Linked Parameters

When creating a Microsoft Excel spreadsheet with parameters, follow these guidelines:

- The data in the spreadsheet can start in any cell, but the cells must be specified when you link or embed the spreadsheet.
- The data can be in rows or columns, but they must be in this order: parameter name, value or equation, unit of measurement, and (if desired) a comment.
- The parameter name and value (equation) are required, but the other items are optional.
- The parameter name cannot include spaces, mathematical symbols, or special characters. You can use these to define the equation.
- Parameters in the spreadsheet must be in a continuous list. A blank row or column between parameter names eliminates all parameters after the blank row or column.
- If you do not specify a unit of measurement for a parameter, the default units for the document will be assigned when the parameter is used. To create a parameter without units, enter "ul" (unitless) in the Units cell.
- Only those parameters defined on the first worksheet of the spreadsheet are linked to the Autodesk Inventor file.
- You can include column or row headings or other information in the spreadsheet, but they must be outside the block of cells that contains the parameter definitions.

The following image on the left shows three parameters that were created in rows with a name, equation, unit, and comment. The image on the right shows the same parameters created in columns.

	A	B	C	D
1	Length	50	mm	Length of Plate
2	Width	Length/2	mm	Width of Plate
3	Depth	10	mm	Depth of Plate

	A	B	C
1	Length	Width	Depth
2	50	Length/2	10
3	mm	mm	mm
4	Length of Plate	Width of Plate	Depth of Plate

Figure 7-6

After you have created and saved the spreadsheet, you can create parameters from it by following these steps:

1. While in a part file click the Parameters command on the Manage tab > Parameters panel. From an assembly file click the Parameters command on the Manage tab > Manage panel.

2. Click Link button [Link] on the bottom of the Parameters dialog box.

3. The Open dialog box appears as shown in the following image.

4. Navigate to and select the Microsoft Excel file to use.

5. In the lower-left corner of the Open dialog box, enter the start cell for the parameter data.

6. Select whether the spreadsheet will be linked or embedded.

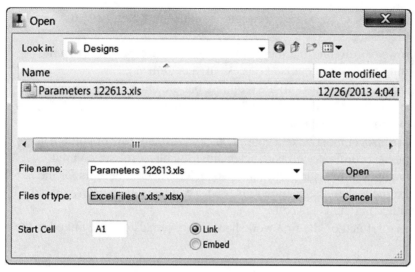

Figure 7-7

7. Click the Open button.

8. A new section showing the linked parameters is added to the Parameters dialog box, as shown in the following image. If you embedded the spreadsheet, the new section will be titled Embedding #.

C:\Designs\Pa...								
Length	mm	50 mm	50.000000	○	50.000000	☐	☐	Length of Plate
Width	mm	Length / 2 ul	25.000000	○	25.000000	☐	☐	Width of Plate
Depth	mm	10 mm	10.000000	○	10.000000	☐	☐	Depth of Plate

Figure 7-8

9. To complete the operation, click Done.

To edit the parameters that are linked, follow these steps:

1. Open the Microsoft Excel file.

2. Make the required changes.

3. Save the Microsoft Excel file.

4. Open the Autodesk Inventor part or assembly file that uses the spreadsheet and if needed click the Update command on the Quick Access toolbar.

You can also follow these steps when a spreadsheet has been linked. If you chose to embed the spreadsheet, the following steps must be used to edit the parameters:

1. Open the Autodesk Inventor part or assembly file that uses the spreadsheet.

2. Expand the 3rd Party folder in the browser.

3. Double-click on the name of the spreadsheet or right-click on the name of the spreadsheet and click Edit from the menu, as shown in the following image.

4. The Microsoft Excel spreadsheet will open in a new window for editing.

5. Make the required changes.

6. Save the Microsoft Excel file.

7. Activate the Autodesk Inventor part or assembly file that uses the spreadsheet.

8. Click the Update command on the Quick Access toolbar.

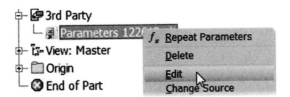

Figure 7-9

EXERCISE 7-1: RELATIONSHIPS AND PARAMTERS

In this exercise, you create a sketch and dimension it. You then set up relationships between dimensions, and define User Parameters in both the model and an external spreadsheet.

1. Create a new file based on the default Standard (in).ipt file.

2. Create a 2D Sketch on the XY origin plane and then draw and dimension the profile as shown in the following image. The lower-left corner should be located at the origin point, and the arc is tangent to both lines.

3. Next create a relation and an equation.

   a. Double-click the **1.5 inch** radius dimension on the arc

   b. With the value in the Edit dimension dialog box highlighted, change it so it has a relationship to the horizontal dimension by selecting the **5.000 inch** dimension, as shown in the following image on the right.

   c. Next you divide the horizontal dimension by four. In the Edit Dimension dialog box type **/4** after the d#. The following image shows the value for the radius dimension equal to "d0/4." The 0 may be a different number in your dimension as this number depends upon the order in which the dimension was placed.

   d. Click the green checkmark to accept the dimension value in the Edit Dimension dialog box.

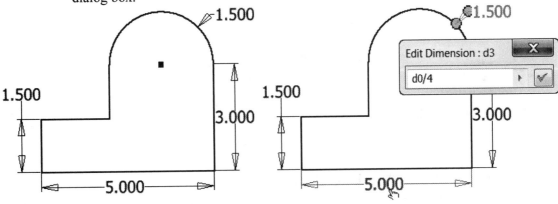

Figure 7-10

4. Add another relationship and equation.

   a. Double-click the **1.5 inch** left vertical dimension.

   b. Change its value by selecting the **3 inch** right vertical dimension and type **/2** after the d#.

   c. Click the green checkmark to accept the dimension value in the Edit Dimension dialog box.

5. Make the following change to these dimensions:

   a. Change the **5 inch** horizontal dimension to **4 inches**.

   b. Change the **3 inch** vertical dimension to **2.5 inches**.

   c. When done, your sketch should resemble the following image on the left. The fx: text denotes that the dimensions are driven by an equation and reference another dimension.

6. To see the underlying equations for the dimensions, click the Expression dimension display option on the bottom of the status bar. When done the equations will be displayed as shown in the following image on the right.

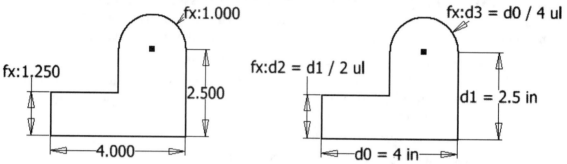

Figure 7-11

7. Next you create two user parameters that will control the sketch.

   a. Click the Parameters command on the Quick Access toolbar or from the Manage tab > Parameters panel.

   b. In the Parameter dialog box, create a User Parameter by clicking the Add Numeric button.

   c. Type the following information for the first parameter:

      i. Parameter Name = **Length**

      ii. Units = **in**

      iii. Equation = **6**

      iv. Comment = **Bottom length**

8. Create a second User Parameter by clicking the Add Numeric button and specify the following information:

   a. Parameter Name = **Height**

   b. Units = **in**

   c. Equation = **Length/3**

   d. Comment = **Height is 1/3 the length**

   e. When done, the User Parameter area in the dialog box should resemble the following image.

   f. Close the Parameter dialog box by clicking Done.

User Parameters									
Length	in	6 in	6.000000	○	6.000000	☐	☐	Bottom length
Height	in	Length / 3 ul	2.000000	○	2.000000	☐	☐	Height is half the length

Figure 7-12

9. Next, you change two dimensions to utilize the parameters you just created.

a. Double-click the bottom-horizontal dimension and click the arrow on the right side of the dialog box. From the menu click List Parameters and click Length from the list, and then click the checkmark in the Edit Dimension dialog box.

b. Double-click the right-vertical dimension, change its value by typing in Height (exactly as you entered it in step 8), and click the green checkmark to make the change to the dimension. When done, your screen should resemble the following image.

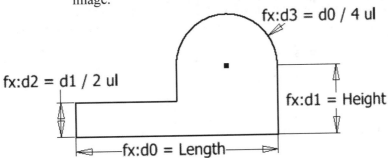

Figure 7-13

10. Start the Parameters command and from the User Parameters area, make the following edits.

   a. Change the Equation value for the parameter "Length" to **4.5**.

   b. Change the Equation value for the parameter "Height" to **2.75**.

   c. Change the comment field of the Height parameter to "Height of the right side". When done making the changes, the User Parameter area should resemble the following image.

   d. Notice that the sketch updates automatically when the values are changed in the Parameters dialog box (if the default option is selected).

   e. Close the Parameter dialog box by clicking Done.

User Parameters								
Length	in	4.75 in	4.750000	○	4.750000	☐	☐	Bottom length
Height	in	2.75 in	2.750000	○	2.750000	☐	☐	Height of the right side

Figure 7-14

11. To see the values of the dimensions, click the Value dimension display option on the bottom of the status bar. The values of the dimensions will be displayed as shown in the following image.

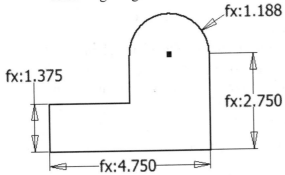

Figure 7-15

---

12. Finish the sketch,

13. Save the file as *ESS_E07_01.ipt* in the Chapter 07 folder

14. Now create a spreadsheet that has two parameters.

    a. Create a Microsoft Excel spreadsheet with the column names Parameter Name, Equation, Unit, and Comment. Then fill in the information as shown in the following image.

	A	B	C	D
1	**Paramter Name**	**Equation**	**Unit**	**Comment**
2	BaseExtrusion	1.25	in	Base extrusion distance
3	Draft	5	deg	Draft angle

Figure 7-16

    b. Save the spreadsheet as *ESS_07_Parameters.xlsx* in the *C:\Inv 2015 Ess Plus\Chapter 07* folder.

    c. Close Excel.

15. Make Autodesk Inventor with the file *ESS_E07_01.ipt* current.

16. Next, you link the parameters to the spreadsheet.

    a. Start the Parameters command.

    b. In the Parameter dialog box, click the Link button and select the *ESS_07_Parameters.xlsx* file, but do not click Open yet.

    c. For the Start Cell, change this to **A2**. If you fail to do this, no parameters will be found. The first row contains the names of the columns and will not be imported.

    d. Click the Open button, and a new spreadsheet area will appear in the Parameters dialog box, as shown in the following image.

    e. Click the Done button to complete the operation.

C:\Inv 2015 E...								
BaseExtrusion	in	1.25 in	1.250000	○	1.250000	☐	☐	Base extrusion distance
Draft	deg	5 deg	5.000000	○	5.000000	☐	☐	Draft angle

Figure 7-17

17. If needed, change to the Home View.

18. Next, you extrude the profile using the linked parameters for the values.

    a. Select an edge of the profile and click Create Extrude from the mini-toolbar.

    b. In the Extrude dialog box, for the value of the extrusion, enter the parameter name **BaseExtrusion** or click the arrow from the menu, click List Parameters, and then click the parameter **BaseExtrusion,** as shown in the following image on the left.

    c. Click the More tab in the Extrude dialog box. For the Taper's value, enter **Draft** or click the arrow from the menu, click List Parameters, and then click the parameter **Draft,** as shown in the middle of the following image.

    d. To complete the operation, click the OK button.

    e. Change the viewpoint so it resembles the image on the right.

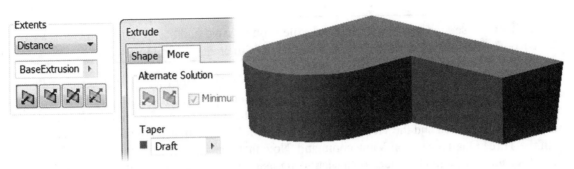

Figure 7-18

19. Next, you edit the spreadsheet.

    a. In the browser, expand the 3rd Party icon.

    b. Double-click on the *ESS_07_Parameters.xlsx* or right-click on *ESS_07_Parameters.xlsx*, and click Edit from the menu.

    c. In the Excel spreadsheet, make the following changes:

        i. Change the Equation value for the parameter "BaseExtrusion" to **2**.

        ii. Change the Equation value for the parameter "Draft" to **-3**.

    d. Save the spreadsheet.

    e. Close Excel.

20. The last step is to update the linked parameters.

    a. Make Autodesk Inventor with the file *ESS_E07_01.ipt* current.

    b. Click the Update command on the Quick Access toolbar. When done, your model should resemble the following image.

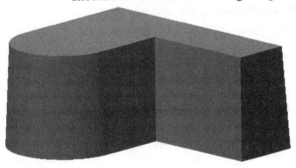

Figure 7-19

21. Close the file. Do not save changes. End of exercise.

SECTIONING A PART OR COMPONENTS IN AN ASSEMBLY

While designing in a part or an assembly file you can visually remove portions of a part or components in an assembly. This is useful especially where features or components are hidden or obscured within chambers. While the part or assembly is sectioned, part and assembly tools can be used to create or modify parts within the assembly. You can use the exposed cut edges, along with the Project Cut Edges command, to assist in sketch construction for additional features that need to be created in a part.

> **TIP:** A section in a part or assembly file is only visual and has no effect on the mass properties of the component and cannot be used to create drawing views from.

There are three types of sections you can create in a part or assembly file; quarter section, half section , or a three quarter section. To access the section commands click on the View tab > Appearance panel, as shown in the following image on the left. The middle image shows a part before being sectioned and the view on the right of the following image shows the part sectioned with the Three Quarter Section View command. Note that the sections are temporary and sketches cannot be actively placed on a sectioned plane. As always, you can create a sketch on an existing planar face or work plane.

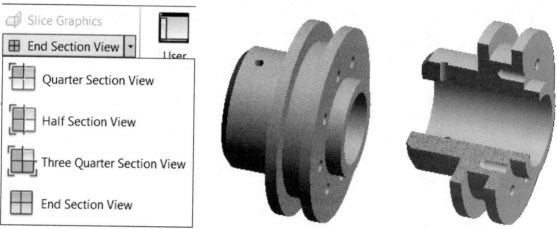

Figure 7-20

To section a part or components in an assembly, follow these steps:

1. Select the desired section command on the View tab > Appearance panel.
2. Select any existing planar face, work plane, or origin plane.
3. Adjust the section depth by clicking and dragging the visible arrow in the graphics window, as shown in the following image on the left or enter a value in the Offset cell in the mini-toolbar. Another option to control the offset is to move the cursor over the Offset cell and scroll the wheel on the mouse. You can control the distance that each step takes when you scroll the wheel by right-clicking and click Virtual Movement > Scroll Step Size.
4. If you are creating a quarter or three quarter section, accept the current location by clicking the right-faced arrow in the mini-toolbar, as shown in the middle image or right-click and click Continue in the marking menu and follow the same process to define a second plane.
5. While still in the command, you can specify which side of the section remains visible by right-clicking and click the Flip Section or change the section type if Quarter or Three Quarter section was selected, as shown in the following image on the right.
6. To finish the command, click the green check mark in the mini-toolbar or right-click and click OK from the menu.
7. To clear the section, click the End Section View command on the View tab > Appearance panel.

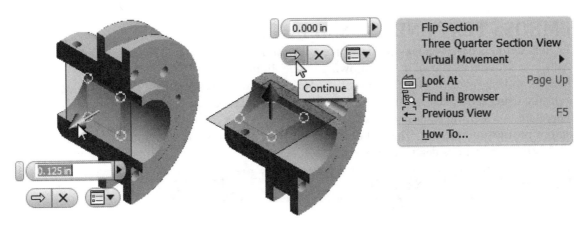

Figure 7-21

DESIGN VIEW REPRESENTATIONS IN A PART OR AN ASSEMBLY FILE

While working on a part or an assembly file, you can save a design view representation that stores information related to the current viewpoint, part color, sections, and work feature visibility. You can save as many design view representations as needed, but only one can be current. By default, there is a design view representation named Master, this master design view cannot be changed, deleted, or locked. To create a design view representation in a part file, follow these steps:

1. To create a Design View in a part file, expand the browser and right-click on View: Master and click New from the menu, as shown in the following image on the left.

2. To create a Design View in an assembly file expand the Representation folder in the browser and right-click on View: Default, as shown in the middle of the following image, and select New from the menu.

3. A design view will be created. You can rename the design view by slowly clicking twice on its name and type in a new name.

4. Once a design view is created, change the view point, section a part, part color, and work feature visibility. These changes will be captured in the current design view.

5. Since these changes are actively captured to the current design view, you can lock a design view so that any change to the current viewpoint, sectioning of a part, part color, or work feature visibility are not saved to the current design view. To lock a design view, right-click on its name in the browser and click Lock from the menu, as shown in the following image on the right.

6. Create as many design views as needed.

7. Lock and unlock the current design view to capture the settings as needed.

8. To make a design view current, in the browser double-click on its name or right-click on its name and click Activate from the menu. The last settings in the design view or the locked settings in the design view will be displayed in the graphics window.

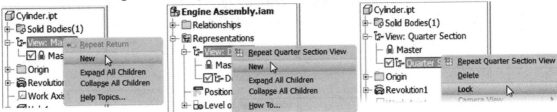

Figure 7-22

EMBOSS TEXT AND CLOSED PROFILES

To help define a part, you may need to have a text or a profile embossed (raised) or engraved (cut) into a model as shown in the following image. In this section, you will learn how you can emboss and engrave text or a closed profile onto a planar or curved face on a part. You can define a profile using the sketch commands on the Sketch tab but note that profiles need to be closed. There are two steps to emboss or engrave: first create the text or profile and then you emboss the text or profile onto the part. The text can be oriented in a rectangle or about an arc, circle, or line. The following sections describe the steps.

Figure 7-23

Step 1: Creating Rectangular Text

To place rectangular text onto a sketch, follow these steps:

1. In a part file, create or activate a sketch.

2. Click the Text command on the Sketch tab > Create panel, as shown in the following image on the left.

3. Pick a point or drag a rectangle where you will place the text. If a single point is selected, the text will fit on a single line and can be grip edited to resize the bounding box. If a rectangle is used, it defines the width for text wrapping and can be modified. The Format Text dialog box will appear.

4. In the Format Text dialog box, specify the text font and format style, and enter the text to place on the sketch. The following image on the right shows text entered in the bottom pane.

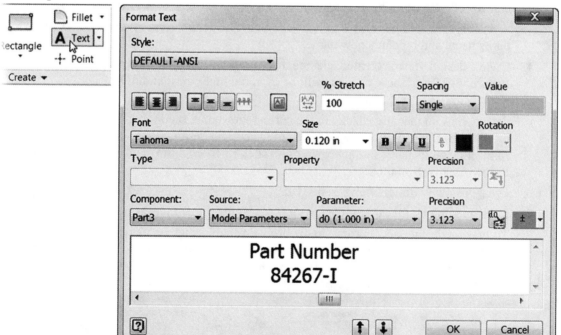

Figure 7-24

5. When you have finished typing the text, click OK to complete the text entry, then right-click and click OK in the marking menu to complete the command.

6. When the text is placed, a rectangular set of construction lines defines the perimeter of the text. You can click and drag a point on the rectangle and change the size of the rectangle. Dimensions or constraints can be added to these construction lines to refine the text's location and orientation, as shown in the following image.

7. To edit the text, double-click on the text or right-click on the text and click Edit text from the marking menu. The same Format Text dialog box that was used to create the text will appear.

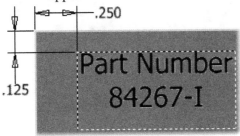

Figure 7-25

Step 2: Creating Text Alongside Geometry

To place text alongside an arc, circle, or line in a sketch, follow these steps:

1. In a part file, create a new sketch or make an existing sketch active.

2. Sketch and constrain an arc, circle, or line that the text will follow; it is recommended to make this geometry using the construction geometry style so that it will not be used as the geometry for the profile.

3. Click the Geometry Text command on the Sketch tab > Create panel > Geometry Text command, as shown in the following image on the left. The command may be under the Text command.

4. In the sketch, select the arc, circle, or line and the Geometry-Text dialog box will appear.

5. In the Geometry-Text dialog box, specify the text font and format style, direction, position, and start angle and enter the text to place on the sketch. The start angle is relative to the left quadrant point of a circle or the start point of the arc. The following image on the right shows the dialog box with text entered in the bottom pane.

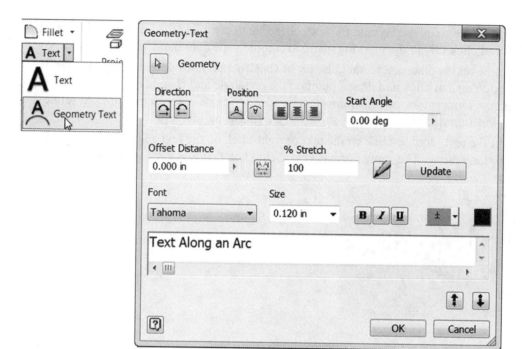

Figure 7-26

6. When you have finished entering text, click the Update button in the dialog box to see the preview in the graphics window.

7. Click OK to complete the operation. The following image shows text placed along an arc.

8. To edit the text, double-click on the text or right-click on the text and click Edit Geometry Text from the marking menu. The same Format Text dialog box that was used to create the text will appear.

Figure 7-27

Step 3: Embossing Text or Closed Profile

To emboss text or a closed profile, click the Emboss command on the 3D Model tab > Create panel, as shown in the following image on the left. The Emboss dialog box will appear, as shown in the following image on the right.

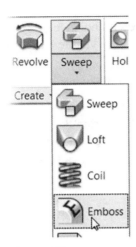

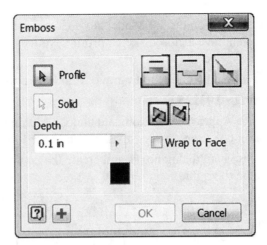

Figure 7-28

To emboss text or a closed shape, follow these steps:

1. Click the Emboss command on the 3D Model tab > Create panel (it may be under the sweep or another command in this group).

2. Define the profile by selecting a closed shape or text. If needed, use the Select Other—Face Cycling command to select geometry that is not selected immediately when the cursor is moved over it.

3. Select the type of emboss: Emboss from Face, Engrave from Face, or Emboss/ Engrave from Plane.

4. Specify the depth, color, direction, and face as needed. If you selected the Emboss/ Engrave from plane option, you can also add a taper angle to the created emboss/engrave feature.

5. You edit the emboss feature like any other feature.

EXERCISE 7-2: CREATING TEXT AND EMBOSS FEATURES

In this exercise, you emboss and engrave closed profiles onto a razor and engrave text on the handle.

1. Open *ESS_E07_02.ipt* in the Chapter 07 folder.

2. First, you emboss a closed profile. From the browser turn on visibility of Sketch11 by right-clicking on Sketch11 and click Visibility from the menu.

3. Change the viewpoint so it resembles the following image.

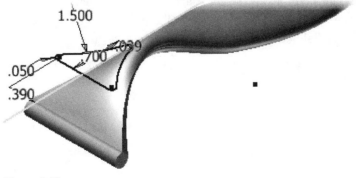

Figure 7-29

4. Click the Emboss command on the 3D Model tab > Create panel (it could be under the sweep or loft icon) to engrave a closed sketch profile. Notice that the only visible closed profile is automatically selected.

   a. In the Emboss dialog box, click the Engrave from Face option (middle button).

   b. Change the Depth to **0.03125 in**.

   c. Click the Top Face Appearance button, and choose Aluminum (Flat) from the Appearance dialog box drop-down list, as shown in the following image on the left.

5. Click OK twice to close both dialog boxes and create the engraved feature, as shown in the following image on the right.

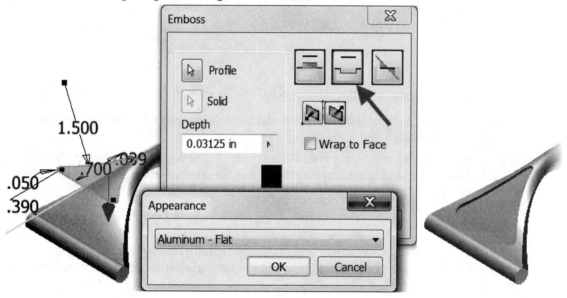

Figure 7-30

6. Click the Home View above the ViewCube.

7. From the browser turn on the visibility of Sketch10.

8. Click the Emboss command from the 3D Model tab > Create panel.

   a. For the profile, click the oblong and the six closed profiles. Be sure to select the left and right halves of the herringbone profiles, as shown in the following image on the left.

   b. In the Emboss dialog box, click the Emboss from Face option (left button).

   c. Change the Depth to **0.015625 in**.

   d. Click the Top Face Appearance button, and select Black from the Appearance dialog box drop-down list, as shown in the following image on the right.

   e. Click OK twice to close both dialog boxes and create the emboss feature.

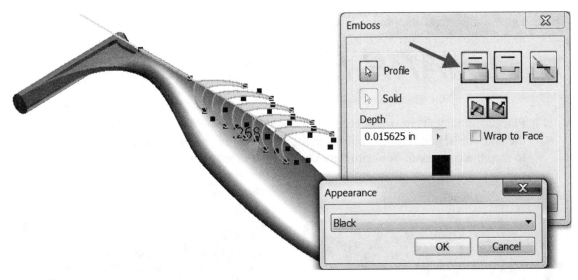

9. Use the Free Orbit command to examine the engraved and embossed features.

10. Next, you create text on a sketch. From the browser turn on the visibility of Sketch9.

11. In the browser, double-click Sketch9 to make it the active sketch.

12. Click the Text command in the Sketch tab > Create panel.

    a. Place the insertion point of the text in an open area below the part and the left edge of the construction rectangle in the sketch, and the Format Text dialog box appears.

    b. In the dialog box, click the Center and Middle Justification buttons labeled (1) and (2) in the following image.

    c. Click the Italic option labeled (3).

    d. Change the % Stretch value to **120** labeled (4).

    e. Click in the text field, and type The SHARP EDGE labeled (5).

    f. In the text field, double-click on the word "The," and change the text size from 1.20 in to **0.09 in** labeled (6).

    g. Click OK to create the text.

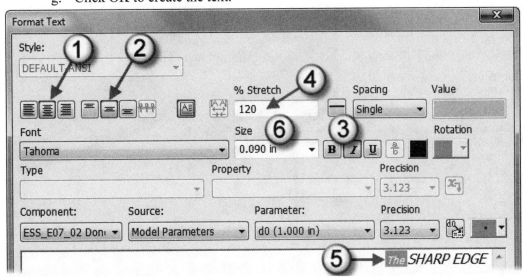

Figure 7-32

13. Draw a diagonal construction line coincident in the text bounding box corners, as shown in the following image.

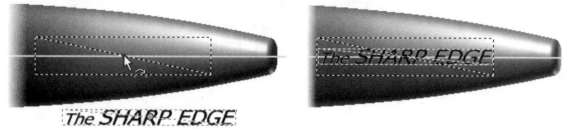

Figure 7-33

14. Place a coincident constraint between the midpoint of the diagonal construction line on the text box and Sketch9, as shown in the following image on the left. Press the ESC key to stop the command. The completed operation is shown in the following image on the right.

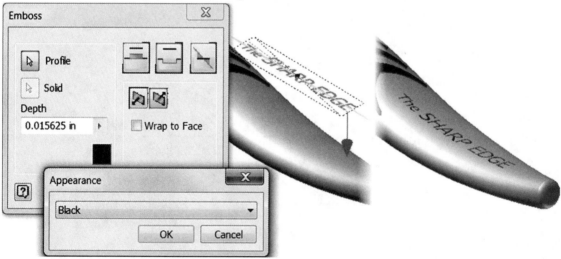

Figure 7-34

15. Finish the sketch by right-clicking and click Finish 2D Sketch from the marking menu.

16. Start the Emboss command.

    a. For the profile, select the text object.

    b. In the Emboss dialog box, click the Engrave from Face option.

    c. Change the Depth to **0.015625 in**.

    d. For the direction, click the right button to change the direction down.

    e. Click the Top Face Color button, and click Black from the Appearance drop-down list, as shown in the following image on the left.

    f. Click OK twice to close both dialog boxes and create the emboss feature as shown in the following image on the right.

Figure 7-35

17. Use the Free Orbit command to examine the engraved text feature.

---

18. Edit Sketch9 – the consumed sketch under the Emboss3 feature you just created by right-clicking on Emboss3 in the browser and click Edit Sketch from the menu.

19. In the sketch, delete the existing text, rectangle and angled lines; do NOT delete the yellow horizontal line in the middle of the part (your color may be different depending upon your color scheme).

20. Sketch and dimension a construction circle as shown.

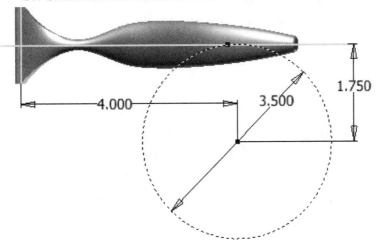

Figure 7-36

21. Click the Geometry Text command from the Sketch tab > Create panel and select the circle for the Geometry selection.

   a. Click the Center Justification button (middle button) labeled (1), as shown in the following image.

   b. Change the Start Angle to **90.00 deg** labeled (2).

   c. Select the Bold button labeled (3).

   d. Change the text height to **0.125 in** labeled (4).

   e. Click in the text field, and enter The SHARP EDGE labeled (5)

   f. To preview the text on the geometry, click the Update button labeled (6) in the Geometry-Text dialog box, as shown in the following image on the right.

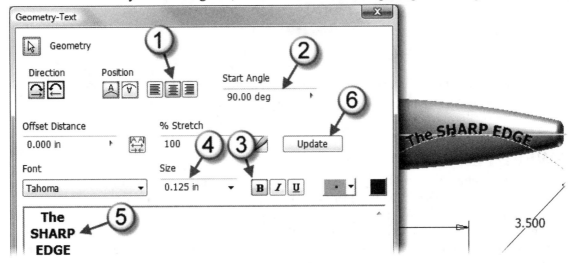

Figure 7-37

g. Click OK to complete the command.

22. Click the Finish Sketch command on the Sketch tab > Exit panel to finish editing the sketch, and then change to the Home View.

23. A dialog box will appear stating that the geometry that the feature was created with cannot be found. Click Accept in the message dialog box.

24. To fix this issue, edit the feature by double-clicking on Emboss3 in the browser.

   a. The Profile button is current, select the text as the new profile.

   b. Click OK to keep the previous settings and close the dialog box. The emboss feature is recreated, as shown in the following image on the right.

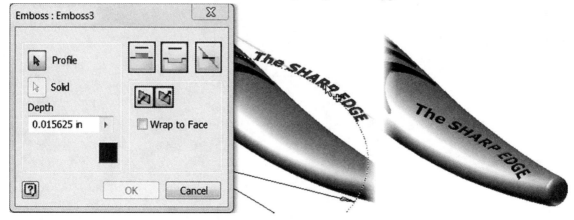

Figure 7-38

25. Use the Free Orbit command to examine the emboss features.

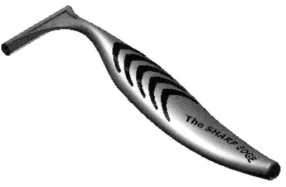

Figure 7-39

26. If desired, edit the sketches and features and try different dimensions and options.

27. Close the file. Do not save changes. End of exercise.

SWEEP FEATURES

As you are designing you will likely need to create more complex geometry beyond extruded or revolved features. In this section you learn how to create sweep features that do not extrude along a straight line such as a hook, cabling, or piping. A sweep feature can be a base or a secondary feature. Unlike extrude and revolve features, a sweep feature usually uses two unconsumed sketches: a profile to be swept and a path that the profile will follow or uses edges on a part for the path. Additional profiles can be used as guide rails or a surface can also be used to help shape the feature. The profile sketch and the path sketch cannot lie on the same or parallel planes. The path can be an irregular shape or use part edges by projecting and including the edges onto the active sketch. The path can be either an open or closed profile and can lie in a plane or lie in multiple planes (3D Sketch). To create a sweep feature, use the Sweep command on the 3D Model tab > Create panel, as shown in the following image on the left and the Sweep dialog will appear, as shown in the following image on the right.

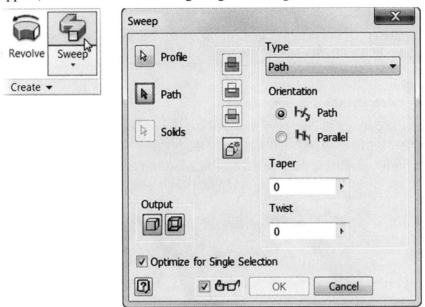

Figure 7-40

The Sweep Dialog Box

The following sections describe the options in the Sweep dialog box.

Profile. Click this button to select the sketch profile to sweep. If the Profile button is depressed and red, it means that you need to select a sketch or sketch area. If there are multiple closed profiles, you will need to select the profile that you want to sweep. If there is only one possible profile, Autodesk Inventor will select it for you and you can skip this step. If you selected the wrong profile or sketch area, depress the Profile button, and deselect the incorrect sketch by clicking it while holding down the CTRL key. Release the CTRL key, and select the desired sketch profile.

Path. Click this button to select the path along which to sweep the profile. The path can be an open or a closed profile on its own sketch, but must pierce the sketch that the profile was drawn on. You can also use edge(s) of a part as a path. The profile is typically perpendicular to and intersects with the start point of the path. The start point of the path is often projected into the profile sketch to provide a reference point.

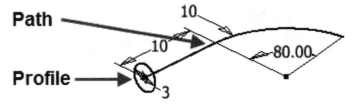

Figure 7-41

Solids. If there are multiple solid bodies, click this button to choose the solid body(ies) to participate in the operation.

Output Buttons. In the Output section, click Solid to create a solid feature or Surface to create the feature as a surface.

Join. Adds material to the part.

Cut. Removes material from the part.

Intersect. Creates a new feature from the shared volume of the sweep feature and existing part volume. Material not included in the shared volume is deleted.

Path Sweep Type

Creates a sweep feature by sweeping a profile along a path.

Path. Holds the swept profile constant to the sweep path. All sweep sections maintain the original profile relationship to the path, as shown in the following image on the left.

Parallel. Holds the swept profile parallel to the original profile, as shown in the following image on the right.

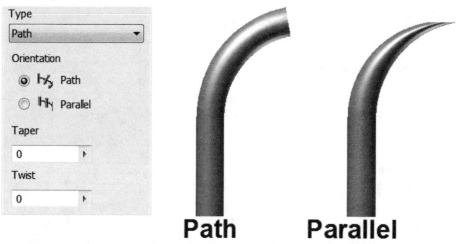

Figure 7-42

Taper. Enter a value for the angle you want the profile to be drafted. By default, the taper angle is zero.

Twist. Use the twist option to spiral the profile along the path the number of degrees or radians you specify. For example, the following image on the left shows a triangle profile and a line as the path, the middle image shows the triangle swept along the line with no twist, and the image on the right shows the same sweep but 360 degrees of twist was added.

Figure 7-43

Path & Guide Rail Sweep Type

Creates a sweep feature by sweeping a profile along a path and uses a guide rail to control scale and twist of the swept profile. The following image shows the options for the path and guide rail type.

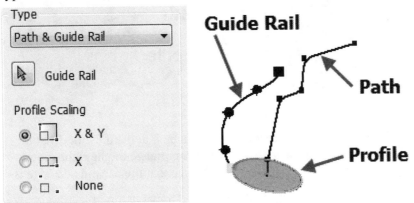

Figure 7-44

Guide Rail. Select a guide curve or rail that controls the scaling and twist of the swept profile. The guide rail must touch the profile plane. If you project an edge to position the guide rail and the projected edge is not the path, change the projected edge to a construction line.

Profile Scaling. Specify how the swept section scales to meet the guide rail. The following image shows the path, the profile, and guide rail along with the three different profile-scaling options.

- **X and Y.** Scales the profile in both the X and Y directions as the sweep progresses.
- **X.** Scales the profile in the X direction as the sweep progresses. The profile is not scaled in the Y direction.
- **None.** Keeps the profile at a constant shape and size as the sweep progresses. Using this option, the rail controls only the profile twist and is not scaled in the X or Y direction.

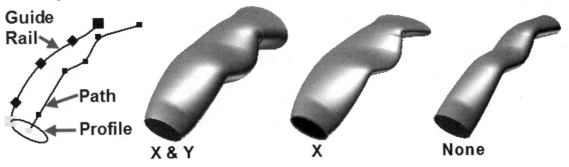

Figure 7-45

Path & Guide Surface Sweep Type

Creates a sweep feature by sweeping a profile along a path and uses a guide surface to control the twist of the swept profile. For best results, the path should touch or be near the guide surface.

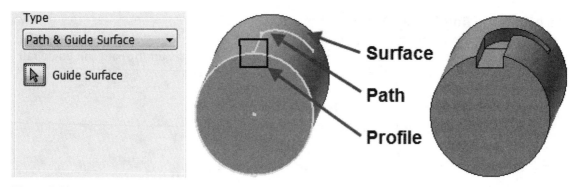

Figure 7-46

The following image on the left shows a sweep feature with only a path defined. Notice that the back inside edge of the cut is angled from the surface. The following image on the right shows the same sweep, but with a guide surface to control the twist. Notice that the back inside edge is parallel to the top of the surface.

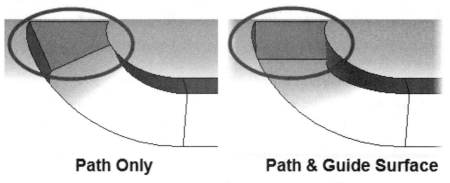

Figure 7-47

Creating a Sweep Feature

To create a sweep feature, follow these steps:

1. Create an unconsumed sketch for the profile and one for the path, or if you are going to use existing part edges for the path, you don't need to create a second sketch for the path. The profile and path sketches must lie on separate nonparallel planes. It is recommended that the profile intersect the path. Use work planes to place the location of the sketches, if required. The sketch that you use for the path can be open or closed. Add dimensions and constraints to both sketches as needed. If needed, create a sketch that will be used as a rail, or create a surface to be used as a guide surface.

2. Click the Sweep command on the 3D Model tab > Create panel.

3. The Sweep dialog box will appear. If two unconsumed sketches do not exist, Autodesk Inventor will notify you that two unconsumed sketches are required.

4. Click the Profile button, and then select the sketch that will be swept in the graphics window. If only one closed profile exists, this step is automated for you.

5. If it is not already depressed, click the Path button, and then select the sketch to be used as the path in the graphics window.

6. Select the type of sweep you are creating: Path, Path & Guide Rail, or Path & Guide Surface.

7. Define whether or not the resulting sweep will create a solid or a surface by clicking either the Solid or the Surface button in the Output area. Select the required options, as outlined in the previous descriptions.

8. If this is a secondary feature, click the operation that will specify whether material will be added or removed or if what is common between the existing part and the new sweep feature will be kept.

9. If you want the sweep feature to have a taper, click on the More tab, and enter a value for the taper angle.

10. Click the OK button to complete the operation.

EXERCISE 7-3: CREATING SWEEP FEATURES

In the first part of this exercise, you create a component with the sweep command. Three sketches will be created, one each for the profile, the path, and the guide rail. In the second part of the exercise you sweep a profile using edges on a part as the path.

1. Start a new part file based on the Standard (in).ipt template file.

2. Create a 2D Sketch on the XY origin plane and draw, constrain, and dimension the geometry as shown in the following image. Place the lower left endpoint of the sketch on the origin point. The arcs are tangent to the adjacent lines and the three arcs have the same radius.

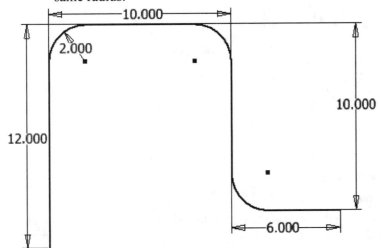

Figure 7-48

3. Finish the sketch.

4. Create a 2D Sketch on the XZ origin plane.

5. Draw two concentric circles that are centered on the origin point and add a **1.5 inch diameter** dimension to the outside circle and add a **.1 inch** dimension between the two circles to define the thickness, as shown in the following image on the left. Note, if the origin point is not on the active sketch, project the origin point or the endpoint of the first line. If needed use the Orbit command to change the viewpoint so you can better see the geometry.

6. Finish the sketch.

7. Click the Sweep command on the 3D Model tab > Create panel.

a. For the profile click a point between the two circles, as shown in the following image on the right.

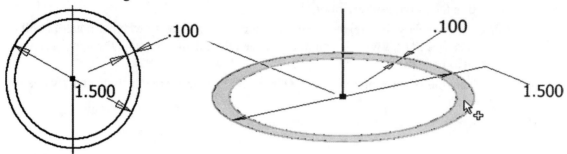

Figure 7-49

b. Next, you define the path, after selecting the profile the Path button in the Sweep dialog box should be current, select one of the lines or arcs of the open profile.

c. Click OK to create the sweep feature.

8. Change the material of the part to steel by selecting Steel from the material list in the Quick Access toolbar, as shown in the following image on the left.

9. Change your viewpoint so you can see the front of the sweep as shown in the following image on the right.

Figure 7-50

10. Close the file. Do not save changes.

11. Open *ESS_E07_03-2.ipt* in the Chapter 07 folder.

12. Create a sketch by zooming into the front right side of the part. Select the front face of the part and click Create Sketch from the mini-toolbar, as shown in the following image on the left.

13. The viewpoint will change so you are looking directly at the sketch. However, it is difficult to see where you are sketching. To return to your previous view, press the F5 key.

14. Sketch a circle on the projected top-right end point and add a **.0625 in** dimension, as shown in the following image on the right. By default, the dimension rounds to three decimal places in the sketch.

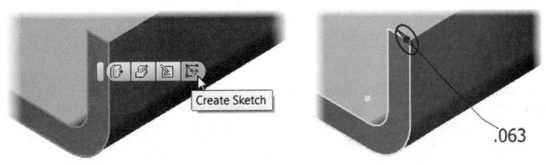

15. Click the Finish Sketch command on the Sketch tab > Exit panel.
16. Next, you sweep the circle along edges of the part using the Sweep command.
    a. Click the Sweep command on the Create panel.
    b. For the profile select inside the circle. The profile may be automatically selected for you.
    c. The Path button will then be active, select the top-right outside edge of the part for the path, as shown in the following image on the left. Note that Inventor will automatically select all of the edges that are tangent to the select edge.
    d. In the Sweep dialog box, click the Cut operation to remove material.
    e. Click the OK button in the Sweep dialog box. The following image on the right shows the completed part.

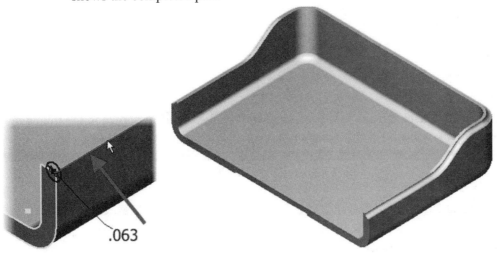

17. Use the Zoom and Free Orbit commands to examine the Sweep feature.
18. Close the file. Do not save changes. End of exercise.

3D SKETCHING

To create a sweep feature whose path does not lie on a single plane, you can create a 3D sketch that will be used for the path. You can use a 3D sketch to define the routing path for an assembly component, such as a pipe or duct work that crosses multiple faces on different planes. You need to define a 3D sketch in the part environment, and you can do this within an assembly or in its own part file. You can use the Autodesk Inventor adaptive technology during 3D sketch creation to create a path that updates automatically to reflect changes to referenced assembly components. In this section, you will learn strategies for creating 3D sketches.

3D Sketch Overview

When creating a 3D sketch, you use many of the sketching techniques that you have already learned with the addition of a few commands. 3D sketches use work points and model edges or vertices to define the shape of the 3D sketch by creating line or spline segments between them. You can also create bends between line segments. When creating a 3D sketch, you use a combination of lines, splines, fillet features, work features, constraints, and existing edges and vertices.

3D Sketch Environment

The 3D sketch environment is used to create 3D or a combination of both 2D and 3D curves. Before creating a 3D sketch, change the environment to the 3D sketch environment by clicking the Start 3D Sketch command on the 3D Model tab > Sketch panel which may be beneath the Start 2D Sketch command, as shown in the following image.

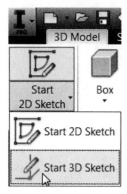

Figure 7-53

In the ribbon, the 3D Sketch tab and new commands will be displayed, as shown in the following image. The commonly used 3D sketch commands are explained in the next sections.

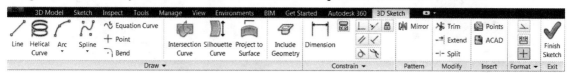

Figure 7-54

3D Sketch from Intersecting Geometry

One method to create a 3D path is to use geometry or features that intersect with faces on the part. If the intersecting geometry defines the 3D path, you can use it. The intersection can be defined by a combination of any of the following: planar or nonplanar part faces, surface faces, a quilt, or work planes. To create a 3D path from an intersection, follow these steps:

1. Create the intersecting features that describe the desired path.

2. Create a 3D Sketch by clicking the Start 3D Sketch command on the 3D Model tab > Sketch panel, it may be under the Start 2D Sketch command.

3. Click the Intersection Curve command on the 3D Sketch tab > Draw panel, as shown in the following image on the left.

4. The 3D Intersection Curve dialog box appears, as shown in the middle of the following image.

5. Select the two intersecting geometries or features.

6. To complete the operation, click OK.

7. The following image on the right shows geometry being created on a cylindrical face where the work plane intersects the cylindrical face.

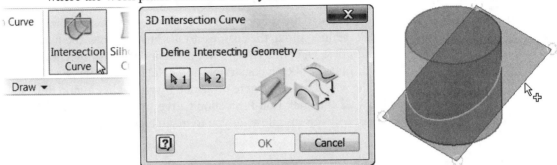

Figure 7-55

Project to Surface

While in a 3D sketch, you can project: curves, 2D or 3D geometry, part edges, and points onto a face or selected faces of a part. To project curves onto a face, follow these steps:

1. Create or open a part onto which the curves will be projected.

2. Create the curves that will be projected onto the part's face(s).

3. Click the Start 3D Sketch command on the 3D Model tab > Sketch panel.

4. Click the Project to Surface command on the 3D Sketch tab > Draw panel, as shown in the following image on the left.

5. The Project Curve to Surface dialog box will appear, as shown in the middle of the following image. The Faces button will be active. In the graphics window, select the face(s) onto which the curves will be projected.

6. Click the Curves Button, and then in the graphics window, select the individual objects to project. The following image on the right shows the face and curves selected.

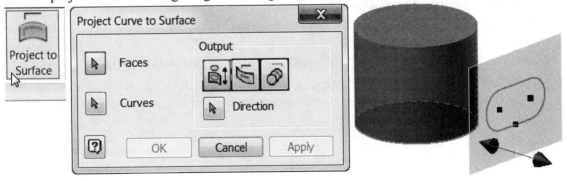

Figure 7-56

7. In the Output area, select one of the following options.

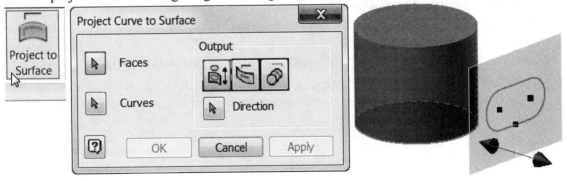	Project along vector	Specify the vector by clicking the Direction button and selecting a plane, edge, or axis. If a plane is selected, the vector will be normal (90°) from the plane. The curves will be projected in the direction of

		the vector.
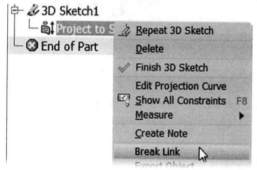	Project to closest point	Projects the curves onto the surface normal to the closest point.
	Wrap to Surface	The curves are wrapped around the curvature of the selected face or faces.

8. Click OK.

By default, the projected curves are linked to the original curve. If the original curves change size, they will be updated. To break the link, move the cursor into the browser over the name of the Projected to Surface entry, right-click, and click Break Link in the menu, as shown in the following image. You could also display the sketch constraints and delete the reference constraints. You can also change the way the curves were projected by right-clicking on the Project to Surface entry in the browser and click Edit Projection Curve from the menu and the Project Curve to Surface dialog box will appear, allowing you to make changes as required.

Figure 7-57

Project to a 3D Sketch

Another method to project 2D geometry onto a non-planar face is to use the Project to 3D Sketch command. While in a 2D Sketch, the Project to 3D Sketch command will project all the geometry on the active 2D sketch geometry onto a nonplanar face and automatically create a 3D sketch. To use the Project to 3D Sketch command, follow these steps.

1. First, create a 2D sketch and sketch and constrain geometry as needed or make an existing sketch active that contains the geometry that you want to project.

2. Click the Project to 3D Sketch command from the Sketch tab > Create panel, as shown in the following image on the left.

3. If needed, in the Project to 3D Sketch dialog box check the Project option.

4. Select a face or faces that the geometry will be projected onto. All of the geometry on the active sketch will preview how it will be projected on the selected face(s), as shown in the following image on the right.

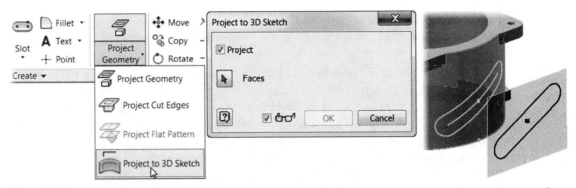

Figure 7-58

5. Click OK to create a 3D sketch and project all the geometry on the active sketch to the selected face(s).

3D LINES

Another option to create a 3D path is to draw 3D lines that are nonplanar. To draw 3D lines follow these steps:

1. While in a 3D Sketch, click the Line command on the 3D Sketch tab > Draw panel, as shown in the following image on the left.

2. Once in the 3D line command, you can create lines by selecting on a plane on the triad, as shown in the following image on the right, and place line segments. After placing the lines you can add dimensions.

Figure 7-59

3. Or while in the line command, you can turn on the Precise Input mini-toolbar. While in the line command click the down arrow on the 3D Sketch tab > Draw panel, as shown in the following image on the left, and from the expanded panel click Precise Input as shown in the middle of the following image. Then, in the Precise Input mini-toolbar enter X, Y, and Z point data, as shown in the following image on the right. Values can be relative to the last point or absolute to 0, 0, 0. Consult the help system "Create a 3D Line" for more information about using Precise Input.

Figure 7-60

4. Dimensions and constraints can be applied to the lines.

5. By default, a bend is not applied between 3D line segments, but this option can be toggled on and off by right-clicking while in the 3D line command and selecting or deselecting Auto-Bend on the menu, as shown in the following image on the left.

6. To set the default radius of the bend, Click the Document Settings command on the Tools tab > Options panel, and change the 3D Sketch Auto-Bend Radius setting on the Sketch tab.

7. To manually add a bend between two 3D lines, use the Bend command on the 3D Sketch tab > Draw panel, as shown in the following image in the middle, or right-click in a blank area of the graphics window and click Bend from the marking menu, as shown in the following image on the right. The Bend dialog box appears, in the Bend dialog box enter a value for the bend, and then select two 3D lines or the endpoint where they meet. To complete the command, right-click and click OK from the marking menu. You can edit the bend by double-clicking on the dimension and entering a new value.

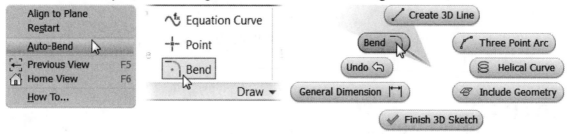

Figure 7-61

CREATE A 3D SWEEP

To create a 3D sweep, follow these steps:

1. Click the Start 3D sketch command from the 3D Model tab > Sketch panel.

2. Create a 3D path using any of the previously discussed techniques.

3. After creating a 3D path, next you create a 2D sketch, draw, and constrain a closed profile.

4. Start the Sweep command on the 3D Model tab > Create panel and use the closed sketch as the profile and 3D lines as the path.

The following image on the left shows a part with 3D lines and dimensions. The image on the right shows the completed sweep.

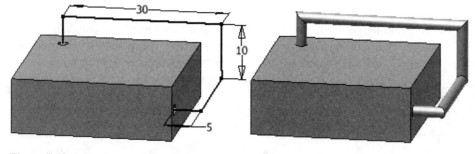

Figure 7-62

IMPORT POINTS

Another option to create geometry is to import X, Y, Z point data from a Microsoft Excel spreadsheet. The imported points can be connected by lines or splines or left as points. The imported points are not associated back to the spreadsheet: if the data in the spreadsheet changes, the imported point data will not update. While in a 2D sketch, only X and Y values are imported. While in a 3D sketch, X, Y and Z values are imported. The data in the spreadsheet must start in cell A1 and be in the first worksheet. Cell A1 can define a unit; if no unit is defined in cell A1 the document unit will be used. Rows can include an X, Y and Z heading if desired, but it is not required. The columns must be in the following order and the C column is not required.

Column A = X value   Column B = Y value   Column C = Z value

The following image on the left shows an example of a spreadsheet with the unit and column heading data and the image on the right shows an example of only the required fields.

	A	B	C
1	in		
2	X	Y	Z
3	0	0	0
4	5	0	0
5	5	5	0
6	5	5	5
7	10	5	5

	A	B	C
1	0	0	0
2	5	0	0
3	5	5	0
4	5	5	5
5	10	5	5

Figure 7-63

To import points from a spreadsheet follow these steps:

1. Create a Microsoft Excel spreadsheet with X, Y and Z point data. The Z data is optional
2. Create or make a 2D or 3D sketch active.
3. Click the Import Point data command using either of the following methods:
   a. In a 2D sketch, click the 2D Sketch tab > Insert Panel > Import Points, as shown in the following image on the left.
      Or
   b. In a 3D sketch, click the 3D Sketch tab > Insert Panel > Import Points, as shown in the image on the right.

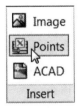
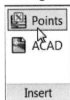

Figure 7-64

4. The Open dialog box appears, navigate to and select the Excel spreadsheet.
5. On the bottom-right corner of the Open dialog box click the Options button and the File Open Options dialog box appears, as shown in the following image. Select the option to Create points (the default), or connect the points by clicking Create lines or connect the points with a spline with the Create spline option.

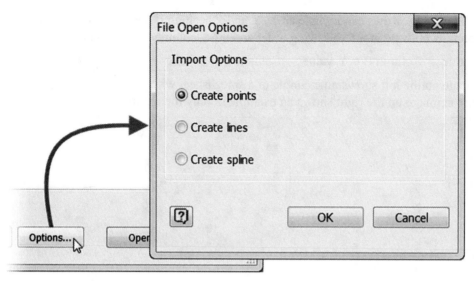

Figure 7-65

6. Click OK to accept the options and then click Open to create the data.
7. Add dimensions and constraints as needed.

EXERCISE 7-4: 3D SKETCH—SWEEP FEATURES

In this exercise, you create geometry in a 3D sketch using different methods.

1. Start a new part file based on the Standard (in).ipt template file.
2. Create a 3D Sketch by clicking the Start 3D Sketch command on the 3D Model tab > Sketch panel.
3. Press the F6 key to change to the Home View.
4. Next you place four lines.
    a. Click the Line command on the 3D Sketch tab > Draw panel.
    b. In the graphics screen select the XY coordinate plane on the 3D coordinator.
    c. For the first point click a point above the Triad and coordinate planes and in the graphics window draw a line in the X direction.
    d. Draw another line in the Y direction with the parallel constraint as shown in the following image on the left.
    e. In the graphics screen select the YZ coordinate plane on the 3D coordinator.
    f. In the graphics window draw a line in the –Z direction with the parallel constraint, as shown in the middle of the following image.
    g. In the graphics screen select the XZ coordinate plane on the 3D coordinator.
    h. In the graphics window draw a line in the X direction with the parallel constraint as shown in the following image on the right.

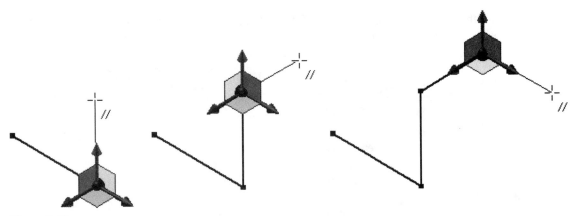

Figure 7-66

5. Start the Dimension command from the 3D Sketch tab > Constrain panel and add the four dimensions to the lines, as shown in the following image. If needed, you can add perpendicular and parallel constraints between the lines.

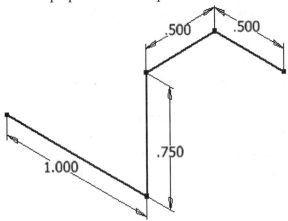

Figure 7-67

6. Delete the lines you just created.

7. Next, you place lines via the Precise Input mini-toolbar.

    a. Click the Line command on the 3D Sketch tab > Draw panel.

    b. If the Precise Input mini-toolbar does not appear, click the down arrow on the 3D Sketch tab > Draw panel and click the Precise Input command. Practice creating lines by entering point data in the Precise Input mini-toolbar.

Figure 7-68

    c. Add dimensions and constraints as desired.

    d. Delete the lines you just created.

8. Next you import point data from an Excel spreadsheet.

    a. Click the Import Point data command from the 3D Sketch tab > Insert Panel.

    b. The Open dialog box appears, navigate to and single click on the Excel spreadsheet *XYZ - Point Data.xlsx* in the Chapter 07 folder.

c. On the bottom-right corner of the Open dialog box click the Options button. In the File Open Option dialog box click the Create lines option, as shown in the following image.

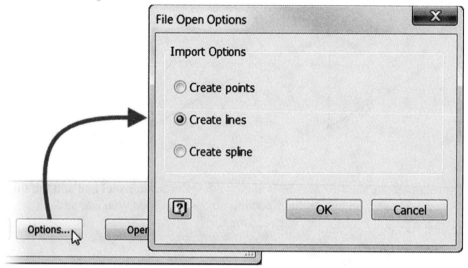

Figure 7-69

d. Click OK to accept the options and then click the Open button in the Open dialog box to create the data.

9. Zoom out and rotate the viewpoint so you can see the imported points with the connecting lines, as shown in the following image.

10. Add dimensions and perpendicular constraints and a parallel constraint between the lines. The following image shows the dimensioned sketch with the constraints visibility on.

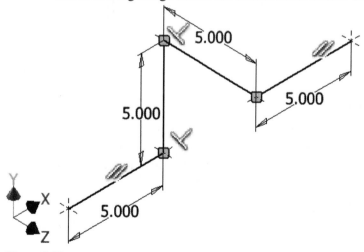

Figure 7-70

11. Close the file. Do not save changes.

In this portion of this exercise, you create geometry on a 3D sketch from intersecting geometry.

12. Open *ESS_E07_04-2.ipt* from the Chapter 07 folder. The part contains a cylinder and an angled work plane.

13. Create a 3D Sketch by clicking the Start 3D Sketch command on the 3D Model tab > Sketch panel.

14. Click the Intersection Curve command from the 3D Sketch tab > Draw panel.

    a.   Select the visible work plane and the circular face of the part.

    b.   Click OK to create the curve.

15. Turn off the visibility of the work plane by right-clicking on an edge of the work plane and click Visibility from the menu. When done, your screen should resemble the following image.

Figure 7-71

16. Finish the 3D sketch by clicking on Finish Sketch on the 3D Sketch tab > Exit panel.

17. Next you create a 2D sketch that the sweep command will use as the profile.

18. Start the Start 2D Sketch command from the 3D Model tab > Sketch panel under the Start 3D Sketch command, and from the Origin folder in the browser click the YZ Plane, as shown in the following image on the left.

19. Change to the Home View by right-clicking and click Home View from the menu.

20. Press the F7 key to slice the graphics.

21. Use the Project Geometry command on the Sketch tab > Create panel and project the geometry that you created previously from the Intersection Geometry command.

22. Change the projected line to a construction line. This will prevent the projected line from being used when you create the sweep.

23. Create a **.5 inch** diameter circle on the bottom left endpoint of the projected geometry as shown in the middle of the following image.

24. Finish the Sketch.

25. Start the Sweep command on the 3D Model tab > Create panel and use the following options:

    a.   The circle should be automatically selected as the profile, if not select the circle as the profile.

    b.   Select the geometry that was created from the intersecting plane and face for the sweep path.

    c.   Change the operation to cut.

    d.   Click OK to create the sweep. When complete, your screen should resemble the following image on the right.

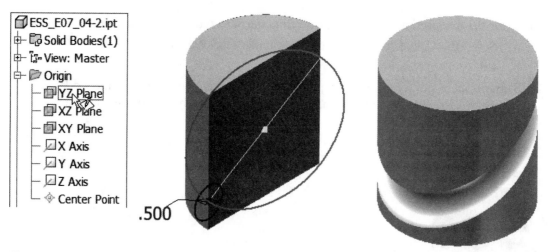

Figure 7-72

26. Close the file. Do not save changes.

In the next portion of this exercise, you will use the Project to 3D Sketch command to project geometry onto a cylindrical face.

27. Open *ESS_E07_04-3.ipt* from the Chapter 07 folder. The part contains an extrusion and a constrained sketch.

28. Make Sketch2 active by clicking on one of the arcs or lines on the sketch, and click Edit Sketch from the mini-toolbar or by double-clicking on Sketch2 in the browser.

29. To better see the part, change to the Home View.

30. Click the Project to 3D Sketch command on the Sketch tab > Create panel. The command may be under the Project Geometry command.

   a. In the Project to 3D Sketch dialog box, the Project option should be checked. In the graphics window select the inside circular face on the part to project the sketch onto, as shown in the following image on the left.

   b. Click OK to complete the operation.

31. Finish the sketch.

32. In the browser, turn off the visibility of Sketch2. When complete, your screen should resemble the following image on the right.

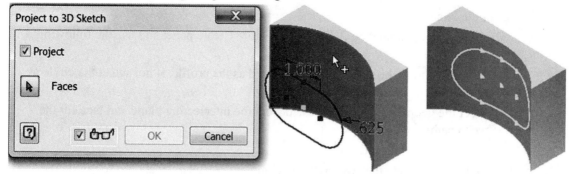

Figure 7-73

33. If desired, you can create a profile and sweep it along the projected geometry as you did earlier in this exercise. Note that you could have also used the Project to Surface command in the 3D sketch tab to project the geometry onto the face.

416

34. Close the file. Do not save changes. End of exercise.

COIL FEATURES

Using the Coil feature, you can easily create many types of helical, coil, spring, or spiral/spring geometry. You can create various types of springs by selecting different settings in the Coil dialog box. You can also use the Coil feature to remove or add a helical shape around the outside of a cylindrical part to represent a thread profile.

To create a coil, you need to have at least one unconsumed or shared sketch available in the part. This sketch describes the profile or shape of the coil feature and can also contain a line that will be used as the coil's axis of revolution. For the axis of revolution you can also use an edge on the part or a work axis. If no unconsumed sketch is available, Autodesk Inventor will prompt you with an error message stating, "No unconsumed visible sketches on the part." After a sketch is available, you can click the Coil command on the 3D Model tab > Create panel, as shown in the following image on the left. The Coil dialog box appears, as shown in the following image on the right, with three tabs. The following sections explain the main options that are available on the tabs.

Coil Shape Tab

The Coil Shape tab allows you to specify the geometry and orientation of the coil.

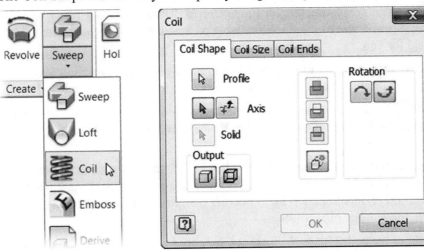

Figure 7-74

Profile. Click to select the sketch that you will use as the profile shape of the coil feature. By default, the Profile button is shown depressed; this tells you that you need to select a sketch or sketch area. If there are multiple closed profiles, you will need to select the profile that you want to revolve. If there is only one possible profile, Autodesk Inventor will select it for you, and you can skip this step. If you select the wrong profile or sketch area, click the Profile button and select a new profile or sketch area. You can only use one closed profile to create the coil feature.

Axis. Click to select a sketched line or centerline, a projected straight edge, or an axis about which to revolve the profile sketch. If selecting an edge or sketched centerline, it must be part of the sketch. If selecting a work axis, it cannot intersect the profile.

Flip. Click to change the direction in which the coil will be created along the axis. The direction will be changed on either the positive or negative X or Y axis, depending upon the edge or axis that you selected. You will see a preview of the direction in which the coil will be created.

Solid. If there are multiple solid bodies, click this button to choose the solid body to participate in the operation.

Output. Click to create a solid or a surface.

Operation. The operation buttons are the column of buttons in the center of the dialog box. These buttons are only available if a feature exists before creating the Coil feature. By default, the Join operation is selected. You can select the other operations to either add or remove material from the part using the Join or Cut options or to keep what is common between the existing part volume and the completed coil feature using the Intersect option.

- **Join**: Adds material to the part.
- **Cut**: Removes material from the part.
- **Intersect**: Keeps what is common to the part and the coil feature.
- **New solid**: Creates a new solid body. The first solid feature that is created uses this option by default. Select it to create a new body in a part file with an existing solid body.

Rotation. Click to specify the direction in which the coil will rotate, either clockwise or counterclockwise.

Coil Size Tab

The Coil Size tab, as shown in the following image on the left, allows you to specify how the coil will be created. You have various options for the type of coil that you can create. Based on the type of coil that you select, the other parameters for Pitch, Height, Revolution, and Taper will become active or inactive. Specify two of the three available parameters, and Autodesk Inventor will calculate the last field for you.

Type. Select the parameters that you want to specify: Pitch and Revolution, Revolution and Height, Pitch and Height, or Spiral. If you select Spiral as the Coil Type, only the Pitch and Revolution values are required.

Pitch. Type in the value for the height to which you want the helix to elevate with each revolution.

Revolution. Specify the number of revolutions for the coil. A coil cannot have zero revolutions, and fractions can be used in this field. For example, you can create a coil that contains 2.5 turns. If end conditions are specified, as mentioned in the following Coil Ends tab section, the end conditions are included in the number of revolutions.

Height. Specify the height of the coil. This is the total coil height as measured from the center of the profile at the start to the center of the profile at the end.

Taper. Specify an angle at which you want the coil to be tapered along its axis.

TIP: A spiral coil type cannot be tapered.

Coil Ends Tab

The Coil Ends tab, as shown in the following image on the right, lets you specify the end conditions for the start and end of the coil. When selecting the Flat option, the helix, not the profile that you selected for the coil, is flattened. The ends of a coil feature can have unique end conditions that are not consistent between the start and the end of the coil.

Start. Select either Natural or Flat for the start of the helix. Click the down arrow to change between the two options.

End. Select either Natural or Flat for the end of the helix. Click the down arrow to change between the two options.

Transition Angle. This is the rotational angle, specified in degrees, in which the coil achieves the coil start or end transition. It normally occurs in less than one revolution.

Flat Angle. This is the rotational angle, specified in degrees, that describes the amount of flat coil that extends after the transition. It specifies the transition from the end of the revolved profile into a flattened end.

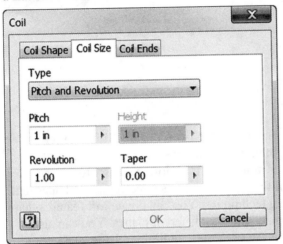 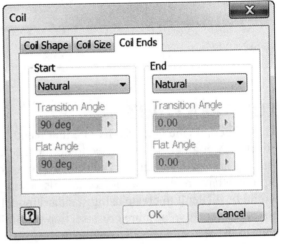

Figure 7-75

The following image shows a coil created as the base feature. The image on the left shows the coil in its sketch stage; it contains a rectangle that will be used as the profile, and a centerline that will be used as the axis of rotation. The finished part, on the right of the following image, shows the coil with flat ends.

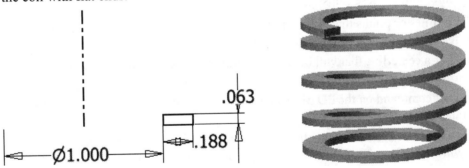

Figure 7-76

The following image shows a coil created as a secondary feature. The image on the left shows the coil in its sketch stage with the Coil dialog box displayed. The sketch, a rectangle, is drawn tangent to the cylinder. The rectangle will be used as the profile, and the work axis will be used as the axis of rotation. The finished part, on the right of the following image, shows the coil with the flat end on the top.

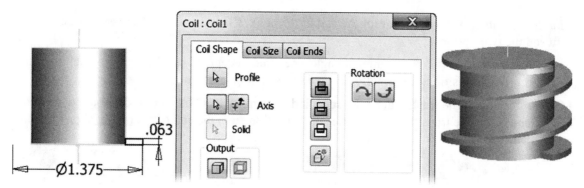

Figure 7-77

LOFT FEATURES

The Loft command creates a feature that blends a shape between two or more different sections or profiles. A point can also be used to define the beginning and ending section of the loft. Loft features are used frequently when creating plastic or molded parts. A loft is similar to a sweep, but it can have multiple sections and rails. Many of these types of parts have complex shapes that would be difficult to create using standard modeling techniques. You can create loft features that blend between two or more cross-section profiles that reside on different planes. You can also control the area of a specific section in the loft. You can use a rail, multiple rails, or a centerline to define a path(s) that the loft will follow. There is no limit to the number of sections or rails that you can include in a loft feature. Four types of geometry are used to create a loft: sections, rails, centerlines, and points. The following sections describe these types of geometry.

Create a Loft

To create a loft feature, follow these steps:

1. Create the profiles or points that will be used as the sections to define the loft. If required, use work features, sketches, or projected geometry to position the profiles.

2. Create rails or a centerline that will be used to define the direction or control of the shape between sections.

3. Click the Loft command on the 3D Model tab > Create panel, as shown in the following image on the left.

4. On the Curves tab of the Loft dialog box, the Sections option will be active. In the graphics window, select the sketches, face loops, or points in the order in which the loft sections will blend.

5. If rails are to be used to define the loft, click the "Click to add" text in the Rails area on the Curves tab, and then in the graphics window select the rail or rails.

6. If needed, change the options for the loft on the Conditions and Transition tabs.

TIP: The loft options are also available by right-clicking in a blank area in the graphics window and clicking an option on the menu.

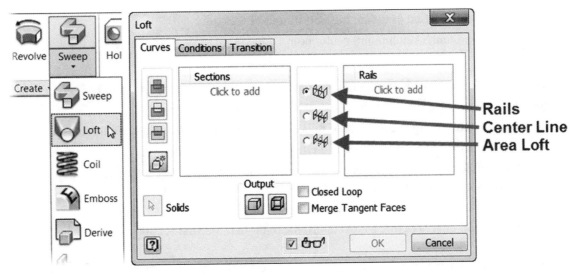

Figure 7-78

The following image shows a loft created from two sections and a centerline rail. The image on the left shows two sections and a centerline in their sketch stages, shown in the top view. The image on the right shows the completed loft.

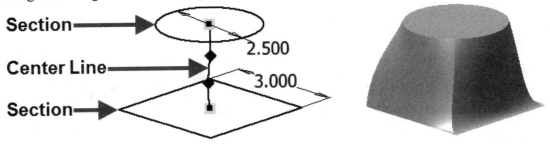

Figure 7-79

The following sections explain the options in the Loft dialog box and on its tabs.

Curves Tab
The Curves tab, as shown in the previous image, allows you to select which sketches, part edges, part faces, or points will be used as sections to select whether or not a rail or centerline will be used and to determine the output condition.

Sections
You can define the shape(s) between which the loft will blend. The following rules apply to sections:

1. There is no limit to the number of sections that you can include in the loft feature.
2. Sections do not have to be sketched on parallel planes.
3. You can define sections with 2D sketches (planar), 3D sketches (nonplanar), and planar or nonplanar faces, edges on a part, or points.
4. All sections must be either open or closed. You cannot mix open and closed profile types within the same loft operation. Open profiles result in a lofted surface.

Points
A point can be used as a section to help define the loft. The following rules apply to points used for a loft profile:

1. A point can be used to define the start or end of the loft.
2. An origin point, sketch point, center point, edge point, or work point can be used.

Rails

You can define rails using the following elements: 2D sketches (planar), 3D sketches (nonplanar), or part faces and edges. The following rules apply to rails:

1. There is no limit to the number of rails that you can create or include in the loft feature.
2. Rails must not cross each other and must not cross mapping curves.
3. Rails affect all of the sections not just faces or sections that they intersect. Section vertices without defined rails are influenced by neighboring rails.
4. All rail curves must be open or closed.
5. Closed rail curves define a closed loft, meaning that the first section is also the last section.
6. No two rails can have identical guide points, even though the curves themselves may be different.
7. Rails can extend beyond the first and last sections. Any part of a rail that comes before the first section or after the last is ignored.
8. You can apply a 2D or 3D sketch tangency or smooth constraint between the rail and the existing geometry on the model.

Center Line

A center line is treated like a rail, and the loft sections are held normal to the center line. When a centerline is used, it acts like a path used in the sweep feature, and it maintains a consistent transition between sections. The same rules apply to center lines as to rails except that the centerline does not need to intersect sections and only one centerline can be used.

Area Loft

Select a sketch to be used as the centerline, and then click on the centerline to define the area of the profile at the selected point. After picking a point, the Section Dimensions dialog box appears, as shown in the following image. You define its position either as a proportional or absolute distance, and you can define the section's size by area or scale factor related to the area of the original profile.

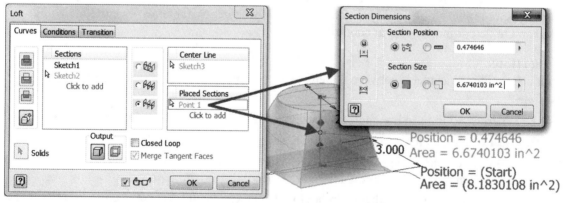

Figure 7-80

Output

Select whether the loft feature will be a solid or a surface. Open sketch profiles selected as loft sections will define a lofted surface.

Operation

Select an operation button to add or remove material from the part, using the Join or Cut options, or to keep what is common between the existing part and the completed loft using the Intersect option. By default, the Join operation is selected.

Closed Loop

Click to join the first and last sections of the loft feature to create a closed loop.

Merge Tangent Faces

This option is available when one of the sketches of the loft is on an existing face of a feature. This option joins the loft feature so it is tangent to the existing feature.

Conditions Tab

The Conditions tab, as shown in the following image, allows you to control the tangency condition, boundary angle, and weight condition of the loft feature. These settings affect how the faces on the loft feature relate to geometry at the start and end profiles of the loft. This may be existing part geometry or the plane or work plane containing the loft section sketch.

Figure 7-81

The column on the left lists the sketches and points specified for the sections. To change a sketch's condition, click on its name, and then select a condition option.

Conditions - Sketch

Two boundary conditions are available when the first or last section is a sketch.

- **Free Condition** (top button): With this option, there is no boundary condition, and the loft will blend between the sections in the most direct fashion.
- **Direction Condition** (bottom button): This option is only available when the curve is a 2D sketch. When selected, you specify the angle at which the loft will intersect or transition from the section.

Conditions - Edge

When a face loop or edges from a part are used to form a section, as shown in the following image on the left, three conditions are available, as shown in the following image on the right.

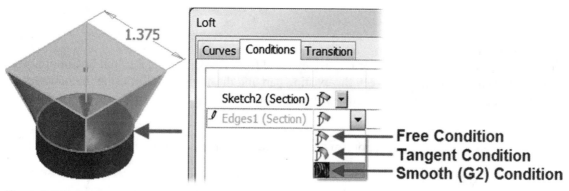

Figure 7-82

- **Free Condition** (top button): With this option, there is no boundary condition, and the loft will blend between the sections in the most direct fashion.
- **Tangent Condition** (middle button): With this option, the loft will be tangent to the adjacent section of the face.
- **Smooth (G2) Condition** (bottom button): With this option, the loft will have curvature continuity to the adjacent section of the face.

Conditions – Point

Three conditions are available when a point is selected for a loft profile, as shown in the following image.

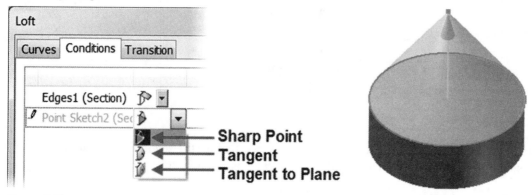

Figure 7-83

- **Sharp Point** (top button): With this option, there is no boundary condition, and the loft will blend from the previous section to the point in the most direct fashion.
- **Tangent** (middle button): When selected, the loft transitions to a rounded or domed shape at the point.
- **Tangent to Plane** (bottom button): When selected, the loft transitions to a rounded dome shape. You select a planar face or work plane to be tangent to. This option is not available when a centerline loft is used.

Angle

This option is enabled for a section only when the boundary condition is Tangent or Direction. The default is set to 90° and is measured relative to the profile plane. The option sets the value for an angle formed between the plane that the profile is on and the direction to the next cross-section of the loft feature. Valid entries range from 0.0000001° to 179.99999°.

Weight

The default is set to 0. The weight value controls how much the angle influences the tangency of the loft shape to the normal of the starting and ending profile. A small value will create an abrupt transition, and a large value creates a more gradual transition. High weight values could result in twisting the loft and may cause a self-intersecting shape.

Transition Tab

The Transition tab, as shown in the following image with the Automatic mapping box unchecked, allows you to specify point sets. A point set is used to define section point relationships and control how segments blend from one section to the segments of the adjacent sections. Points are reoriented or added on two adjacent sections.

Map Points

You can map points to help define how the sections will blend into each other. The following rules apply to mapping points:

Point Set. The name of the point set appears here.

Map Point. The corresponding sketch for the selected point set appears here.

Position. The location of the selected map point appears here. You can modify the position by entering a new value or by dragging the point to a new location in the graphics window.

To modify the default point sets or to add a point set, follow these steps:

1. Click on the Transition tab, and uncheck the Automatic Mapping box. The dialog box will populate the automatic point data for each section. The list is sorted in the order in which the sections were specified on the Curve tab, as shown in the following image on the left.

2. To modify a point's position, select the point set in which the point is specified. When you select its name, it will become highlighted in the graphics window.

3. Click in the Position section of the map point that you want to modify, and enter a new value or drag the point to a new location in the graphics window.

4. To add a point set, select Click to add in the point set area.

5. Click a point on the profile of two adjacent sections. As you move the cursor over a valid region of the active section, a green point appears. As the points are placed, they are previewed in the graphics window, as shown in the following image on the right.

6. You can modify the new point set in a similar way to the default point set.

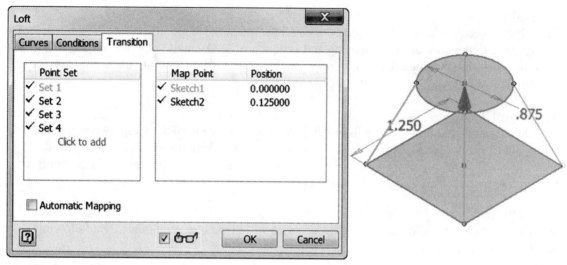

Figure 7-84

EXERCISE 7-5: CREATING A LOFT FEATURE

In this exercise, you use the loft command to define the shape of a razor handle.

1. Open *ESS_E07_05.ipt* in the Chapter 07 folder.
2. Edit the Sketch1 by double-clicking on Sketch1 in the browser.
3. Click the Point, Center Point command on the Sketch tab > Create panel.
4. Place a point so it is coincident on the spline near the bottom-right of the curve, making sure that the coincident glyph is displayed as you place the point, as shown in the following image.

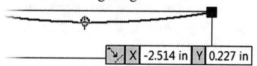

Figure 7-85

5. Draw two construction lines that are coincident with the sketched point you just placed and the nearest spline points on both sides of the point, as shown in the following image.

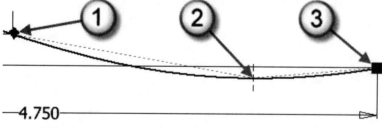

Figure 7-86

6. To parametrically position the sketched point midway between the spline points, place an equal constraint between the two construction lines you just created.
7. Change the 4.750 horizontal dimension to **5 inches**, and verify that the sketched point moves along the spline to maintain its position on the spline.
8. Finish editing the sketch by right-clicking and click Finish 2D Sketch from the menu.

9. Next, you create a work plane that a new profile will be located on. The work plane will be perpendicular to the spline and located at the point you just created.

   a. Click the Work Plane - Normal to Curve at Point command on the 3D Model tab > Work Features panel.

   b. Locate the work plane by selecting the point you just created.

   c. Position the work plane so it is perpendicular to the spline by selecting the spline, as shown in the following image on the left (do not select the construction line).

10. Next, create a profile for a loft section on the new work plane.

    a. Create a new sketch on the work plane you just created.

    b. To see the sketch better, change to the Home View.

    c. Use the Project Geometry command on the Sketch tab > Create panel and select the Point, Center Point you created in step 4.

    d. Draw an ellipse with its center coincident with the projected point and the second point so the ellipse's axis is horizontally constrained to the Point. Click a third point, as shown in the image on the right.

    e. Place **.1875 inch** and **.375 inch** dimensions to control the size of the ellipse, as shown in the following image on the right.

    f. Finish the sketch.

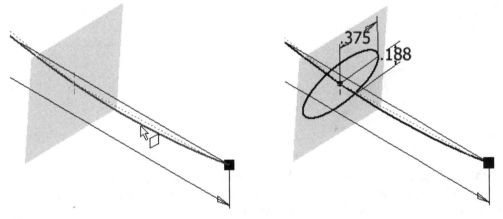

Figure 7-87

11. Click the Loft command on the 3D Model tab > Create panel.

    a. For the first section, click the concave 3D face, as shown in the following image.

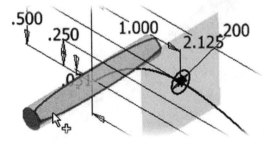

Figure 7-88

    b. To define the remaining sections, select the other three profile sections from left to right, and then click the point on the right end of the spline.

c. Click the Center Line option in the Loft dialog box, as shown in the following image on the left and select the spline. When finished, the preview should resemble the following image on the right.

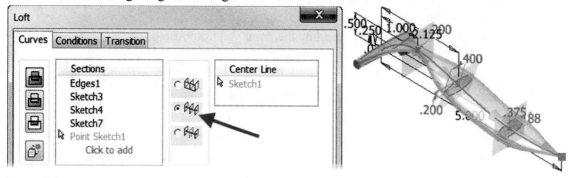

Figure 7-89

d. Click OK to create the loft.

12. Turn off the visibility of all the work planes by pressing the ALT and] keys and then use the Free Orbit command to examine the loft. Notice that the end of the loft on the right side is sharp.

Figure 7-90

13. To edit the loft, select a face on the Loft in the graphics window, and click Edit Loft from the mini-toolbar that is displayed. Click the Conditions tab, and change the Point entry to a Tangent condition, as shown in following image on the left.

14. Click OK to update the loft. The bottom of the handle should resemble the following image on the right.

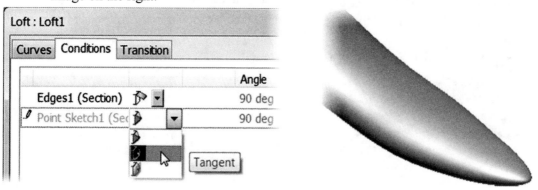

Figure 7-91

15. Next, edit the loft again and add another section that defines the section's area. In the browser, double-click on the entry Loft1.

a. From the Curves tab, click the Area Loft option labeled (1) in the following image.

b. In the Placed Sections area, click in the Click to add area labeled (2).

c. In the graphics window, click a point near the middle of the spline labeled (3).

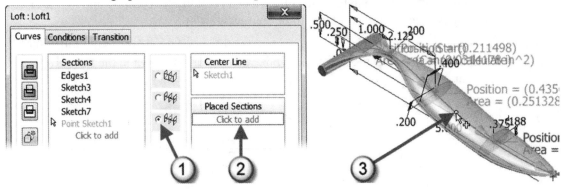

Figure 7-92

d. The Section Dimensions dialog box appears, in the Section Position area change the Proportional Distance option to **0.5** labeled (1) in the following image.

e. In the Section Size area change the Area option to **0.375 in^2** labeled (2).

f. Click OK in the Section Dimensions dialog box.

g. In the graphics window, notice the values of each section and new section half way through the loft.

16. In the Loft dialog box, click OK. The following image on the right shows the updated loft.

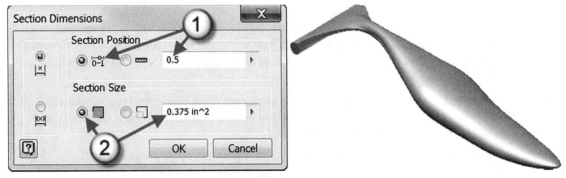

Figure 7-93

17. Close the file. Do not save changes. End of exercise.

SPLIT A PART OR FACE

The Split command allows you to split a part into two solids, split the solid by removing one portion of the part, to split individual faces, or to split all faces. A typical application to split a face is to allow the creation of face drafts to the split faces of a part. You can use the Split command to perform the following:

• Split a solid into multiple solid bodies.

• Remove a section of the part by using a surface, planar face, or a work plane and to cut material from the part in the direction you specify. The side that is removed is suppressed rather than deleted. To create a part with the other side removed, edit the split feature, redefine it to keep the other side, save the other half of the part to its own file using the Save Copy As option, or create a derived part.

- Split individual faces by using a surface, sketching a parting line, or placing a work plane, and then selecting the faces to split. You can edit the split feature and modify it to add or remove the desired part faces to be split.

The Split command is located on the 3D Model tab > Modify panel, as shown in the following image on the left. Once selected, the Split dialog box will appear, as shown in the following image on the right.

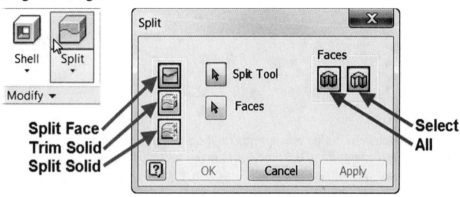

Figure 7-94

The Split dialog box contains the following sections:

Method

Split Face. Click this button to split individual faces of a part by selecting a work plane, surface, or sketched geometry and then selecting the faces to split. The split face method can split individual faces or all the faces on the part. When you select the split face method, the Remove area in the dialog box will be replaced with the Faces area, which allows you to select all or individual faces.

Trim Solid. Click this button to split a part using a selected work plane, surface, or sketched geometry to cut or remove material. If you select this option, you are prompted to choose the direction of the material that you want to remove.

Split Solid. Click this button to split a solid into two solid bodies. Use a surface, plane, or work plane that at least touches the outside edges of the solid; it can exceed the exterior faces of the part.

Remove. The option to remove material is only available when you use the Trim Solid method. After splitting a part, you can retrieve the cut material by editing the split feature and clicking to remove the opposite side or by deleting the split feature.

Faces

The Faces option is available only when you select the split face method.

All. Click this button to split all faces of the part that intersect the Split command.

Select. Click this button to enable the selection of specific faces that you want to split. After clicking the Select button, the Faces to Split command becomes active.

Faces. Click this button, and select a surface, work plane, or sketch that you want to use to split the part.

EXERCISE 7-6: SPLITTING A PART INTO MULTIPLE SOLID BODIES

In this exercise, you split a part into multiple solid bodies and export them to an assembly. For more information about working with multi-body parts consult the help system.

1. Open *ESS_E07_06.ipt* in the Chapter 07 folder.

2. First, you use an origin plane to split the part into two solids.

   a. Start the Split command from the 3D Model tab > Modify panel (may be under the Combine command).

   b. Click the Split Solid method button, as shown in the following image.

   c. For the Split Tool, click XY Plane from the Origin folder in the browser.

   d. Click OK to split the part into two solids.

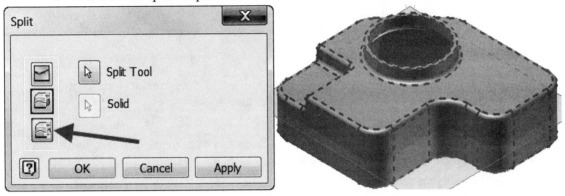

Figure 7-95

3. In the browser, expand the Solid Bodies folder and click on Solid2 and then Solid3 to verify that another solid has been created.

4. Next, you turn off the visibility of a solid. In the browser, in the Solid Bodies folder, right-click Solid2 and click Visibility on the menu.

5. Use the Zoom and Free Orbit commands to examine the solid.

6. Next, you switch the visibility of the solids. In the browser, in the Solid Bodies folder, right-click Solid2 and on the menu click Hide Others.

7. Use the Zoom and Free Orbit commands to examine the solid.

8. Turn the visibility of Solid3 back on, under the Solid Bodies folder, right-click Solid3 and click Visibility or Show All on the menu.

9. Next, you create a hole feature.

   a. From the 3D Model tab > Modify panel click the Hole command.

   b. Add a Through All **.25 inch** diameter hole that is concentric to the top right edge of the top solid, as shown in the following image.

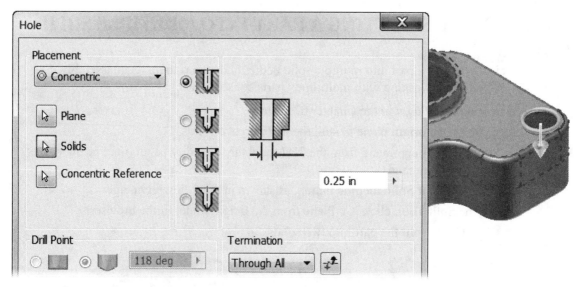

Figure 7-96

10. After creating the hole, use the Free Orbit command to examine the bottom solid and notice that the hole does not go through the bottom solid.

11. Change to the Home View.

12. In the browser, expand the Solid Bodies folder and expand the Solid2 and Solid3 entry. Notice that Hole1 is only under Solid2, as shown in the following image on the left.

13. Edit the hole feature.

    a. In the Hole dialog box click the Solids button, as shown in the middle of the following image.

    b. Select the bottom solid (Solid3) in the graphics window, as shown in the following image on the right.

    c. Click OK to complete the edit.

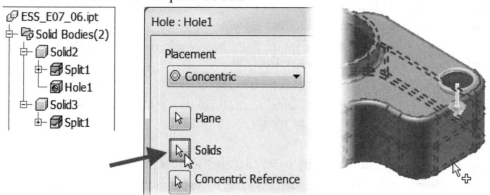

Figure 7-97

14. Use the Free Orbit command to ensure that the hole now goes through both solids.

15. In the browser, also notice that the Hole1 feature is now listed under both Solid2 and Solid3.

16. Next, you export the solids into an assembly file. The solids in a part file are not individual part files, but they can be exported to individual files with the Make Part or Make Component commands.

a. Click the Make Components command on the Manage tab > Layout panel.

b. In the graphics window or in the browser select the top solid and then the bottom solid. The order the solids are selected will be the order they are displayed in the dialog box.

c. Change the Target assembly location to *C:\Inv 2015 Ess Plus\Chapter 07* as shown in the following image. Click Yes when prompted to create a new assembly file and then save the new file with the default name.

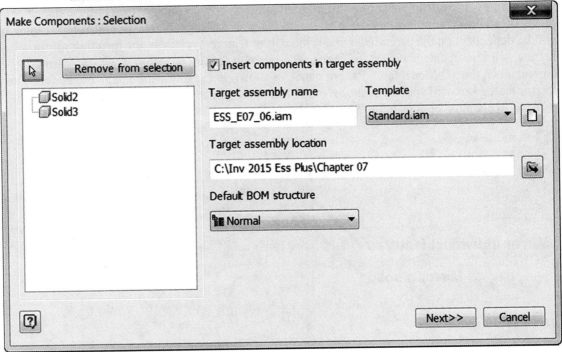

Figure 7-98

17. In the dialog box, click the Next button and click in each of the Component Name Cells and enter new components names, as shown in the following image. Note that you can rename the solids in the browser of the part file and the names will be reflected in the Make Components dialog box.

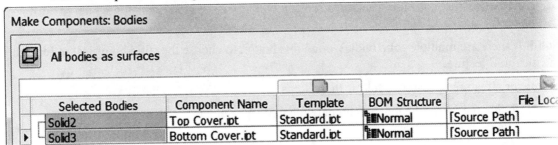

Figure 7-99

18. Click OK to create the parts and assembly files.

19. The assembly will be the active file. Examine the parts. Additional features can be added to the parts as needed but the new part's size and shape are derived from the original part file. If the features in the original part change, the linked parts will update to reflect the change.

20. Close the files. Do not save changes. End of exercise.

MIRROR FEATURES

When creating a part that has features that are mirror images of one another, you can use the Mirror Feature command to mirror a feature(s) about a planar face or work plane instead of recreating the features from scratch. Before mirroring a feature, a work plane or planar face that will be used as the mirror plane must exist. The feature(s) will be mirrored about the existing plane; it can be a planar face, a work plane on the part, or an origin plane. The mirrored feature(s) will be dependent on the parent feature—if the parent feature(s) change, the resulting mirror feature will also update to reflect the change. To mirror a feature or features, use the Mirror command on the 3D Model tab > Pattern panel, as shown in the following image on the left. The Mirror dialog box will appear, as shown in the following image on the right. The following sections explain the options in the Mirror dialog box.

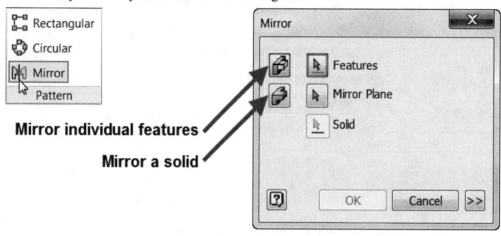

Figure 7-100

Mirror Individual Features. Click this button to mirror a feature or features.

Mirror a Solid. Click this button to mirror the solid body.

Features. Click the button to select the feature or features to mirror.

Mirror Plane. Click this button and then select a planar face or work plane on which to mirror the feature(s) about.

Solid. If there are multiple solid bodies, click this button to choose the solid body(ies) to receive the mirrored feature.

To mirror a feature or features, follow these steps:

1. Click the Mirror Feature command on the 3D Model tab > Pattern panel. The Mirror dialog box will appear.

2. Click the Mirror individual features option or the Mirror the entire solid option.

3. Select the feature(s) or solid body to mirror.

4. Click the Mirror Plane button, and select the plane on which the feature(s) will be mirrored about.

5. Click the OK button to complete the operation. The following image on the left shows a part with the features that will be mirrored, the middle image shows the part with a work

plane that the features will be mirrored about, and the image on the right shows the mirrored features.

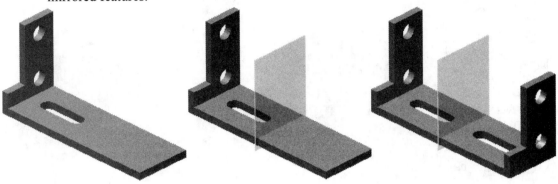

Figure 7-101

SUPPRESSING FEATURES

You can suppress a model's feature or features to temporarily turn off their display and not calculate them. Feature suppression can be used to simplify parts, which may increase system performance. This capability can also be used to access faces and edges that you would not otherwise be able to access. If you need to dimension to a theoretical intersection of an edge that was filleted, for example, you could suppress the fillet and add the dimension and then unsuppress the fillet feature. If the feature you suppress is a parent feature for other dependent features, the child features will also be suppressed. Features that are suppressed appear gray in the browser and have a line drawn through them, as shown in the following image on the right. A suppressed feature will remain suppressed until it is unsuppressed, which will also return the features to their unsuppressed state. The following image on the left shows a part with no features suppressed and the following image on the right shows the suppressed extrusion and its dependent features suppressed.

To suppress and unsuppress a feature in a part, use one of these methods:

1. Right-click on the feature in the browser, and select Suppress Features from the menu, as shown in the following image on the left.

2. To unsuppress a feature, right-click on the suppressed feature's name in the browser, and select Unsuppress Features from the menu.

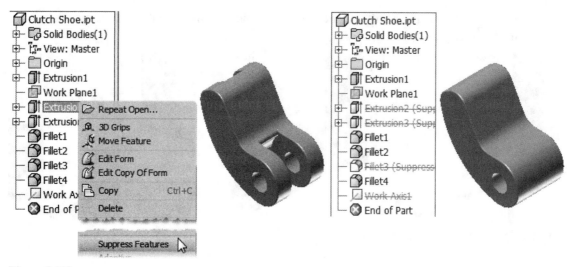

Figure 7-102

REORDERING A FEATURE

While designing, you may create features in an order that you would like to change, Inventor allows you to reorder a feature in the browser as long as there are no dependent features. For example, if you created a fillet feature using the All Fillets or All Rounds option and then created an additional extruded feature, such as a boss, you can reorder the fillet feature so it is below the boss in the browser. By reordering the fillet feature, so it is after the extrusion of the boss, the edges of the boss will be filleted. To reorder features, follow these steps:

1. Click the feature's name or icon in the browser. Hold down the left mouse button and click and drag the feature to the desired location in the browser. A horizontal line will appear in the browser to show you the feature's relative location while it is being reordered. The following image on the left shows a hole feature being reordered in the browser.

2. Release the mouse button and the model features will be recalculated in their new sequence. The following image on the right shows the browser and the reordered hole feature.

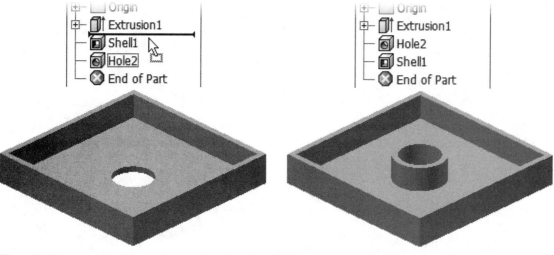

Figure 7-103

If you cannot move the feature due to parent-child relationships with other features, Autodesk Inventor will not allow you to drag the feature to the new position. In the browser, the cursor will change to a No symbol instead of a horizontal line, as shown in the following image.

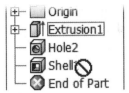

Figure 7-104

FEATURE ROLLBACK

While designing, you may not always place features in the order that your design later needs. In the last section you learned how to reorder features, but reordering features will not always allow you to create the desired results. To help solve this issue, you can roll back the design to an earlier state and then place the additional new features. To roll back a design, follow these steps:

Note that the following image on the left shows the original part.

1. Move the cursor over the End of Part marker in the browser.

2. With the left mouse button depressed, drag the End of Part Marker to the new location in the browser. While dragging the marker, a line will appear, as shown in the middle of the following image.

3. Release the mouse button, and the features that are below the End of Part marker are temporarily removed from calculation of the part. The End of Part marker will be moved to its new location in the browser.

4. Another method is to right-click on a feature in the browser and click Move EOP Marker from the menu, as shown in the following image on the right. The End of Part Marker moves below the selected feature.

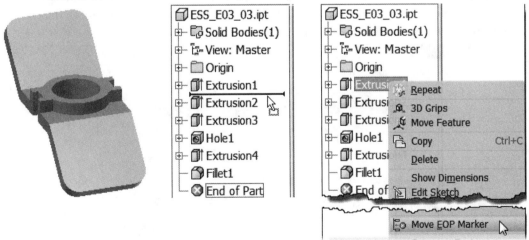

Figure 7-105

5. The following image on the left shows the browser and part after moving the End of Part Marker below Extrusion 1. Then you can create new features as needed. The new features will appear in the browser above the End of Part Marker.

6. To return the part to its original state, including the new features, drag the End of Part marker below the last feature in the browser or right-click on the End of Part marker and click Move EOP to End.

7. If needed, you can delete all features below the End of Part marker by right-clicking on the End of Part marker and click Delete All Features Below EOP, as shown in the following image on the right.

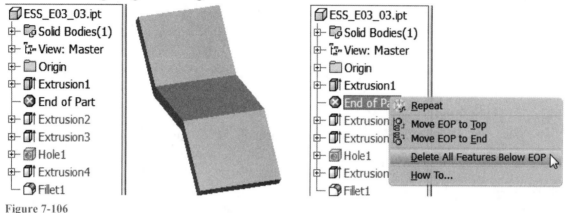

Figure 7-106

CONTENT CENTER

Autodesk Inventor's Content Center contains a number of standard components. It contains thousands of parts such as screws, nuts, bolts, washers, pins, and so on. You can place these standard components into an existing assembly using the Place from Content Center command that is found on the Assemble tab > Component panel, as shown in the following image on the left.

After the command is selected, the Place from Content Center dialog box opens, as shown in the following image on the right, and you can navigate between items that are either included or published to the Content Center. Select the item you want to place, click OK, and place the part as you would any other assembly component.

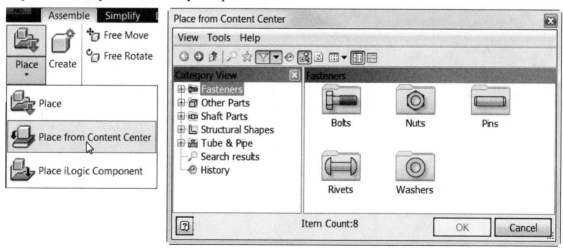

Figure 7-107

In addition to using the default items in the Content Center, you can publish your own features and parts to the Content Center. You publish parts and features using the Editor or Batch Publish commands, found on the Manage tab > Content Center panel as shown in the following image.

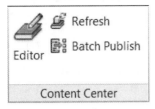

Figure 7-108

In order to publish content to the Content Center, a read/write library must exist and be added to the active project file.

 TIP: For more information about the Content Center, publishing features, publishing parts, or configuring libraries, refer to Autodesk Inventor's Help system.

INTRODUCTION TO STRESS ANALYSIS

Autodesk Inventor Professional has the functionality to simulate the stress that will be applied to a part or an assembly which it will encounter when used in a real world environment. Before a simulation can be performed, a material must be assigned, constraints established, and a load applied, as shown in the following image on the left. Autodesk Inventor uses Finite Element Analysis (FEA) to create a grid across the surface, called a mesh, as shown in the middle of the following image. The mesh divides the object into a continuous set of elements. Using properties of the assigned materials, Inventor calculates the stress in each element as shown in the following image on the right. Note that Inventor allows you to create multiple simulations on the same part or assembly, allowing you to test different designs and determine which design is best.

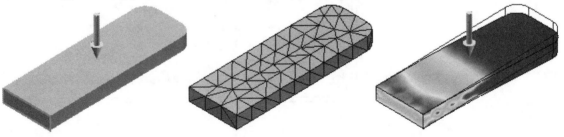

Figure 7-109

The following sections review the steps to run a stress analysis / simulation in Inventor Professional.

Create a Simulation – Step 1

The first step when performing a Stress Analysis is to create a simulation. Follow these steps to create a simulation in a part or an assembly file.

1. First, you show the simulation tools by clicking the Stress Analysis command on the Environments tab > Begin panel, as shown in the following image on the left. The Stress Analysis tab will be current.

2. Start a simulation by clicking the Create Simulation command on the Stress Analysis tab > Manage panel, as shown in the middle of the following image.

3. The Create New Simulation dialog will appear, as shown in the following image on the right.

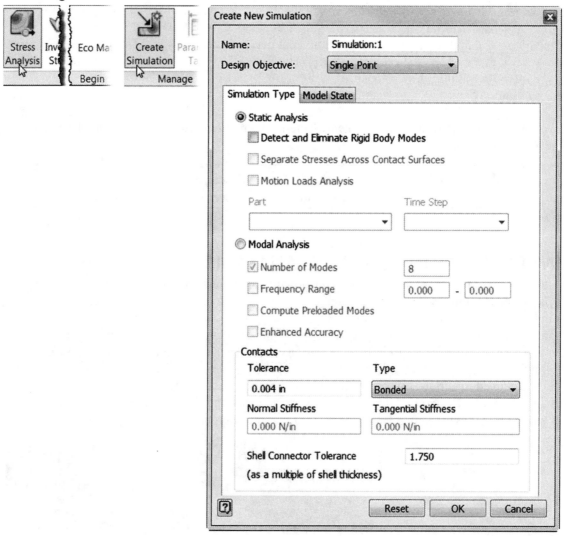

Figure 7-110

4. Before a simulation can be created, you must select the type of simulation that will be created; Static or Modal Analysis. After selecting the type of simulation, click OK.

The following description explains the two types of simulations.

Static Analysis

Static analysis performs a simulation that calculates stresses and displacement. The simulation helps you determine the simple structural loading conditions of the part without motion and the load is constant (no impact or changing of the load values).

Modal Analysis

Modal Analysis performs a simulation that calculates the dynamic properties of a model with different frequencies of vibration. Rigid body movements are also a consideration within this type of analysis.

Assign Material – Step 2

The second step is to define the material. Before an analysis can be performed, a material must be assigned to each part. The material can be applied at the part level as was discussed in Chapter 3 - Part Material, Properties And Appearance section, or you can override the material in the simulation. To assign a material while in a simulation, click the Assign command on the Stress Analysis tab > Material panel, as shown in the following image on the left. The Assign Materials dialog box will appear, as shown in the following image on the right. From the Override Material drop down menu, select the desired material. The material selected in the override will not change the material set in the part's iProperties.

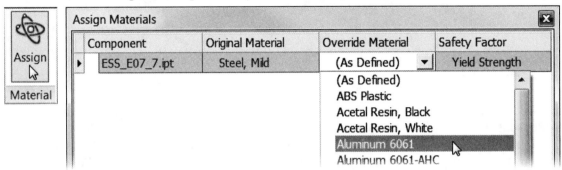

Figure 7-111

Applying Constraints – Step 3

The third step after the material(s) is assigned, is to constrain the model. These constraints represent the conditions the part or assembly will experience in the real world. Inventor has three constraints within the Stress Analysis environment; fixed, pin and frictionless. These constraints are located in the Stress Analysis tab > Constraints panel, as shown in the following image.

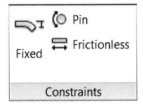

Figure 7-112

Fixed, Pin, and Frictionless constraints constrain the part or assembly to assure that the model reacts to an applied force in a realistic manner. Before the proper constraint can be applied, you must determine how the constraints will limit the movement of the model. You need to understand the three constraints that you can apply to the model that emulate the real world scenario that the simulation represents. A brief description of each constraint follows.

Fixed

A fixed constraint removes all the degrees of freedom on the selected face(s) or edge (s). You apply a fix constraint when no translational or rotational movements are permitted. You may apply multiple fix constraints on different faces or edges on the same model.

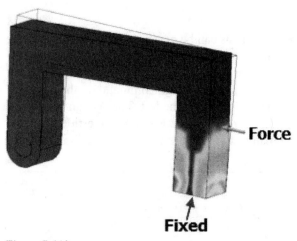

Figure 7-113

Pin

A Pin constraint removes translation degrees of freedom along the axes of a cylindrical face (no linear or sliding movement is allowed) but allows rotation. Apply this constraint if rotational movement is desired. A pin constraint can only be applied to a cylindrical face. A Pin constraint can work in conjunction with the other constraints.

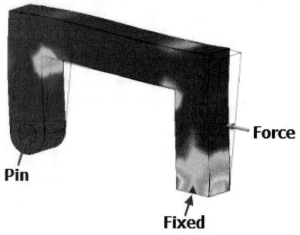

Figure 7-114

Frictionless

A Frictionless constraint limits a face to a rotation or translation movement (slide) along a plane. The face is prevented from moving or deforming perpendicular to the plane. A Frictionless constraint can be used in conjunction with the other constraints.

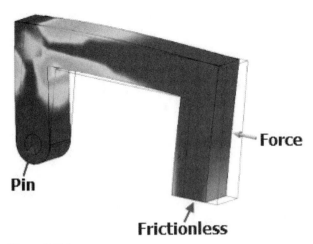

Figure 7-115

Applying a Load – Step 4

The next step to setup a stress analysis is to apply a load to the model. Inventor has different loads that can be applied to the model; force, pressure, bearing, moment and gravity. These constraints are located on the Stress Analysis tab > Loads panel, as shown in the following image. Review the following descriptions to determine the type of load that closely resembles the desired load you need to apply.

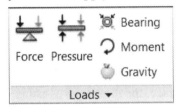

Figure 7-116

Force

Applies a user-defined load to a face or edge. A Force load is perpendicular to the surface, and parallel to an edge.

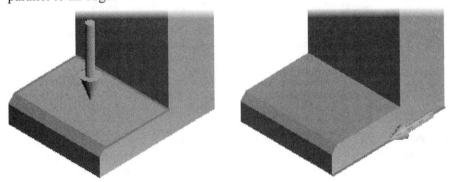

Figure 7-117

Pressure

Applies a user-defined pressure to a face. Pressure is a uniform load applied perpendicular to the whole surface.

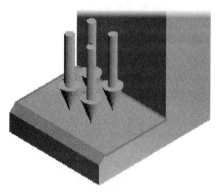

Figure 7-118

Bearing

Applies a user-defined axial or a radial load to a cylindrical face.

Figure 7-119

Moment

Applies a user-defined rotational load around an axis. If applied to a face, the momentary load is perpendicular to the surface.

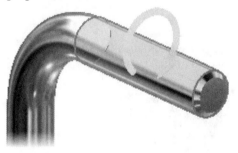

Figure 7-120

Gravity

Applies a user-defined gravitational pull on a part. The gravitational pull is perpendicular to the surface, or parallel to an edge.

Figure 7-121

Mesh Options – Step 5

This step is optional, if you skip this step, Inventor will automatically mesh the part(s). As you gain experience performing simulations you may want to adjust the mesh to fine tune the results. There are four mesh commands that you can use from the Stress Analysis tab > Mesh panel, as shown in the following image.

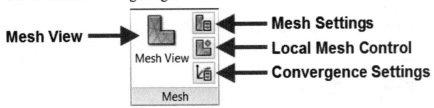

Figure 7-122

Mesh View

Use the Mesh View command to compute the mesh of the model. If this step is not done before a simulation is performed, Inventor will mesh the model automatically before doing the simulation. After the model has been meshed, click the Mesh View command to toggle the display of the mesh on and off.

Mesh Settings

Use the Mesh Settings command to adjust the average element size, minimum element size, grading factor, maximum turn angle, and if a curved mesh should be generated.

Local Mesh Control

Use the Local Mesh Control command to set the average element size for a face or an edge.

Convergence Settings

Use the Convergence Settings command to specify the maximum number of refinements, stop criteria, h refinement threshold, select the results to converge (Von Misses Stress, 1st Principal Stress, 3rd principal Stress or Displacement) and select the geometry that will be utilized.

Run Simulation – Step 6

After materials are assigned, loads and constraints applied, and if needed, mesh adjusted, the last step is to run the simulation. To run a simulation, click the Simulate command from the Stress Analysis tab > Solve panel, as shown in the following image on the left. The Simulate dialog box will appear. Click the Run button as shown in the following image on the right.

Simulate

Solve

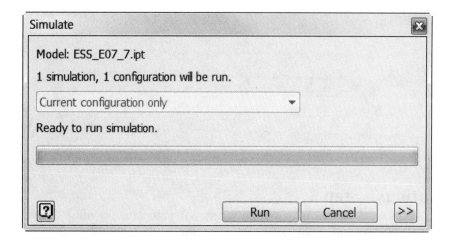

Figure 7-123

Simulation Results – Step 7

After a simulation is performed, several results can be displayed. To view the results from a different simulation, activate the desired test result in the browser, under the results section, as seen in the following image.

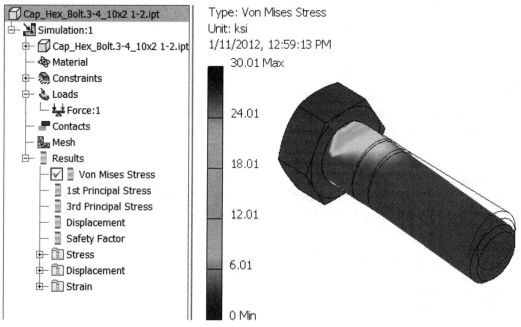

Figure 7-124

Display Results – Step 8

The results of the simulation can be analyzed by comparing the colors on the part to the color bar on the left side of the Graphics Window. How the simulation is displayed can be changed by selecting one of the options under the Stress Analysis tab > Display panel, as shown in the following image.

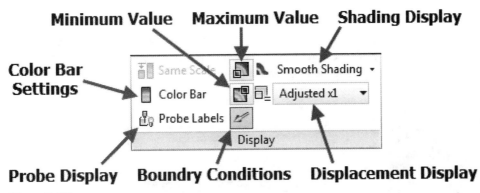

Figure 7-125

Color Bar Settings
Opens the Color Bar Settings Menu.

Minimum Value
Displays the location of the minimum value.

Maximum Value
Displays the location of the maximum value.

Shading Display
Allows the user to change the quality of the shading.

Displacement Display
Adjusts the level of model deformation.

Boundary Conditions
Toggles the display of glyphs for the loads applied.

Probe Display
Toggles the display of user probes.

Animate or Probe Results
To further analyze the results, you can run an animation of the simulation or probe a specific point(s) for information. These commands are located in the Stress Analysis tab > Result panel, as shown in the following image.

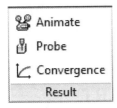

Figure 7-126

Animate
The Animate command plays an animation of the results. Once the Animate Results dialog opens, click the play button to view animation. If desired, an animation can be recorded.

Probe

The Probe command creates a probe to measure the simulation results. The probe will measure the exact value of the simulation at the selected point. To place a probe, select the area of the model where the exact measurement is to be displayed.

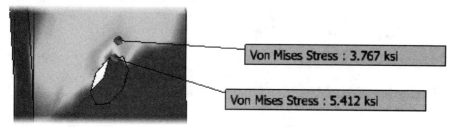

Figure 7-127

Report

Once the Simulation is complete, a report can be generated and exported. The Report command is located under the Stress Analysis tab > Report panel, as shown in the following image on the left. To determine what simulation results to include in the report, click the options desired on the Simulations tab in the report dialog, as shown in the image on the right. From the Format tab select the file type to export; html, mhtml or rtf. Click the OK button to create the report.

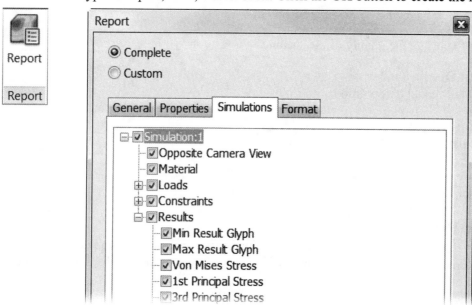

Figure 7-128

EXERCISE 7- 7: RUN A STRESS ANALYSIS ON A PART

In this exercise, you will use the Stress Analysis commands to create a simulation, add constraints, loads, simulate, animate and create a report of a lifting claw that was used in the assembly constraint exercise in chapter 6.

1. Open *ESS_E07_07.ipt* in the Chapter 07 folder.
2. Create a new simulation.
    a. Click the Environments tab.

   b. Begin a simulation by clicking the Stress Analysis command on the Environments tab > Begin panel, as shown in the following image on the left.

   c. Create a new simulation by clicking the Create Simulation command on the Environments tab > Manage panel, as shown in the following image on the right.

   d. In the Create New Simulation dialog box, click OK to create a new static analysis.

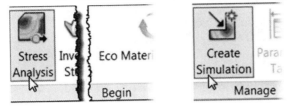

Figure 7-129

3. Verify that a material has been applied to the part by clicking the Assign Materials command on the Stress Analysis tab > Material panel. Verify that the Original Material assigned to the part via the iProperties is Steel, Mild, as shown in the following image, and then click OK.

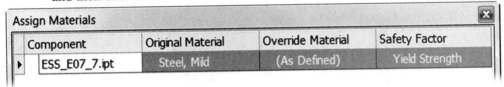

Assign Materials			
Component	Original Material	Override Material	Safety Factor
ESS_E07_7.ipt	Steel, Mild	(As Defined)	Yield Strength

Figure 7-130

4. Next, you constrain the part.

   a. Click the Pin command from the Stress Analysis tab > Constraints panel.

   b. Select the two circular faces of the bottom hole, as shown in the following image on the left, and click Apply.

   c. While still in the Pin Constraint dialog box, select the two circular faces of the top hole, as shown in the following image on the right.

   d. Then click OK to create the pin constraint.

Figure 7-131

5. Next, you apply a load to the part.

   a. Click the Force command on the Stress Analysis tab > Loads panel.

   b. Select the bottom horizontal face and change the Magnitude to **200 N,** as shown in the following image. The direction of the force should be directed down.

   c. Click OK to create the force.

Figure 7-132

6. Next, run the simulation.

    a. Click the Simulate command from the Stress Analysis tab > Solve panel.

    b. In the Simulate dialog box click the Run button.

    c. The result of your simulation should resemble the following image.

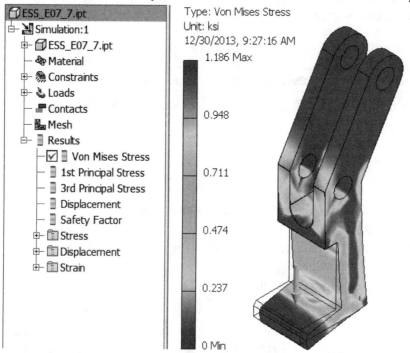

Figure 7-133

7. From the browser analyze the results of the simulation by double-clicking different results. When done make the Von Mises Stress results method current.

8. Next, you animate the simulation results.

    a. Click the Animate command from the Stress Analysis tab > Result panel.

    b. Start the animation by clicking the Play button in the Animate Results dialog.

    c. You can adjust the speed by selecting different options from the drop list.

    d. Click OK to finish the animation.

9. Next, you copy the simulation, override the material of the part, and rerun the simulation.

    a. Copy the simulation by right-clicking on Simulation:1 in the browser and click Copy Simulation, as shown in the following image.

    b. Simulation:2 (the new simulation) will be current.

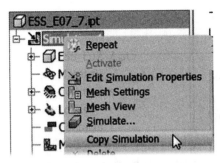

Figure 7-134

10. Next, you override the material.

    a. Click the Assign Materials command on the Stress Analysis tab > Material panel.

    b. In the Override Material cell click in the cell and from the list of materials click Aluminum 6061 as shown in the following image.

    c. To complete the operation click OK.

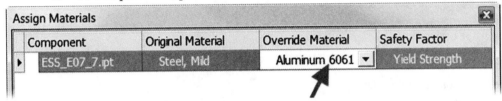

Figure 7-135

11. The constraints and the load were copied from the first simulation and do not need to be reapplied, but you need to run the new simulation to reflect the change in material. Run the simulation by clicking the Simulate command from the Stress Analysis tab > Solve panel and then click the Run button in the Simulate dialog box.

12. From the browser analyze the results of the simulation by selecting the different results method.

13. Lastly, generate a report. Click the Report command from the Stress Analysis tab> Report panel and then click OK.

14. To return to the part file environment, click the Finish Stress Analysis command on the Stress Analysis tab > Exit panel.

15. Close the file. Do not save changes. End of exercise.

EXERCISE 7-8: RUN A STRESS ANALYSIS ON AN ASSEMBLY

In this exercise, you will use the Stress Analysis commands to analyze a design of a plant hook to determine how much displacement there will be with and without a brace.

1. Open *ESS_E07_08.iam* in the Chapter 07 folder.

2. Create a new simulation.

    a. Click the Environments tab.

    b. Begin a simulation by clicking the Stress Analysis command on the Environments tab > Begin panel.

    c. Create a new simulation by clicking the Create Simulation command on the Environments tab > Manage panel, as shown in the following image on the right.

    d.   In the Create New Simulation dialog box that appears, click OK to create a new static analysis.

3.   Verify that a material has been applied to both parts.

    a.   Click the Assign Materials command on the Stress Analysis tab > Material panel.

    b.   Verify that the Original Material assigned to both parts is Steel, Mild.

    c.   Dismiss the dialog box by clicking the Cancel button.

For the first simulation, you simulate how far the plant hook will displace without the brace.

4.   In the browser, expand *ESS_E07_8.iam* and exclude the Brace part by right-clicking on Brace:1 in the browser and click Exclude From Simulation from the menu, as shown in the following image.

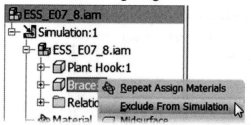

Figure 7-136

5.   Next, you constrain the plant hook.

    a.   Click the Fixed Constraint command on the Stress Analysis tab > Constraints panel.

    b.   Select the two circular faces of the holes labeled (1) and (2), as shown in the following image on the left.

    c.   Create the constraints by clicking OK.

6.   Next, you apply a load to the part, click the Force command from the Stress Analysis tab > Loads panel. To create the force, make the following changes:

    a.   For the location, select the inside circular face on the left end of the plant hook labeled (3) in the following image on the right.

    b.   To set the direction of the force based on a vector of the components coordinates click the More button on the lower right corner of the dialog box, and then click the Use Vector Components option labeled (4).

    c.   In the Fy option (Y vector) enter **-5.000 lbforce** labeled (5) and select in another cell to verify the direction of the force is pointing down.

    d.   Create the force by clicking OK.

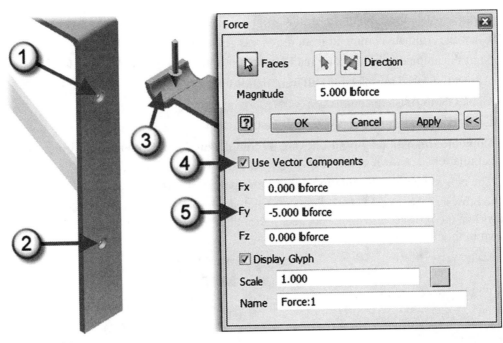

Figure 7-137

7. Next, you run the simulation.
   a. Click the Simulate command from the Stress Analysis tab > Solve panel.
   b. Click the Run button in the Simulate dialog box.
   c. From the Results entry in the browser, double-click Displacement and the results of your simulation should resemble the following image.

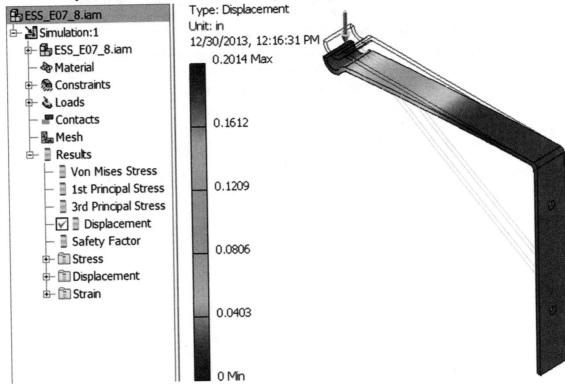

Figure 7-138

8. Next, you animate the simulation results.

    a. Click the Animate command from the Stress Analysis tab > Result panel.

    b. Start the animation by clicking the Play button in the Animate Results dialog.

    c. Adjust the speed by selecting different options from the drop list.

    d. Click OK to finish the animation.

9. Next, you copy the simulation to include the brace and run the simulation.

    a. Copy the simulation by right-clicking on Simulation:1 in the browser and click Copy Simulation, as shown in the following image on the left.

    b. The new simulation, Simulation:2 will be active.

10. In the browser, expand *ESS_E07_8.iam* and include the Brace part by right-clicking on Brace:1 in the browser and click (uncheck) Exclude From Simulation from the menu, as shown in the following image on the right.

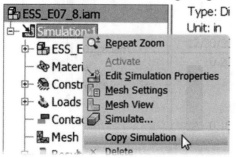 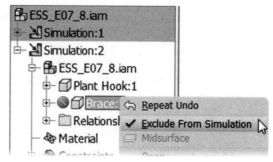

Figure 7-139

11. The constraints and the load were copied from the first simulation and do not need to be reapplied, but you need to run the simulation to reflect the inclusion of the brace. Run the simulation by clicking the Simulate command from the Stress Analysis tab > Solve panel and then click the Run button in the Simulate dialog box.

12. From the Results entry in the browser, click Displacement and your results of your simulation should resemble the following image. As you can see, the displacement went from approximately 0.20 inches without the brace to approximately 0.003 inches with the brace.

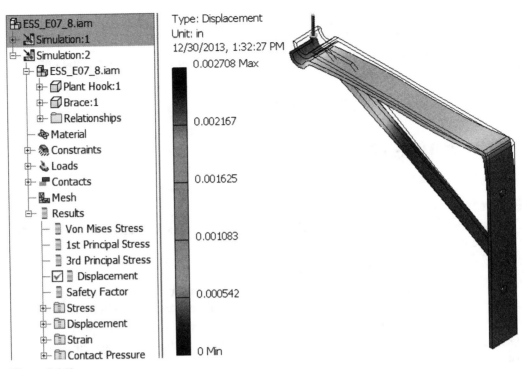

Figure 7-140

13. To see where the maximum and minimum value of the active simulation click the Maximum Value and the Minimum Value command from the Stress Analysis tab > Display panel, as shown in the following image on the left.

14. To see a leader point to the location of the result click and drag the result away from the part. The following image on the right shows the maximum and minimum results moved away from the part.

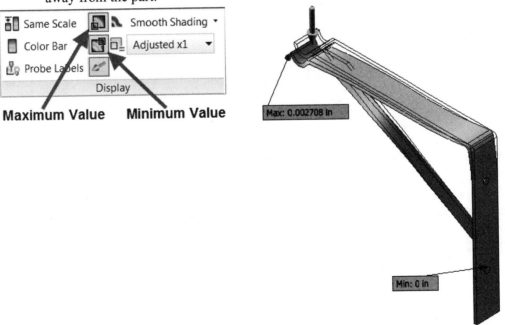

Figure 7-141

---

15. If desired, copy the simulation, assign different materials to the parts and edit the location of the holes to see if you can further minimize the displacement.

16. To return to the part file environment click the Finish Stress Analysis command on the Stress Analysis tab > Exit panel.

17. Close the file. Do not save changes. End of exercise.

APPLYING YOUR SKILLS

Skill Exercise 7-1

In this exercise, you use the knowledge you gained through this course to create a joystick handle. You will use the loft, split, and a few plastic part commands.

1. Open *ESS_Skills_7-1.ipt* from the Chapter 07 folder.

2. Create a loft, for the sections using the two elliptical shapes and circle in order from top to bottom as profiles and for the rails use the splines. Your preview should resemble the following image on the left.

3. Create a **0.1875 inch** fillet around the top edge, as shown in the following image on the right.

Figure 7-142

4. Shell the part towards the inside with a thickness of **0.0625 inches**. Do not remove any faces.

5. Next, create a **0.5 inch** diameter hole that is concentric to the bottom circular face and terminates at the inside face of the shell (use the To termination option), as shown in the following image.

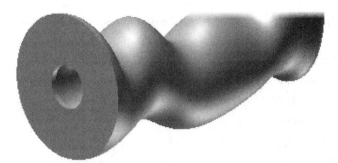

Figure 7-143

6. Use the Split command and the XY Origin plane to split the part into two solid bodies, as shown in the following image on the left.

7. Use the Move Bodies command (found by clicking the down arrow on the 3D Model tab > Modify panel) to move one of the solid bodies **1.5 inches** in the Z direction, as shown in the middle of the following image.

8. Turn off the visibility of the front solid and your screen should resemble the following image on the right.

9. If desired, use the Make Components command to export the solids into an assembly.

10. Close the file. Do not save changes. End of exercise.

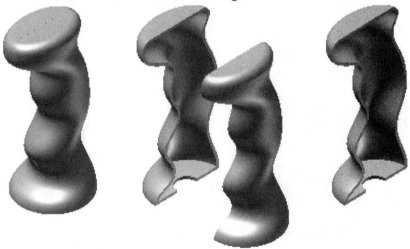

Figure 7-144

CHECKING YOUR SKILLS

Use these questions to test your knowledge of the material covered in this chapter.

1. When creating an equation, what does it signify when the equation is red in color?

2. What is the difference between a Model Parameter and a User Parameter?

3. True__ False__ You can only emboss text on a planar face.

4. True__ False__ A sweep feature requires three unconsumed sketches.

5. True__ False__ In a 3D Sketch, the Project Geometry command is used to project curves onto a circular face.

6. True__ False__ You can create a 3D curve with a combination of both 2D and 3D curves.

7. Explain how to create a 3D path using geometry that intersects with a part.

8. True__ False__ The easiest way to create a helical feature is to manually create a 3D path and then loft a profile along this path.

9. True__ False__ You can control the twisting of profiles in a loft by defining point sets.

10. Explain how to split a part into two solid bodies and then save them to their own part file.

11. Explain the difference between suppressing and deleting a feature.

12. True__ False__ After mirroring a feature, the mirrored feature is always independent from the parent feature. If the parent feature changes, the mirrored feature will NOT reflect this change.

13. Explain how to reorder features.

14. When creating a sweep with the Path & Guide Surface option, what does the surface control?

15. True__ False__ With Inventor Professional you can only run a stress analysis on a single part.

Index